ULTRASONIC WELDING OF LITHIUM-ION BATTERIES

Wayne W. Cai
Bongsu Kang
S. Jack Hu

Library of Congress Cataloging-in-Publication Data

Names: Cai, Wayne W., author.
Title: Ultrasonic welding of lithium-ion batteries / [edited] by Wayne W. Cai.
Description: New York : ASME Press, [2017] | Includes bibliographical references.
Identifiers: LCCN 2016043603 | ISBN 9780791861257
Subjects: LCSH: Lithium ion batteries–Design and construction. | Ultrasonic welding.
Classification: LCC TK2945.L58 U58 2017 | DDC 621.31/2423--dc23 LC record
  available at https://lccn.loc.gov/2016043603

TABLE OF CONTENTS

Chapter 10: Fundamental Dynamics of Ultrasonic Welding   **163**

Bongsu Kang, Wayne Cai, and Chin-An Tan

Chapter 11: Dynamics and Vibrations of Battery Tabs under Ultrasonic Welding   **191**

Bongsu Kang, Wayne Cai, and Chin-An Tan

PREFACE

Since its commercialization in the early 1990s, the lithium-ion (li-ion) battery has seen rapid growth due to its advantages of high voltage and high power/energy density. The growth has become particularly strong during the past decade with the development of li-ion battery powered electric vehicles. In 2016, the global li-ion battery industry generates about 90 GWh output with $20B revenue for a combined consumer electronics (60%), electric vehicles (35%), and grid (5%) usage. It is estimated that the global li-ion battery output for electric vehicles alone will grow to 195 GWh or about $35B in 2020, translating to 3 million pure electric vehicles out of a market of 100 million units per year. With the prevailing consensus that battery electric vehicles will become mainstream by 2050, the economical impact of li-ion battery industry will be at trillion dollar levels. Hence, the li-ion battery technologies including the associated manufacturing technologies are deemed very critical.

Ultrasonic metal welding (USMW), a process in which high-power ultrasonic vibration is used to produce relative tangential motion and then frictional heat to create bonds between two or multiple metal sheets, has rapidly become one of the key manufacturing technologies for joining li-ion battery cells, modules, and packs. Being a solid state joining process, USMW is firstly ideal in dissimilar materials joining largely due to its ability to avoid or significantly reduce the amount of brittle and non-conductive intermetallic compounds commonly formed in fusion welding. When applied to li-ion battery cell, module, and pack joining in battery electric vehicles, the advantages of USMW become even more evident due to its excellent characteristics for joining thin, multiple, and highly conductive materials such as copper, aluminum, and nickel. While it is well known that successful USMW depends on such design and manufacturing process parameters as the materials, stack-up configurations, tool knurl geometry, vibration amplitude, welding force, and welding time/energy, the underlying physics of the USMW process has not been fully understood and trial-and-error is still the dominant engineering practice. In particular, issues such as the interfacial bond failure, excessive thinning and fracture, and system vibratory responses are both perplexing and elusive to predict and prevent. Therefore, scientific understanding of the USMW mechanism, process, and thereafter sound engineering design and manufacturing guidance are much needed.

This book hence seeks to make an original contribution to the knowledge base underpinning USMW, particularly for the manufacturing of li-ion battery cells, modules, and packs as used in electric vehicles. More specifically:

1. From a physics point of view, the book (Chapters 2–7) strives to significantly advance the fundamental understanding of the USMW mechanism and subsequently the weld quality predictability by using a combined mechanics-materials approach including cyclic

plasticity and microstructural simulations. Throughout the chapters, a number of state-of-the-art metrology techniques are employed to measure key product/process characteristics in order to better understand the process and to validate the theoretical results. To detect transient temperature and heat flow of the workpieces and the tool, a novel in-situ thin-film thermocouple and thermopile sensing method is developed. Super-high-speed field imaging establishes real-time phenomenological observation on the multi-layer USMW process by analyzing the vibration behavior of metal layers through direct measurement of the lateral displacement of each metal layer. Advanced SEM/EDX methods provide the essential microscopic information to exam the bonding mechanism and fracture behaviors. The classification of the ultrasonic weld quality and the analyses of two limiting factors affecting ultrasonic weld quality (i.e., the interfacial bonding strength between metal layers and the metal perforation/fracture on top layer(s)) from these chapters shed great light on ultrasonic weld formation and quality.

2. The book (Chapters 10–11) attempts to establish the relationship between the weld tool vibration (input) and the system vibration (output) by studying the fundamental aspects of dynamics involved in USMW. Nonlinear dynamics analyses clearly indicate that both the product design (e.g., the materials, geometries, boundary conditions, and damping) and the process design (e.g., the tool stiffness and placement) significantly impact the system stresses which can exert strains on the system components and, in certain conditions, cause system failure. Laser scanning vibrometry provides much first-hand validation data.

3. As a critical element of the ultrasonic weld quality evaluation, data-drive approaches were adopted (Chapters 8–9) to establish a correlation between USMW signal features and the USMW process conditions and eventually joint quality. The book also develops the algorithms for monitoring welding process and its impact on weld quality, based on the tool wear conditions.

The book focuses mainly on two-layer and multi-layer aluminum (with and without anodizing) and copper (with and without nickel coating) welding configurations. Thus, its value to the practitioners in li-ion batteries and battery electric vehicles is self-evident. Nevertheless, the theories and methods presented in the book are highly transferable and extendable to all other li-ion battery applications, and can be of significant values to battery manufacturers and the automotive industry in general for judicious implementations. Furthermore, the new knowledge generated can drive the development of such innovative technologies as single-sided USMW, and thermally enhanced USMW for multiple layers of thick-sheets and hard-to-weld materials. It is expected that the book may have even broader implications in understanding and developing more effective solid state joining processes such as cladding, impact welding, friction stir welding, and ultrasonic consolidations for additive manufacturing, which are all strongly governed by the similar solid-state physics.

The key contributors to the book represent a team of leading experts in the field.

 **Dr. Wayne Cai**, is a Staff Researcher at General Motors Global R&D Center, and guest professor at Shanghai Jiaotong University (China). He is well-recognized for his innovation in automotive technologies, particularly li-ion battery design and manufacturing technologies with over thirty US and international patents (or patent pending) and over sixty peer-reviewed research papers. He is currently Chair of SAE Hybrid Electric Vehicle Committee, and Vice Chair of ASME Manufacturing Process Technical Committee. He also serves as an Associate Editor for ASME Journal of Manufacturing Science and Engineering and SME Journal of Manufacturing Processes.

Dr. Bongsu Kang is a Professor of Mechanical Engineering at Indiana University - Purdue University Fort Wayne. His research interests include dynamics and vibrations of distributed parameter systems. He has conducted various academic and applied research projects on friction-induced vibration problems including the work on modeling and vibration analysis of elastic bodies under ultrasonic excitation with application to ultrasonic metal welding of battery tabs in manufacturing of battery pack modules for electric vehicles.

Dr. S. Jack Hu is the J. Reid and Polly Anderson Professor of Manufacturing at the University of Michigan, Ann Arbor, USA. He is also professor of Mechanical Engineering and professor of Industrial & Operations Engineering. Dr. Hu has made significant contributions to advanced manufacturing research and education. He is a member of US National Academy of Engineering, an elected Fellow of the American Society of Mechanical Engineers (ASME) and of the International Academy for Production Engineering (CIRP).

We wish to express our gratitude to all the co-authors of the book, whose enthusiasms and contributions have really made this book possible. Special thanks also go to Mary Grace Stefanchik of ASME Press and other editorial staff who have made this strenuous process a pleasant experience.

Wayne Cai, GM Global R&D, Warren, MI, USA
Bongsu Kang, Purdue University Fort Wayne, Fort Wayne, IN, USA
S. Jack Hu, The University of Michigan, Ann Arbor, MI, USA

Chapter 1

INTRODUCTION[1]

Wayne Cai[1], Shawn Lee[2], and S. Jack Hu[3]
[1]Manufacturing Systems Research Lab, General Motors Global R&D Center
[2]Intellectual Property Prosecution, McDermott Will & Emery LLP
[3]Department of Mechanical Engineering, The University of Michigan

ABSTRACT

Automotive battery packs for electric vehicles typically consist of a large number of battery cells. These cells must be assembled together with robust mechanical and electrical joints. This chapter provides a comprehensive review of joining technologies for automotive lithium-ion battery manufacturing. It compares the advantages and disadvantages of the different joining technologies as related to battery manufacturing, including ultrasonic welding, resistance welding, laser beam welding, wire-bonding, and mechanical joining. Joining processes for electrode-to-tab, tab-to-tab, tab-to-busbar, and module-to-module assembly are discussed with respect to cell types and pack configuration. This chapter also describes the basic concepts in ultrasonic welding, serving as the foundation for the rest of the book.

Keywords: joining technology, lithium-ion battery manufacturing, ultrasonic metal welding

1.1 THE ERA OF VEHICULAR ELECTRIFICATION

During the last few decades, environmental concern of the petroleum-based transportation has led to renewed and stronger interest in electric vehicles (EV). In an EV, energy storage devices (such as batteries, super-capacitors) or conversion devices (such as fuel cells) are used to store or generate the electricity to power the vehicle. The first highway-capable EV with mass production in the modern age was GM's EV1 [2], using lead-acid-based batteries as onboard energy storage. With the advancement of newer generations of high-density energy storage batteries such as the metal-hydride batteries, and most recently the lithium-ion (li-ion) batteries, battery EVs (BEVs) have seen tremendous growth in the past decade. Batteries used as the power and energy sources to drive BEVs are called traction batteries.

A BEV falls into one of following four categories, hybrid EV (HEV), plug-in HEV (PHEV), extended range EV (EREV), and pure BEV. An HEV, is generally powered by an internal combustion engine and a battery pack. The internal combustion engine is the primary source of energy during medium or high-speed driving conditions with the batteries serving as the main power source in stop-and-go traffic as well as power assist in vehicle acceleration, where the batteries are also called power batteries. The battery pack in a HEV is relatively small and re-charged by the internal combustion engine and regenerative braking. An exemplary HEV is the Toyota Prius (2015 model year), offering an EPA-estimated 50 mpg

---

[1] Part of the content presented in this chapter has previously appeared in Ref. [1].

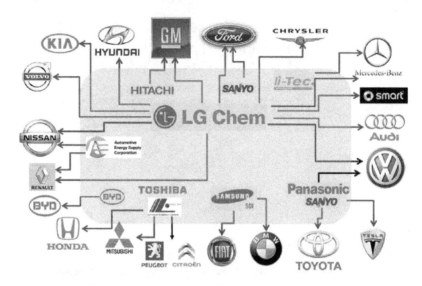

Figure 1.1. Major BEV manufacturers and li-ion battery suppliers, updated from [3].

fuel economy using a small 4.3 kWh of li-ion battery pack [4]. A PHEV, or Plug-in EV, operates under the battery mode, the internal combustion engine mode, or a combination of the two modes. The battery pack, however, can be charged via an external electrical power grid. Toyota's Prius Plug-in [4] is such an example. Depending on the design intent and the size of the battery pack, the traction batteries in PHEV can be either power or energy batteries. An EREV, or Extended Range EV, differs from a PHEV in that the battery pack is relatively large and the vehicle operates primarily under the electric mode. The internal combustion engine in the vehicle is used exclusively or primarily to charge the traction batteries (although the internal combustion engine can also be used to assist the battery mode driving in special circumstances). Exemplary Chevrolet Volt is such an EREV [5]. A pure BEV is powered entirely electrically by an onboard battery pack through the traction motors. The battery pack is typically recharged via an external electrical power grid. Although many automakers are producing BEVs for the marketplace, the most notable models are Tesla Model S [6], Nissan LEAF [7], and BMW i3 [8]. Figure 1.1 shows the landscape of major BEV manufacturers and their li-ion battery cell suppliers, based upon [3] (as updated in 2016). At the end of 2014, Panasonic, AESC, LG Chem and BYD are the four largest traction battery cell manufacturers in the world, supplying batteries to Tesla Model S (pure BEV), Nissan LEAF (pure BEV), GM Chevrolet (EREV), and BYD (pure EV and PHEV), among others [9].

1.2 LI-ION BATTERY CELLS, MODULES AND PACKS

There exist primarily three different cell formats for a traction battery cell: cylindrical, prismatic, and pouch. Due to legacy reasons, the cylindrical format has been the mainstream ranging from alkaline (such as AA cells) to NiMH to li-ion (such as 18650) cells. However, when rechargeable batteries such as NiMH and lithium-ion batteries are considered in automotive battery applications, other formats of battery cells such as prismatic and pouch types are developed to improve the volumetric efficiency, accommodate thermal management, and/or packaging requirement. Inside the cells, multiple layers of pre-cut positive/negative electrodes and separators are stacked with electrode leads (or tabs) and then welded. Then, the edges of the battery cover or pouch (made of aluminum laminated films) are heat sealed. Similar to prismatic cells, no standards exist as to the size of pouch cells. Figure 1.2 shows the joining and assembly process for pouch-type battery cells.

A module is a group of two or more battery cells joined together that can be replaced in maintenance and repair without impacting the rest of the battery pack. A module is also typically the minimum unit that is installed with safety components, power and heat management electronics. Modules can vary in size. A pack is a collection of all battery modules in the BEVs. The enclosure of a battery pack is sealed and water-tight so that it can protect the modules inside in the event of vehicle impact or crash. Due to excessive flexibility and softness of the pouch cells, holding components are generally needed to prevent pouch cells from having dimension and alignment issues. Such holding components can include frames, rigid cases, and supporting trays, an example of which is shown in Fig. 1.3.

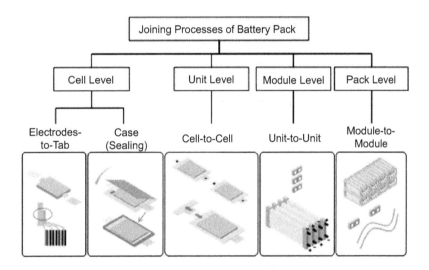

Figure 1.2. Joining processes of pouch type cells [3].

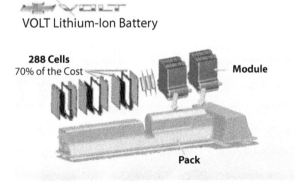

Figure 1.3. GM Chevy Volt: battery cells, modules and pack [10].

1.3 BATTERY JOINING

1.3.1 Inside a Cell

Welding occurs for the following four scenarios inside a battery cell:

- For all cell formats: between an electrode lead/tab and multiple (such as 10 to 100) layers of current collectors [11]. Thickness of each layer ranges from 10 to 30 microns [11], depending on the design and materials used, and the cathode foils are thicker than the anode foils when Al and Cu are used. The thickness of the lead/tab is 0.1 to 0.2 mm. Ultrasonic welding is commonly used.
- For all cell formats: for multiple layers of foils themselves. Ultrasonic welding is commonly used.
- For cylindrical cells only: between a positive tab and a positive terminal, or a negative tab and the bottom of the enclosure case. Laser welding or resistance spot welding is commonly used.
- For prismatic cells only: between the enclosure case and the cover. Laser welding is commonly used.

1.3.2 Module Assembly (Cell-to-Cell)

The following is a list of battery cell components requiring joining.

- For all cell formats:
  Cathode current collector (i.e., foil):   commercial grade pure Al (e.g., 1100)
  Anode current collector (i.e., foil):   commercial grade pure Cu (e.g., CDA 110)
  Positive electrode lead (i.e., tab):   commercial grade pure Al (e.g., 1100)
  Negative electrode lead (i.e., tab):   commercial grade pure Cu (e.g., CDA 110), or Ni
- For cylindrical and prismatic cells only:
  Enclosure case (i.e., container):   steels, stainless steels, aluminum alloys
  Enclosure cover (i.e., top plate):   steels, stainless steels, aluminum alloys

A number of battery cells are normally grouped together, either in parallel or series, to form a module. Often, circuitry sensors and safety devices, along with busbars or conduction plates are also joined together with the cell tabs or terminals. The busbars or conduction plates are made of Cu or Al. On the other hand, busbars are usually much thicker than those of battery cell tabs. Therefore, tab-to-busbar joining is a high gauge ratio's joining, which may limit the choice of joining method. In addition, for pouch cells, positive battery tabs are typically made of aluminum while negative tabs are copper, thus requiring dissimilar materials joining. Figure 1.4 shows the Tesla Model S pack [12] where each of the 18650 cylindrical cells is wire-bonded to the Cu bus plate. Figure 1.5 shows GM's Chevy Volt modules where three pouch cells are ultrasonically welded to the Cu busbar for each weld [10]. Figure 1.6 shows a Nissan LEAF battery module consisting four battery cells [13], two of which are connected in series and two in parallel. Figure 1.7 shows BMW i3 battery modules.

1.3.3 Pack Assembly (Module-to-Module)

Module-to-module assembly is normally mechanically joined via bolts/nuts with busbars. In fact, welding is not recommended in this stage due to the need of disassembly of battery packs. Figure 1.8 shows Nissan LEAF's battery pack [7].

Figure 1.4. Partial view of Tesla motor's battery pack.

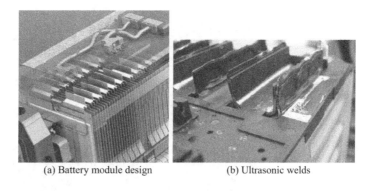

(a) Battery module design   (b) Ultrasonic welds

Figure 1.5. Chevy Volt battery modules and ultrasonic welds.

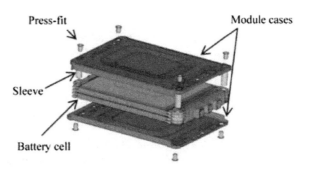

Figure 1.6. Nissan LEAF's battery module.

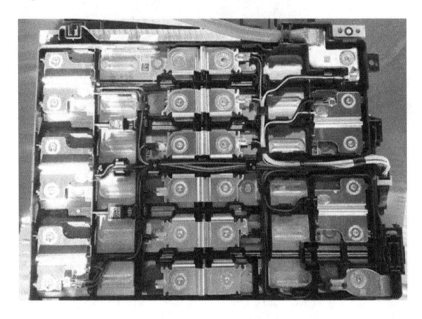

Figure 1.7. Partial view of BMW i3 battery module.

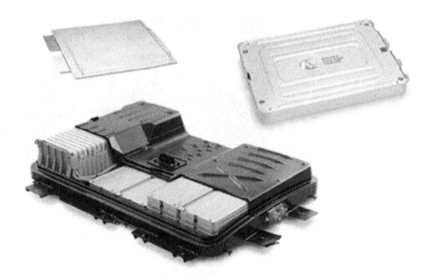

Figure 1.8. Nissan Leaf Battery cell, module and pack [7]: a laminated battery cell (upper left); a battery module set of four laminated battery cells (upper right); and a battery pack made up of 48 modules (bottom).

1.4 BATTERY JOINING TECHNOLOGIES

Joining technologies pertinent to li-ion battery cell and pack manufacturing, i.e., ultrasonic welding, resistance welding, laser welding, wire bonding and mechanical joining, are discussed in this section.

1.4.1 Ultrasonic Metal Welding

Overview

Ultrasonic metal welding (USMW) is a process in which a high frequency, usually 20 kHz or above, of ultrasonic energy is used to produce relative lateral motions to create solid-state bonds between two or more metal sheets clamped under pressure. The high-frequency shear force induces alternating metal surface friction and heat to produce a weld. A schematic of the ultrasonic metal welding system is shown in Fig. 1.9, which can be used to join a wide range of metal sheets or thin foils, see Fig. 1.10.

USMW is considered a solid-state welding. In contrast to fusion welding processes, USMW has several inherent advantages. The main advantage of USMW lies in its excellent welding quality for thin, dissimilar, and multiple layers of highly conductive metals (such as Cu and Al), which is crucial in battery cell joining and for battery tab joining [14]. Another advantage is the low heat-affected zone. USMW also produces a very thin layer of bonding interfaces (typically a few microns) and therefore eliminates metallurgical defects that commonly exist in most fusion welds such as porosity, hot-cracking, and bulk intermetallic compounds. Therefore, it is often considered the best welding process for li-ion battery applications.

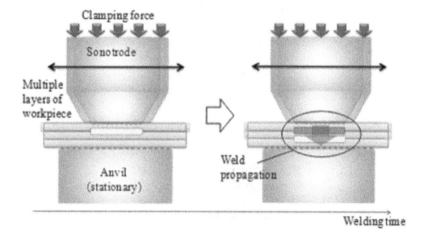

Figure 1.9. A schematic of ultrasonic metal welding system [3].

Figure 1.10. Ultrasonic welding can be used to join a wide range of metal sheets or thin foils [3].

Ultrasonic Welding Physics

There are three important physical attributes pertaining to the quality of ultrasonic welding:

- The interfacial bonding quality of an ultrasonic weld:
  The interfacial bonding strength (such as lap-shear or U-tensile) is the first attribute to gauge a weld quality. However, the bonding mechanism for USMW is not completely understood. A combination of the following four mechanisms may attribute to the bonding: (a) micromelting (e.g., a few microns of thin interface layer melting); (b) metal interlocking (due to plastic deformation, particularly the severe deformation caused by sonotrode knurls); (c) metallic bonding; and (d) chemical bonding (such as covalent bonding). This will be further discussed in Chapters 2 and 3.
- Fracture and perforation of the metals at the weld spot:
  Another attribute critical to the weld quality is the fracture and perforation of the metals. Figure 1.11 is a sketch of a two-layered circular ultrasonic weld whose size is dictated by the sonotrode knurl area. According to reference [14], if the welding parameters (e.g., vibration amplitude, welding pressure and welding time) are set too high, excessive plastic deformation and/or higher temperatures can result in metal fracture and perforation at the weld spots and consequently poor joint strength, although the interfacial bonding strength can be higher. This will be discussed in detail in Chapter 2.
- Dynamic stresses and system failure induced by USMW:
  One unique feature in ultrasonic welding is the detrimental effect to the system due to the dynamic stresses from the ultrasonic waves. Because the ultrasonic vibration is a mechanical wave that can propagate to cause stresses throughout the entire system, it is important to ensure that the structure (under specific boundary conditions) does not have a natural frequency at or near the ultrasonic frequency. The details of structural dynamics and stresses during ultrasonic welding will be discussed in Chapters 10 and 11.

Ultrasonic Welding Quality Evaluation

Standards and guidelines for destructive, post-weld quality evaluation are well-established [15] for many types of welds, including ultrasonic spot welds [16, 17]. They generally prescribe the quality evaluation and testing procedures. As for Non-Destructive Evaluation (NDE), a variety of methods are developed using ultrasonic probes, eddy current, X-ray/CT, electrical resistance, etc. Validity of any of the methods largely depends on the nature

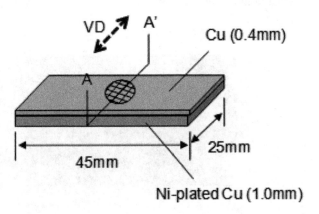

Figure 1.11. Two layers of metals with sonotrode knurl marks [14].

of the weld and defect types, and significant challenges exist in interpreting the test data. In terms of real-time, online welding process monitoring and NDE, neither standards nor guidelines exist although many sensors such as temperature sensors (including thermo-couples, Infrared), force sensors (such as load cells), displacement (such as linear variable differential transformer [LVDT]), accelerometers, and acoustic sensors are reportedly used [18]. In particularly, online monitoring and quality assurance methods were developed for GM's Chevy Volt [19] and Cadillac ELR [20]. The relationship between online sensor signals and the joint quality will be discussed in Chapter 8.

1.4.2 Resistance Welding

Resistance welding relies on a higher contact resistance at the joint interface to induce a localized joule heating and fusion of materials when the electrical current is applied through two electrodes. Resistance welding process is fast and generally automated. It has wide applications in sheet metal industries, particularly for steels welding. Though resistance welding has also been used in the battery welding for decades, conventionally its usage was primarily limited to low current-carrying applications, rather than high-power/high-energy BEVs. Resistance welding/welds using single-side welding electrodes [21], i.e., two electrodes are on the same side of the metals to form a closed current conducting circuit instead of the more conventional process of two-sided resistance welding (not shown) with the two electrodes on each side of the metals is shown if Fig. 1.12.

The following are three important characteristics of resistance welding for battery welding:

1. Li-ion battery metals use highly electrically and thermally conductive materials such as aluminum and copper. These metals are difficult to weld using the conventional resistance spot welding technology, particularly when the contact resistance(s) at the metal interface(s) becomes low. It hence requires very large electrical current density (i.e., current versus weld size) to be applied in the welding circuit to generate enough joule heat at the intended weld interfaces. A steady stream of recent advances has given users much improved capabilities to control various aspects of the process. For example, projection resistance welding method can sometimes be used where a small metal projection is introduced at one of the metals to reduce the total contact area of the metals and hence

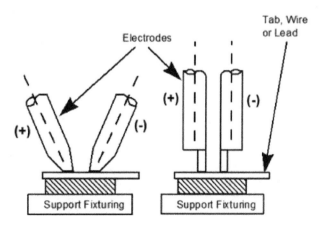

Figure 1.12. Resistance spot welding of battery and electronic assemblies [21].

increase the current density. Another solution is to increase the current density by using a special type of resistance welder called Capacitive Discharge welder [22] to provide very high welding current (such as 10 to 100 kA) in a very short period (such as 10 ms). Nevertheless, it is still very difficult to produce a large-sized weld nugget for battery metals because of the extremely high electrical current density required.

2. As is the case for all fusion welding technologies of dissimilar materials, welds are difficult to form due to different melting temperatures; in addition, a large amount of intermetallics is typically produced making the weld brittle with very high electrical resistivity.

3. When welding multiple layers, it is very difficult to ensure homogenous melting at all the interfaces.

1.4.3 Laser Beam Welding

Laser beam welding, or simply laser welding, is a welding technique to join workpieces through the use of the high power beam of laser. The process has been frequently used in high volume applications, but recently has also been used in electronics and battery industries. Figure 1.13 shows laser welding of busbars to cylindrical battery cans [23]. Figure 1.14(a) shows a laser seam welding of an aluminum can [23]. In battery tab welding as described in Fig. 1.14(b), weld penetration must be controlled accurately so that the weld nugget does not penetrate into the can [23].

Laser welding can offer significant advantages in process precision, throughput, and noncontactness. It also produces a small heat affected zone, resulting low weld distortion, and low residual stress. Low heat input and low weld penetration can also reduce the adverse effect of heat flux on the structure and the chemistries of battery cells. However, the need of precise joint fit-up and the high reflectivity of the battery materials (e.g., Cu and Al) make laser welding challenging in battery applications. More critically, due to the large amount of intermetallics from the fusion welding process, weld defects such as porosity and hot-cracking can be significant [24].

1.4.4 Wire-Bonding

Wire-bonding is a single-sided ultrasonic welding that bonds an auto-fed small diameter (typically 0.01 to 0.5 mm) Ag, Cu or Al wire to one substrate first (called the first bond) and then to the second or more substrates in sequence (i.e., the second bond, the third bond, etc.) to establish an interconnect between the substrates through the bonding wire. Wire bonding is widely used in micro-electronics industry and generally considered the most cost-effective and flexible interconnect technology. For high power applications such as BEVs, heavy gauges of feed wires (either Al or Cu) are needed. For example, Tesla Model S uses 0.381 mm diameter of Al wires as interconnects between its 18650 li-ion battery cells and the bus plate, shown in Fig. 1.4.

Figure 1.13. Laser welding of busbars to cylindrical battery cans.

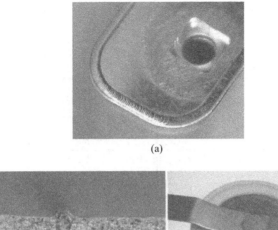

(a)

(b)

Figure 1.14. (a) laser seam welding of an aluminum can; (b) a nickel battery tab laser-welded to a stainless steel casing.

1.4.5 Mechanical Joining

Mechanical joining can be categorized by two distinct groups: fasteners and integral joints. Fasteners include nuts, bolts, screws, pins and rivets. Integral joints include seams, crimps, snap-fits, and shrink-fits that are designed into the components to be connected. For battery module-to-module connection, mechanical joining is preferred for the ease of disassembly for maintenance and repair.

1.4.6 Summary of Battery Joining Technologies

Table 1.1 summarizes the key characteristics of the selected battery joining technologies.

1.5 CHAPTER SUMMARY

This introductory chapter provides an overview on the state-of-the-art of battery EV (BEV) manufacturing, with emphasis on the joining, assembly and packaging of lithium-ion battery packs.

1. Li-ion battery and battery EV marketplace are growing and evolving rapidly. As of 2014, Panasonic, AESC, LG Chem and BYD are the four largest traction battery cell manufacturers in the world, supplying batteries to Tesla Model S (pure BEV), Nissan LEAF (pure BEV), GM Chevrolet (EREV), and BYD (pure EV and PHEV), respectively.
2. There are three major cell formats for li-ion traction batteries, i.e., cylindrical, prismatic, and pouch. The manufacturing processes for cylindrical and prismatic cells are substantially similar, but deviate meaningfully from that for the pouch-type cells. The

TABLE 1.1. Summary of battery joining technologies [1].

Joining Methods	Advantages	Disadvantages
Ultrasonic welding	• Excellent for dissimilar materials due to minimal intermetallics • Excellent for thin sheets or wires • Excellent for multiple wires or multi-layered sheets • Low heat-affected zone: low thermal distortion and low residual stresses • Excellent for highly conductive materials	• Double-sided • May have severe knurl perforation at the top and/or bottom weld surface • May cause structural vibration • Has an upper limit in total joint thickness • Most suitable for soft materials
Resistance welding	• Can be single-sided welding • Relatively mature technology with established weld quality monitoring and/or control methods • Low cost	• Large heat-affected zone: large thermal distortion and residual stresses • Large amount of intermetallics for dissimilar materials • Difficult for highly conductive materials • Difficult for multiple layers • Difficult to produce large welds • Electrode sticking/wear
Laser welding	• Relatively small heat-affected zone: small thermal distortion and residual stresses • Single-sided and non-contact • High throughput	• Large amount of intermetallics for dissimilar materials • Porosity and hot-cracking • Requiring very tight sheets fit-up • High initial cost
Wire bonding	• Low heat-affected zone: low thermal distortion and low residual stresses • No or very little intermetallics for dissimilar materials • Excellent for highly conductive materials • Single-sided • Built-in bond strength evaluation	• Only light gauges of wires can be bonded onto the substrates (such as the bus bars or bus plates) and thus the electrical current carrying capability is limited • Most suitable for soft materials • Substrate needs to have rigidity to sustain the bonding force
Mechanical joining	• Joint strengths can be very high • Easy disassembly	• Added parts and mass • Labor-intensive • Corrosion

exact manufacturing process for any format is determined by the designs, materials, and cell and BEV manufacturers' preferences.

3. The traction li-ion battery joining is an important manufacturing process at three different levels, i.e., cell level (inside cell joining), module level (cell-to-cell joining), and pack level (module-to-module).

4. Ultrasonic welding, laser beam welding, resistance welding, wire bonding, and mechanical joining are the commonly used joining techniques for li-ion battery cells, modules, and packs.

1.6 ORGANIZATION OF THE BOOK

This book is organized as follows. Chapter 2 begins with defining ultrasonic weld quality and uncovering the attributes that affect weld quality. Chapter 3 presents microstructures of weld interface to study weld mechanisms with a focus on Al/Cu dissimilar joints. Chapter 4 identifies the effect of transient temperature variations during the welding process on joint quality utilizing thin-film microsensors. Chapter 5 shows further experimental studies on weld development of multi-layered battery tabs using high speed imaging. Chapter 6 develops a coupled thermo-mechanical simulation model of multi-layered ultrasonic welding process. Chapter 7 further develops a physics-based model of weld interface to present microstructural evolution. Chapter 8 characterizes sensor signals and their relationships to joint quality in online process monitoring. Chapter 9 develops a tool wear monitoring system to study how tool wear affects the final joint quality. Chapters 10 and 11 discuss the effects of ultrasonic welding dynamics on the system. More specifically, these chapters focus on the battery tab dynamics by employing sophisticated analytical models. Chapter 12 concludes the book and presents the outlook on the ultrasonic welding technology for battery welding.

Although the intention of this book is to present a comprehensive coverage of all topics pertinent to the ultrasonic welding for batteries, its main focus is given towards the related sciences and theories rather than engineering. This also explains that performance evaluations of ultrasonic welds (such as mechanical, electrical, and corrosion) are scantly discussed in the book.

REFERENCES

[1] W. Cai, 2017, "Chapter 1: Lithium-ion Battery Manufacturing for Electric Vehicles: A Contemporary Overview." In *"Advances in Battery Manufacturing, Service, and Management Systems,"* Edited by J. Li, S. Zhou, and Y. Han, ISBN 978-1-119-05649-2, Wiley-IEEE Press.

[2] GM EV1, from http://en.wikipedia.org/wiki/General_Motors_EV1

[3] Lee, S. S., Kim, T. H., Hu, S. J., Cai, W. W., and Abell, J. A., 2010, "Joining Technologies for Automotive Lithium-Ion Battery Manufacturing—A Review," *Proceedings of the ASME 2010 International Manufacturing Science and Engineering Conference*, Erie, PA, Paper No. MSEC2010-34168, October 12–15.

[4] Toyota Prius PHEV, from http://en.wikipedia.org/wiki/Toyota_Prius_Plug-in_Hybrid

[5] Chevy Volt, from http://en.wikipedia.org/wiki/Chevrolet_Volt

[6] Tesla Model S, from http://en.wikipedia.org/wiki/Tesla_Model_S#Battery

[7] Nissan Technology Magazine, from http://www.nissan-global.com/EN/TECHNOLOGY/MAGAZINE/ev_battery.html

[8] BMW i3, batteries and charging solutions from http://www.bmwblog.com/2013/04/18/bmw-i3-batteries-and-charging-solutions/

[9] 2014 Global Traction Battery Market, from http://m.d1ev.com/37935.html?from=timeline&isapp installed=0

[10] Lev, L., 2012, "New Areas of Automotive NDE: Li-ion Batteries and Composite Materials," NASA In-Space Non-Destructive Inspection Technology Workshop, Houston, TX.

[11] Massey, S., 2013, Ultrasonic Metal Welding for Lithium-Ion Battery Cells. http://ewi.org/ultrasonic-metal-welding-for-lithium-ion-battery-cells/. January 17.

[12] https://chargedevs.com/features/a-closer-look-at-wire-bonding/

[13] Kinoshita, Y., Hirai, T., Watanabe, Y., Yamazaki, Y., Amagai, R., and Sato, K., 2013, "Newly Developed Lithium-Ion Battery Pack Technology for a Mass-Market Electric Vehicle," SAE Technical Paper 2013-01-1543.

[14] Lee, S. S., Kim, T. H., Hu, S. J., Cai, W., Abell, J. A., and Li, J., 2013, "Characterization of Ultrasonic Metal Weld Quality for Lithium-Ion Battery Tab Joining," ASME *Journal of Manufacturing Science and Engineering*, **135**(2), p. 021004002E.

[15] American Welding Society, 2007, "Standard Methods for Mechanical Testing of Welds," AWS B4.0.

[16] US Department of Defense Military Standard, 1985, "Ultrasonic Welding of Aluminum and Aluminum Alloy Materials," MIL-STD-19471985.

[17] Society of Automotive Engineers, 2009, "Performance Specification for Ultrasonically Welded Wire/Cable Termination," SAE/USCAR-38.

[18] Cai, W., Abell, J. A., Tang, C. H. J., Wincek, M. A., Boor, P. J., Spacher, P. F., and Hu, J., 2014, "Method and System for Online Quality Monitoring and Control of a Vibration Welding Process," US Patent 8,702,882.

[19] University of Michigan Record Update, 2011, "GM, CoE create technology to maximize Volt's battery weld quality," from http://www.ur.umich.edu/update/archives/110624/battery

[20] Green Car Congress, 2013, "Ultrasonic Welding in the Battery Pack for the Cadillac ELR," from http://www.greencarcongress.com/2013/08/elr-20130802.html

[21] NASA Johnson Space Center, 2004, "Process Specification for the Resistance Spot Welding of Battery and Electronic Assemblies," NASA PRC-009 REV D.

[22] Amada Miyachi America, 2016, http://www.amadamiyachi.com/products/resistance-welding/rw-power-supplies/adp-series

[23] Industrial Laser Solutions, 2015, "Battery Welding: Selecting Laser, microTIG, and Resistance technologies," from http://www.industrial-lasers.com/articles/print/volume-30/issue-1/features/battery-welding-selecting-laser-microtig-and-resistance-technologies.html

[24] Mys, I., 2006, "Laser Micro Welding of Copper and Aluminum," Proc. SPIE 6107, Laser-based Micropackaging, 610703.

Chapter 2

DEFINING JOINT QUALITY USING WELD ATTRIBUTES[1]

S. Shawn Lee[1], Tae Hyung Kim[2], S. Jack Hu[2], Wayne Cai[3], Jeffrey A. Abell[3], and Jingjing Li[4]
[1]Intellectual Property Prosecution, McDermott Will & Emery LLP
[2]Department of Mechanical Engineering, The University of Michigan
[3]Manufacturing Systems Research Lab, General Motors Global R&D Center
[4]Department of Industrial and Manufacturing Engineering, The Pennsylvania State University

ABSTRACT

Manufacturing of lithium-ion battery packs for electric or hybrid electric vehicles requires a significant amount of joining, such as welding, to meet the desired power and capacity needs. However, conventional fusion welding processes such as resistance spot welding and laser welding face difficulties in joining multiple sheets of highly conductive, dissimilar materials to create large weld areas. Ultrasonic metal welding overcomes these difficulties by using its inherent advantages derived from its solid-state process characteristics. Although ultrasonic metal welding is well-qualified for battery manufacturing, there is a lack of scientific quality guidelines for implementing ultrasonic welding in volume production. In order to establish such quality guidelines, this chapter first identifies a number of critical weld attributes that determine the quality of welds by experimentally characterizing the weld formation over time using copper-to-copper welding as an example. Samples of different weld quality were cross-sectioned and characterized with optical microscopy, scanning electronic microscopy, and hardness measurements in order to identify the relationship between physical weld attributes and weld performance. A novel microstructural classification method for the weld region of an ultrasonic metal weld is introduced to complete the weld quality characterization. The methodology provided in this chapter links process parameters to weld performance through physical weld attributes.

Keywords: lithium-ion battery assembly, ultrasonic metal welding, weld attributes, weld quality

2.1 INTRODUCTION

Battery electric vehicles (BEVs) including electric, hybrid electric, and plug-in hybrid electric vehicles have received a great deal of attention in the automotive industry. The performance of these BEVs relies on the power and energy capacities of their batteries. Among the various battery technologies, lithium-ion batteries have the advantages of being compact and light weight for the same power requirement. In order to meet the desired power and capacity needs for BEVs, a lithium-ion battery pack is assembled from a large

---

[1] The content presented in this chapter has previously appeared in Ref. [1].

15

number of battery cells, sometimes several hundreds, even thousands depending on the cell configuration and pack size. Several cells are usually joined together to form a module with common bus-bars, and tens of modules are then assembled into a battery pack [2]. Hence, a significant amount of battery joining is needed in battery pack manufacturing. However, battery joining is faced with several challenges [2]: joining of highly conductive materials such as copper, aluminum, and nickel; dissimilar and multi-layer materials with varying sheet thickness combinations; and large weld areas to decrease current density and to increase mechanical strength. In addition, reliable joints are required for batteries to stand for harsh environments such as vibration, severe weather, and humidity. Hence, it is essential to develop robust and reliable technologies for battery joining.

In this study, ultrasonic metal welding is applied to battery joining because of its advantages over other fusion welding methods such as resistance spot welding and laser welding. First, highly conductive materials with thin, dissimilar, and multi-layer sheets can be welded by ultrasonic metal welding. Second, ultrasonic metal welding does not generate a large amount of heat since high heat may damage the battery. Finally, ultrasonically welded joints typically eliminate metallurgical defects that commonly exist in most other fusion welds, such as formation of intermetallic compounds, brittle phases, or porosities in the fused zone. Although ultrasonic metal welding is well-suited for battery manufacturing, scientific quality guidelines do not yet exist for volume production of batteries. Therefore, it is necessary to develop understanding of the mechanisms of weld formation and the resulting quality characteristics for battery joining.

A commonly accepted weld quality definition does not yet exist for ultrasonic welding, but methods have been established for other joining processes. The quality for spot welds is assessed by whether the performance of a weld meets the specific requirements or by the size of a weld nugget usually obtained from the peel test [3]. Although there are not as many quality guidelines as in spot welding, some research has been carried out to define the weld quality in ultrasonic metal welding. Kong et al. [4, 5] proposed the "linear weld density," the proportion of bonded line to the entire weld along the weld interface, as a quantitative quality criterion for ultrasonic welds. Based on this linear weld density, Yang et al. [6] developed an analytical energy model for metal foil deposition in ultrasonic consolidation and studied the effects of process parameters on weld quality. Hetrick et al. [7] used several microstructural features of a weld cross section to characterize ultrasonic metal welding process in auto body fabrication. Bakavos and Prangnell [8] performed a microstructural analysis on the mechanisms of weld formation in ultrasonic metal welding of aluminum alloys. Zhou et al. [9, 10] developed finite element models of the welded samples to predict performance based on two distinct failure modes: interfacial fracture and pull-out fracture of ultrasonic welds. Kim et al. [11] attempted to develop a quality criterion for ultrasonic metal welding of conductive materials such as copper and nickel plated copper by identifying failure modes in T-peel tests. Nevertheless, none of these studies has established an explicit relationship between physical weld attributes and weld performance, and scientific quality guidelines of ultrasonic welds are still lacking, particularly for battery applications. Physical weld attributes can be defined as any measurable characteristics of the weldment that may affect the weld performance, which refers here to the mechanical strength at the joint [12]. Therefore, this chapter identifies a number of critical weld attributes that determine the quality of welds by experimentally characterizing the weld formation over time using copper-to-copper welding as an example and establishes a quality classification for ultrasonically welded joints. A microstructural classification method for the weld region is introduced to complete the weld quality characterization.

The remainder of this chapter is organized as follows: Section 2.2 describes the materials and experimental procedures; Section 2.3 defines the attributes in an ultrasonic metal weld, summarizes the microstructural observations on weld cross-sections. Section 2.4 discusses the relationship between weld attributes and quality.

2.2 MATERIALS AND EXPERIMENTS

To simulate the joining of battery tabs and bus-bars, as shown in Fig. 2.1(a), 0.4 mm C11000 copper sheets (Cu, 99.9%) and nickel-plated 1.0-mm copper sheets of the same copper alloy (ASTM B689) were used for the welding experiments. Nickel coating, approximately of 3 μm, was intended originally for corrosion resistance, but it also served as an indicator of surface separation between the two similar materials during the microscopic analysis. For example, the bond density over the weld interface can be measured by (1) the interfacial area where the nickel layer is broken and two copper surfaces are fused together, and (2) the area where the nickel layer is distorted so that it leads to a mechanical interlocking between materials. It is difficult to determine these bonded regions between two copper surfaces without the nickel layer.

The experimental procedure is as follows:

1. Coupon sheets of Cu and Ni-plated Cu were ultrasonically welded at different levels of clamping pressure (40, 50, and 60 psi) and welding time (0.2, 0.4, 0.6, 0.8, and 1.0 second);
2. The produced weld samples were then subjected to U-tensile tests to identify the failure types and to evaluate the weld quality; and
3. The weld zones were characterized by optical microscopy (Fig. 2.1(c)), SEMs and micro-hardness tests.

2.2.1 Experiments

Test coupons, 25-mm wide and 45-mm long, with complete overlap (Fig. 2.1(b)), were welded by an AmTech Ultraweld®L-20 high power welder with a vibration frequency of 20 kHz and a vibration direction along the shorter side of the coupon. The dimensions and configurations of weld samples were designed to allow the U-tensile test, as illustrated in Fig. 2.2(a). According to the screening tests performed prior to this study, the clamping pressure and welding time were selected as input variables while the vibration amplitude was kept constant at 30 μm throughout the experiment, as detailed in Table 2.1. Using a full factorial design, 15 test conditions in total and 10 replicates at each condition were conducted.

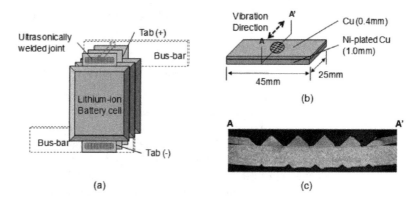

Figure 2.1. Ultrasonic welding configuration: (a) an example of battery tab joining; (b) dimension and configuration of weld coupons; and (c) cross-section image (AA′).

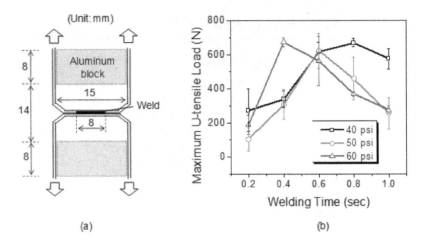

(a)   (b)

Figure 2.2. Weld performance testing: (a) U-tensile test configuration; (b) maximum U-tensile load plotted against welding time for three different clamping pressures.

TABLE 2.1. Factors and levels for experimental design.

Factor	Factor name	Level
P	Clamping pressure (psi)	40, 50, 60
T	Welding time (sec)	0.2, 0.4, 0.6, 0.8, 1.0

2.2.2 Weld Performance Testing

In order to evaluate the mechanical strength, welded samples were subjected to U-tensile tests performed using an *Instron* testing machine with a 5-kN load cell. A pulling speed of 20 mm/min was selected to minimize unnecessary dynamic effects for weld failure. The peak load during the test was recorded as a measure of weld performance. After the weld had failed, photo images were taken and examined to record different failure types.

Figure 2.2(b) shows the maximum U-tensile load against welding time for three different clamping pressures. The load at each clamping pressure increases as welding time increases, and begins to decrease beyond a critical welding time due to material thinning and crack formations. For 40 psi of clamping pressure, the maximum U-tensile load is achieved at 0.8 second of weld time, and this optimum welding time decreases with higher clamping pressures: 0.6 second for 50 psi and 0.4 second for 60 psi, respectively.

2.2.3 Sample Preparation/Microscopy/Hardness Testing

To identify weld attributes, SEM and metallurgical examination were conducted. The weld samples were sectioned across their center, parallel to the direction of welding vibration, by a low speed diamond wheel saw without creating any residual stresses. The cross-sectioned specimens were then cold-mounted in epoxy, carefully ground until the plane of the maximum sonotrode indentation depth was reached. Then they were polished down to 1 μm diamond, and further polished to 0.25 μm colloidal silica. Following etching using ammonium hydroxide mixed with dilute hydrogen peroxide, optical images were obtained from a fluorescent microscope (Olympus BX51 W/DP71) to provide metallographs of the samples. More detailed microstructural analysis was performed with a SEM with a Philips XL30 FEG-SEM at 30 kV to characterize the circumferential defect of the weld. Finally, to identify the mechanical property change within the weld zone, microhardness was measured by using a Vickers microhardness tester (Clark, CM-400AT) with an indentation load of 25 g for 15 seconds.

2.3 DEFINITION OF ATTRIBUTES AND WELD CHARACTERIZATION

In this section, critical weld attributes that impact on the weld performance are defined first. Then, the ultrasonically welded joints of Cu and Ni-plated Cu are characterized using microstructural images and hardness distribution. The bond mechanisms for these particular materials and the metallurgical characteristics, such as material flow in the metal surface of the top sheet and hardening/softening during the weld development, are discussed as those are associated with the formation of weld attributes.

2.3.1 Definition of Weld Attributes

Weld strength can be determined by the physical attributes of the weldment [12]. Several weld attributes of ultrasonically welded joints are defined in Table 2.2. Each weld attribute was quantitatively measured or qualitatively estimated by using the cross-section images and microhardness profiles in the weld zone.

- *Bond density*: the relative bond density for different welding time is estimated by distinguishing bonded and unbonded regions at the weld interface and measuring the proportion of bonded portion projected onto the horizontal line to the entire sonotrode width, as described in Table 2.2(a).
- *Post-weld thickness*: the post-weld thickness is the thickness of the indented material by the sonotrode's pressing force. The indented thickness of the upper sheet for each weld sample produced in different welding time is measured from the microscope and averaged over the whole bonding line, and then the deformed material thickness is calculated as,

$$\text{post weld thickness}\,(\%) = \frac{t_{indented}}{t_{original}} \times 100 \tag{2.1}$$

TABLE 2.2. Definitions of ultrasonic weld attributes and schematic diagrams of attribute measurement.

Attribute	Definition	Schematic diagram
(a) Bond density	The proportion of projected bonded region to entire weld interface	
(b) Post-weld thickness	The average thickness of the top material after weld	
(c) Weld nugget size	The entire width of ultrasonically bonded area under sonotrode	
(d) TMAZ size	The entire width of thermo-mechanically affected zone outside the weld nugget	

where $t_{indented}$ is the minimum distance from indented surface to weld interface and $t_{original}$ is the original unwelded thickness, which is a constant value. Table 2.2(b) provides a schematic explanation of the post-weld thickness.

- *Weld nugget size*: the weld nugget size is measured using the cross-section length where the actual ultrasonic weld is formed. A schematic diagram of this weld nugget size is described in Table 2.2(c). This attribute is one of the most decisive factors that determine the failure types in the U-tensile test.

- *Thermo-mechanically affected zone*: the size of thermo-mechanically affected zone (TMAZ), as illustrated in Table 2.2(d), is the width of the entire area influenced by both plastic deformation and heat. Both weld nugget and TMAZ size are indirectly measured from the hardness profile where the mechanical property change in the weld zone was reflected. Detailed weld region classification will be discussed in the later section (2.4.3).

2.3.2 Characterization of Ultrasonic Welds Using Weld Attributes

To understand the relationship between physical weld attributes and weld performances, multiple weld samples of different weld quality were cross-sectioned and characterized with optical microscopy, SEMs, and hardness measurements. The cross-section samples were selected from the weld samples produced in 50 psi clamping pressure with increasing weld time (0.2–1.0 second) since they revealed various failure types within the entire range of weld time. Observations from the selected samples are shown in Fig. 2.3. Gaps along the weld interface are clearly visible due to the lack of bonding (0.2 second weld time). As weld time increases, these gaps become less distinct since materials are now in intimate contact. The imprints from the horn (Fig. 2.4) and the anvil, however, become intense for the 1.0 second case, and the outer edges of top sheet are thinned due to excessive welding energy input. Detailed joint characteristics including the bond mechanism, material flow, and hardening and softening behaviors are discussed in this section. The formation process

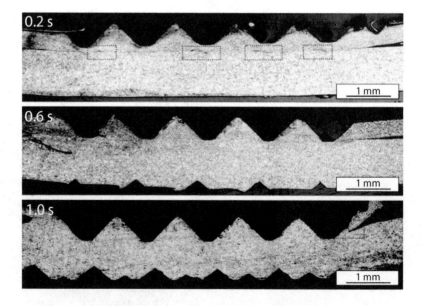

Figure 2.3. Optical images of Cu and Ni-plated Cu weld cross-sections produced with a pressure of 50 psi, with increasing welding times (0.2 second, 0.6 second, and 1.0 second).

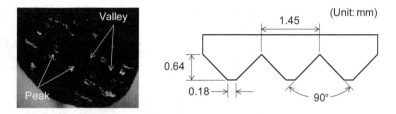

Figure 2.4. Knurl pattern of sonotrode (left) and its dimension (right).

of each weld attribute as defined in Section 2.3.1 has a deep affinity with those joint characteristics. For example, the bond density is measured by identifying the bonded region, which is based on the bond mechanisms discussed in this section. The formation process of indention in the weld zone is closely related to the material flow occurred on the metal surface. Lastly, the rationale behind the weld region classification such as weld nugget (WN) or TMAZ grounds on the hardness change resulted from such phenomenon as work hardening and softening happened during the welding process.

Bond Mechanism

There are several theories of weld formation in ultrasonic metal welding, which include metallurgical adhesion derived from a significant amount of plastic deformation [4, 13, 14], diffusion across the weld interface [15–17], local melting [18, 19], and mechanical interlocking [20]. Among these theories, metallurgical adhesion and mechanical interlocking are observed in this cross-sectioning analysis. Diffusion bonding is excluded in this study because the diffusion between materials of the same kind, copper-to-copper in this study, is hardly observable in the microscopic analysis. The microstructures of the weld specimen produced in 0.4 second of welding time are shown in Fig. 2.5, which describes the formation process of bonding lines between two metal surfaces. Three different stages during the formation process are identified along the weld interface in the same cross-section sample: (1) micro-bond development, (2) curvy bonding line initiation, and (3) completion

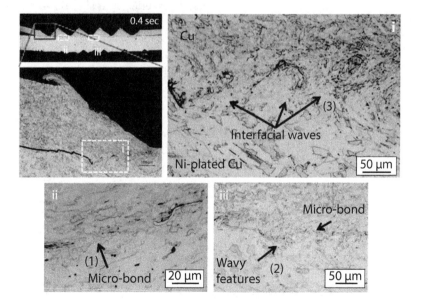

Figure 2.5. Optical images of the formation process of micro-bonds and interfacial waves along the bonding line.

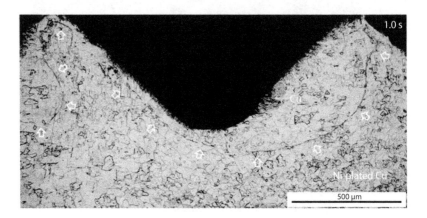

Figure 2.6. Convoluted bonding line in the weld samples produced in 1.0 second weld time.

of interfacial wave formation. In Fig. 2.5, the local micro-bonds are developed through the broken Ni layer, and by continuing shear oscillations around the micro-bonds, the bonding line forms into a twisted, rolled shape, so called "interfacial waves." This compound phenomenon agrees with the previous study [8]. Hence, the bonding strength of ultrasonically welded joints is a result of a synergistic effect of (1) metallurgical adhesion (micro-bonds) and (2) mechanical interlocking (interfacial waves).

Figure 2.6 shows a special case of bonding line appearances when the weld time or the energy input exceeds its optimum range within which good weld quality is achieved. The cross-section image exhibits an extremely convoluted bonding line, which appears to be different from typical bonding lines with good weld quality. This macroscopic convolution of the bonding line is caused by the similar process of interfacial waves formation, but in a much greater scale. In other words, as the locally bonded regions (used to be concentrated on the peaks of the sonotrode teeth) grow over the entire weld interface, the bonding line of the highly softened materials experiences a significant amount of deformation by the combined forces in shear and normal directions. Therefore, the forming mechanism of these convoluted bonding lines is summarized as (1) an expansion of bonding line through the entire interface; (2) macroscopic deformation of the bonding line by continuous vibrations and clamping forces from the sonotrode; (3) the completion of a very complex-shaped bonding line.

Material Flow

In an ultrasonic weld, there exist imprints by the knurl patterns of the sonotrode and anvil, which was customized for the material type and thicknesses of the test coupons. By analyzing optical micrographs of the cross-sectioned weld samples, the deformation process of these imprints is as follows: (1) a shear force is exerted to the metal surface by friction as the sonotrode starts to vibrate; (2) plastic deformation begins at the material surface around the peaks of the sonotrode teeth and expands outwards from each teeth through a repetition of friction and sliding; (3) the indentation of the sonotrode is intensified as the plastically deformed areas grow. Figure 2.7(a) describes a layer of deformed material overflowing onto the edge of sonotrode tip, while Fig. 2.7(b) shows a captured image of the material flowing along the inclined surface. As such, the flows of material layers occur in local sonotrode tooth areas throughout the entire knurl plane. It is seen that the regions close to the contact surface have elongated grains parallel to the slopes, and the regions where the materials actually flow have very fine grains due to high local strain (high magnification images of Fig. 2.7(a–b)).

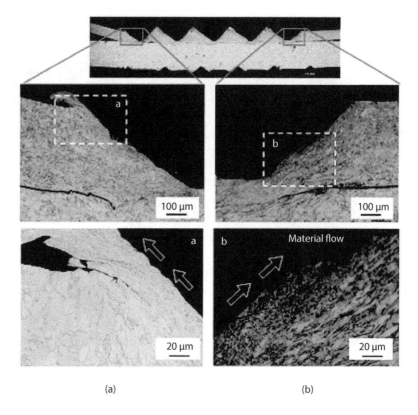

(a)   (b)

Figure 2.7. Optical images of Cu and Ni-plated Cu joints produced in 0.4 second weld time: the layer of deformed material (a) overflowing onto the edge of sonotrode edge (b) starting to flow along the inclined plane.

As shown in Fig. 2.8(a), the vertical position of the sonotrode during the welding with 1.0 second process time and 50 psi clamping pressure was obtained from a LVDT sensor equipped in the welder. The sonotrode's position rapidly decreases at the beginning (0–0.2 second), slows down in the middle (0.2–0.6 second), and then decreases again after that (0.6–0.9 second). This indentation rate is related to how the knurl imprint is formed during

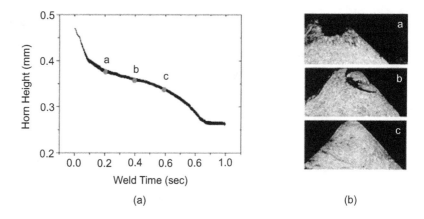

(a)   (b)

Figure 2.8. Material flow during the welding process: (a) a LVDT signal for 1 second process time; (b) optical images of valley areas of the sonotrode knurl pattern for different welding time (a: 0.2 second, b: 0.4 second, c: 0.6 second).

the welding process. The initial fast indentation is resulted from the fact that there exists enough space (i.e., sonotrode valleys) for the deformed material layers to flow in. However, once this space is filled up, the material flow cannot extensively occur any longer, and the indentation slows down its rate. The filling process of the material is clearly shown in a series of optical images of the sonotrode's valley area with increasing weld time (Fig. 2.8(b)). Regaining the indentation rate after 0.6 second is caused by intensified material softening due to an annealing effect, which will be further discussed.

In conclusion, the process of material flow with extensive plastic deformation is one of the important characteristics in ultrasonic metal welding, because it improves gripping of the specimens so that more frictional work can be done at the weld interface. Nonetheless, an excessive material flow causes the material thinning, which negatively affects the weld quality.

Work Hardening and Softening

In this study, an extensive microscopic analyses and microhardness measurements were performed to observe microstructural changes during the ultrasonic metal welding process. Figure 2.9 shows a series of optical cross-section images over time (0–1.0 second), focused on the weld interface area. Figure 2.9(a) shows microstructures of the as-received materials for Cu and Ni-plated Cu. As ultrasonic excitation begins, the interface experiences the shear forces due to friction resulting in a significant amount of plastic deformation. Elongated grains along the bonding line are observed in the initial stage of the welding process (Fig. 2.9(b–c)). As welding proceeds, the elongated grains disappear and new crystal structures are shown with uniform grain size and with similar lattice structure to the original undeformed grains (Fig. 2.9(d)). This recrystallization process is due to the continuous ultrasonic power input into drastically deformed grains with elevated temperature. However, as welding continues beyond this point, the grain sizes in Fig. 2.9(e–f) grow and the material softening is accelerated as a result of the continuous temperature rise. These microstructural changes are related to the mechanical performance of ultrasonically welded joints. The weld samples produced in short welding time (~0.4 second), showing cold worked microstructures, failed at the interface during U-tensile test. These "undeveloped" welds were classified as "under" weld. The weld samples produced with 0.6 second welding time were confirmed as "good" weld in which recrystallization was identified. Finally, the samples produced with 0.8 second or 1.0 second welding time, showing their microstructures with enlarged grains, were assessed as "over" weld quality.

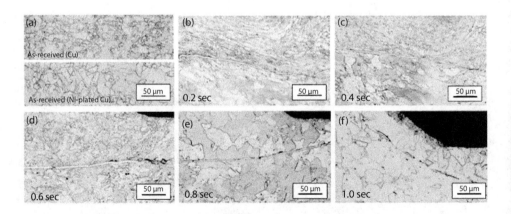

Figure 2.9. Optical images of Cu and Ni-plated Cu joints with increasing welding time: (a) as-received condition (b) 0.2 second; (c) 0.4 second; (d) 0.6 second; (e) 0.8 second; (f) 1.0 second.

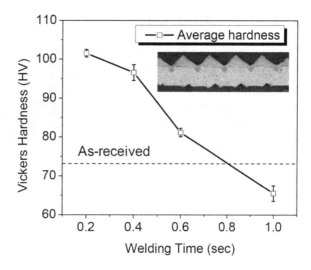

Figure 2.10. Hardness profile of weld samples for different welding time. The hardness is averaged over the peaks of the sonotrode (dots in the cross-section image).

Microhardness measurements were taken on the cross-sectional samples in order to verify the existences of hardening and softening during the weld process that were observed in the microstructures. The Vickers hardness profile measured at the peaks of the sonotrode tip, where the highest strain rate is expected, is plotted against the welding time (Fig. 2.10). The hardness of the initial welding stages shows almost over 40% increase from the as-received condition, which is caused by a large amount of cold working along the weld interface. Then, it is dramatically decreased as the welding time increases, and falls even below the original hardness. The results shown in the hardness profile together with the microscopic analysis in grain size demonstrate the plastic behaviors (i.e., work hardening and softening) that any soft metals in the ultrasonic metal welding process can show.

Hardness Profile in Horizontal Locations
Figure 2.11(a) shows the hardness variation along the bonding line, and the micrographs for 0.4 second and 1.0 second are represented in Fig. 2.11(b). For short welding time (i.e., 0.2 second or 0.4 second), the hardness values of the regions below the peaks of the sonotrode are higher than those below the valleys. This is because the plastic deformation

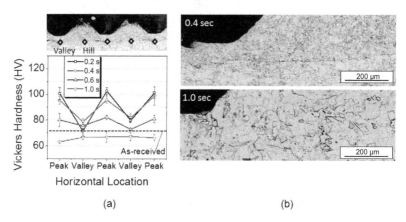

(a)　　　　　　　　　　　　　　　　　　(b)

Figure 2.11. Hardness variation in horizontal locations: (a) horizontal hardness profile of the weld cross-sections; (b) Optical images for 0.4 second and 1.0 second.

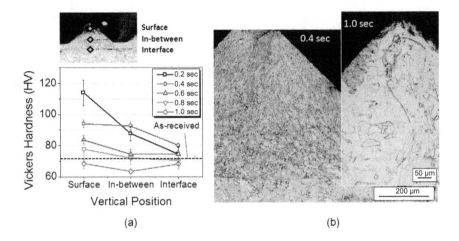

Figure 2.12. Hardness variation in vertical locations: (a) vertical hardness profile of the weld cross-sections; (b) Optical images at the valley area of the sonotrode for 0.4 second and 1.0 second.

begins at the centers of each peak and expands outwards as welding proceeds, so the valley areas of the weld interface are not as much work hardened as the peak areas are. However, as welding time increases, this local fluctuation in hardness value is diminished, and the overall hardness profile is lowered simultaneously due to material softening. Micrographic evidences in Fig. 2.11(b) substantiate the hardness result, by having more distorted grains in the peak area than the valley for shorter welding time (0.4 second), and evenly grown grain size for higher welding time (1.0 second).

Hardness Profile in Vertical Locations

In addition, the hardness profiles in the vertical direction were also measured in order to complete the entire two-dimensional hardness map of the weld cross-sections. The results shown in Fig. 2.12(a) describe how the hardness changes over the vertical measurement locations below the valley area, and over the welding time. For shorter weld time (e.g., 0.2 second), the hardness of the area close to the surface is much higher than that of the interface area, whereas this hardness difference with space is not so severe for longer weld time (e.g., 0.8 or 1.0 second). This is mainly because there is a tremendous amount of cold working at the surface of the valley area (i.e., material flow), as discussed in the previous section. As seen in the optical images in Fig. 2.12(b), the grains of the weld specimen for 0.4 second welding time are vertically elongated while the area close to interface does not seem affected by plastic deformation. In contrast, the microstructure of the weld specimen with 1.0 second weld time does not show any differences in terms of grain size in vertical direction although the overall grain size is much increased than 0.4 second.

To summarize, the materials undergone high ultrasonic energy exhibit instant work hardening due to the cold working at the joint and then softening with the continuous temperature rise. This ultrasonic metal welding process resembles a cold work and subsequent annealing process, where the cold worked metals are recovered to the strain free stage through the recrystallization and grain growth with the application of heat.

2.4 CORRELATION BETWEEN WELD ATTRIBUTES AND QUALITY

In this section, weld quality is correlated to the joint characteristics (i.e., attributes). An ultrasonic metal weld with good weld quality should have dense interfacial bonds without having any severe symptoms of material thinning and surface cracks around the weld zone. Detailed discussions on each attribute including bond density, post-weld thickness, sizes of critical weld regions, and surface cracks are followed with microstructural analyses using optical images, SEMs, and microhardness measurements.

2.4.1 Bond Density

Per previous discussion (Section 2.2), an ultrasonically welded joint of Cu and Ni-plated Cu is created along the interface by breakage of nickel layers followed by severe plastic deformation and metallurgical adhesion with partial aid of mechanical interlocking. Hence, the high density of bonded area through these mechanisms should be critical for higher weld performances.

There was an attempt to quantify the ultrasonic weld quality by directly measuring the percentage of contact points showing diffusion, so called "linear weld density" [4, 5]. This linear weld density is relatively easy to measure because the samples are produced by ultrasonic consolidation process where the bonding lines are almost straight. However, the quantification of bond density for ultrasonic spot welding applications is much difficult due to the complex shape of the bonding line (interfacial waves). Therefore, in this study, the relative bond density was qualitatively estimated for different welding conditions through the microscopic examination of cross-sectioned weld samples.

In Fig. 2.13, the microstructural images of the bonding line for different welding time, 0.2 second (under), 0.6 second (good), and 1.0 second (over), are shown. Distinct gaps between the sheets, referred as unbonded regions, were found along the bonding line in the under weld specimens, whereas there were multiple regions of metallurgical bonds between clean copper surfaces, forming a unified grain structure, in good and even in over weld specimens. There were also very complicated appearances (i.e., mechanical interlocking) throughout the bonding line, which could give additional bonding strength to the joint. However, the densities of metallic bonds and interlocking in the over welds were much larger than those in the good welds, even though the U-tensile test showed the opposite result (i.e., higher weld performance in good welds). Therefore, the weld performance of ultrasonic metal welds is not a function of the bond density alone.

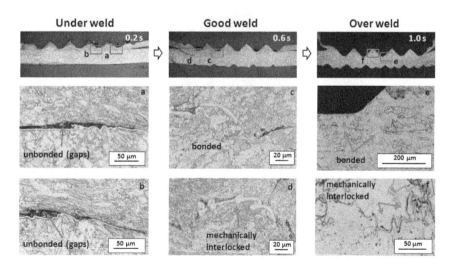

Figure 2.13. Optical images of welded joints made in different weld qualities (i.e., "under," "good," and "over" weld).

2.4.2 Post-Weld Thickness

The post-weld thickness in the knurl imprints is another important attribute that can affect the weld performance of the ultrasonic metal weld. The percentile thickness of post-weld samples, as defined in Section 2.1, is plotted against the welding time in Fig. 2.14.

As welding time increases the upper workpiece is deformed more and more until its thickness becomes less than 10% of the original thickness. It is also noted that a similar trend of indentation is observed from both the LVDT signal and the measured thickness in optical cross-section images. More than 60% of the original thickness is deformed by the indentation during the first 0.2 second, and then the deformation rate slows down as welding proceeds. This fast indentation rate in the initial stage of the welding process is mainly because there is a plenty of room for the material to flow in between each valley area of the sonotrode tip. As referred to the weld performance, under weld quality is resulted during the initial fast deformation stage, and gradually changed into good quality of weld with high tensile strength as the deformation rate becomes stable. The indented thickness for the over weld case (1.0 second) was not able to measure because of the vague bonding line due to the complete breakage of the nickel layer and the blending into copper.

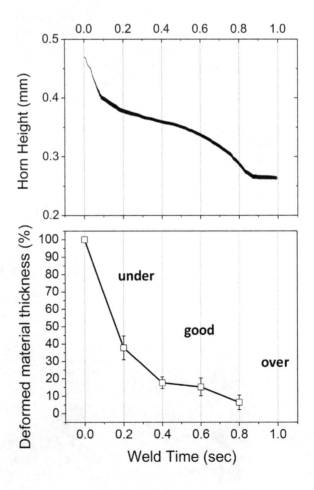

Figure 2.14. Vertical position of sonotrode obtained from LVDT sensor (upper); percentile ratio of indentation measured from optical cross-section images (lower).

2.4.3 Thermo-Mechanically Affected Zone (TMAZ) and Weld Nugget

The microstructures and mechanical properties of metal weldment are difficult to measure due to locality sensitivity [21]. In addition, the preparation of microscopic mechanical testing specimens for ultrasonic metal welds is not easy. Therefore, the material properties of the welds such as yield strength can be obtained by empirical relationships between material strength and hardness [21]. As a linear relationship (i.e., *Hardness* = $c\sigma_y$) [22], the relative change in yield strength can be estimated by the relative change of hardness, which can be expressed as

$$\frac{\sigma_y}{\sigma_{y,as-received}} = \frac{t_{measured}}{HV_{as-received}} \qquad (2.2)$$

where σ_y is the yield strength and HV is the hardness value. From this relationship and the hardness profiles of the weld specimens, the plastic behavior of the material for each different zone can be indirectly estimated.

Hardness Distribution

Hardness profiles over the entire weld region for different weld times (0.2, 0.6, and 1.0 second) were collected and presented in Fig. 2.15. Figure 2.15(b) shows the hardness variation along the weld interface (inside the weld zone), and the hardness profile along the center line of the top material (outside the weld zone) is in Fig. 2.15(c). The test locations selected for those hardness measurements are shown in the schematic drawing of weld cross-sections (Fig. 2.15(a)). To compare the hardness profiles at two different scales, it should be noted that the interval of each peak and valley in Fig. 2.15(b) is 1.45 mm for the selected design of the sonotrode tip, and the hardness for Fig. 2.15(c) was measured in every 0.1 mm.

The hardness profile on the weld interface for under weld case in Fig. 2.15(b) shows a large variation from peak to valley, whereas the hardness profile gradually levels off as shifted to good and over weld case. In addition, an overall degradation in absolute hardness value over time is shown at the same time. These simultaneous variations in hardness

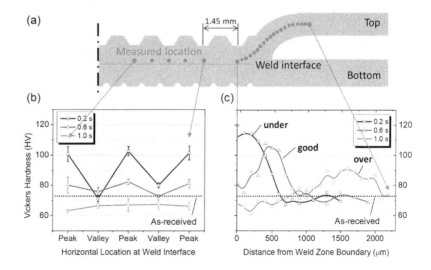

Figure 2.15. Hardness distribution of the weld samples for different weld time: (a) a schematic diagram of ultrasonically welded joint; (b) hardness profile of the weld interface; (c) hardness profile outside of weld zone.

profile, in terms not only of the regional difference within the bonding line but of the weld process time, are resulted from the work hardening due to severe plastic deformation and the softening from intense ultrasonic energy input, as discussed in the prior section (2.2).

Figure 2.15(c) shows a result on the hardness variation of the region outside the weld zone. It can be seen as an extension of the horizontal hardness profile at the weld interface of Fig. 2.15(b). Each weld sample produced in different welding time experiences a different pattern of work hardening and softening. For shorter weld time (0.2 second) the increased hardness can be read at the region very close to the boundary of weld zone, and then lowers its value back to the original hardness of as-received materials. However, as welding time becomes longer, the region where the highest hardness value is found to move outwards away from the boundary. In an "over" weld, high hardness value outside the weld region exists because of the work hardening in the metal sheets due to the plastic deformation. At the same time, the absolute value of the peak hardness is slowly decreasing, but still higher than any of hardness inside the weld zone. The hardness increase in this area is resulted from the cold working due to the cyclic stresses exerted both horizontally (ultrasonic vibration) and vertically (clamping force). However, the hardness decreases at the boundary due to the softening with the temperature rise. The hardness in this region for over weld case falls even below the original hardness value because the material experiences higher stress right under the sonotrode tip. Therefore, the regions outside the weld zone are also thermally and mechanically affected by the ultrasonically oscillating tools.

Weld Region Classification

Various zones in an ultrasonic metal weld were distinguished by their mechanical properties and micrographs. As depicted in a schematic diagram of an ultrasonically welded joint (Fig. 2.16(a)), the weld is divided into three primary regions. Area "A" is called "weld nugget (WN)" where an actual interfacial bonding between the metals occurs. It is found that an extensive amount of plastic deformation due to friction between surfaces creates a metal-to-metal bonding, and recrystallized grain structures due to increased temperature are also observed in this area. Area "B" is affected by both heat and plastic deformation and named as the "thermo-mechanically affected zone." This terminology, normally used in other solid state welding process especially in friction stir welding (FSW) [23–25], is

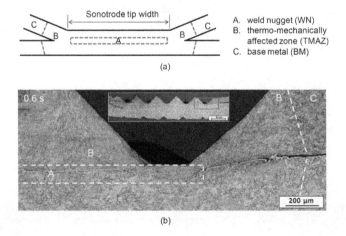

(a)

(b)

Figure 2.16. Weld region classification: (a) a schematic diagram of weld region classification; (b) optical micrograph of an ultrasonic weld produced in 0.6 second welding time, giving an overview of classified weld regions.

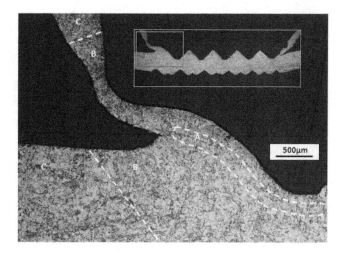

Figure 2.17. Optical micrograph of an ultrasonic weld produced in 1.0 second welding time with classified weld regions.

selected here because the basic material behaviors under the influence of the welding tools (e.g., a sonotrode tip or an anvil) are similar in ultrasonic metal welding, although the intensity of deformation in FSW is much higher due to the direct stirring motion of the tool. From the hardness distribution previously shown in Fig. 2.15, evidence of thermo-mechanical effects is found in this area, and the degree of affection in the area is also identified. The microstructure of the TMAZ on the upper sheet of workpiece as in Fig. 2.16(b) shows an elongated grain structure parallel to the vibration direction. Area "C" is base metal (BM) which is affected neither by heat nor by deformation in terms of microstructure or mechanical properties (e.g., hardness).

Figure 2.17 shows an optical image of the microstructure of the weld cross-section, which was ultrasonically welded for 1.0 second (over weld case). The same weld region classification can be applied to this figure: WN, TMAZ, and BM. However, the micrograph is slightly different from that of Fig. 2.16(b) which is a typical microstructure of the good weld case. The area of the TMAZ of over weld case has been much enlarged than that of good weld case, and so has the WN.

Relationship between Size of TMAZ or WN and Weld Performance
High performance of an ultrasonic weld tends to be associated with the failure type when performing destructive tests for their joint strengths [8]. The previous U-tensile test showed a good quality weld failed near the outermost sonotrode teeth while a under or an over quality weld experienced different failure types. The failure type variation can be related to the changes in microstructure and mechanical properties with space and time, so the location for stress concentration will vary with the different weld quality. Therefore, a relationship between weld performance and the size variation of each classified weld region (i.e., WN, TMAZ, and BM) within the weldment can be qualitatively established.

The boundaries between each zone (e.g., WN/TMAZ or TMAZ/BM) are determined by the areas where the hardness profile changes its value in a relative gradient as shown in Fig. 2.15(c). For example, the hardness for the weld specimen of 0.6 second weld time shows a sudden increase at the location slightly off the outermost teeth (~350 μm). The hardness passes its peak point and then decreases back to the hardness of as-received condition at the location away from the sonotrode (~1300 μm). The first transition zone is regarded as the boundary of the WN, and the latter one as the boundary between the TMAZ and the BM.

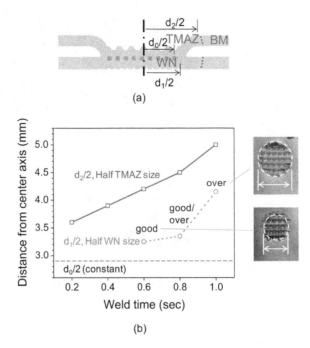

(a)

(b)

Figure 2.18. Classified weld regions associated with failure types: (a) a schematic diagram indicating dimension of each weld region (TMAZ and WN); (b) half TMAZ size and half WN size over weld time, with failed weldment images after U-tensile test.

Figure 2.18(b) shows the approximate half sizes of these zones, which is schematically indicated in Fig. 2.18(a), measured from the hardness profile plotted against the welding time. It should be noted that the half WN size for 0.2 second and 0.4 second was not applicable since the weld specimens in this condition showed interfacial separation during the performance testing. This is because the WN zone has not been grown well. As shown in Fig. 2.18(b), the half TMAZ size increased proportionally to the weld process time and the half WN size also grew with time. Of these two, the half WN size is more related to the stress concentration area which plays a role in the failure type of the weld specimen during the performance test. The failure type of circumferential fracture may be resulted from the crack initiation along the boundary of WN. The photo images of the failed parts showing their weldments adhered to the bottom sheets have a good agreement with the measured sizes of half WNs.

2.4.4 Surface Cracks

As discussed in the previous section, a good quality weld was not always achieved as the WN size grew. Instead, the excessive welding time or energy input caused extra thinning around the TMAZ area, and eventually led to lower weld strength during the performance testing. In addition to material thinning, various sizes of cracks can be generated on the surface of the material, especially on the outer TMAZ area, due to the high strain rate caused by an intense forming action from the sonotrode. These surface cracks are referred as one of the defects that an ultrasonic metal weld with excessive condition may have.

Figure 2.19 shows a series of SEM images of an ultrasonic weld produced in an over weld condition (1.0 second weld time), focusing on the outer TMAZ area. The images in

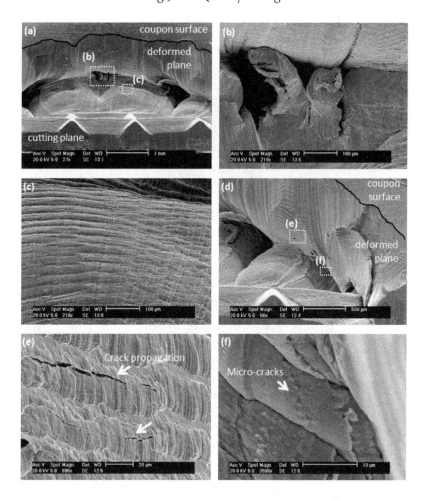

Figure 2.19. SEM images of deformed surfaces around the weld zone from the "over" weld: (a) a front view image (vibration direction: out-and-in-plane); (b) "island" features; (c) fatigue striation marks; (d) another front view image of the right hand side of image-(a); (e) crack propagations; (f) micro-cracks.

Fig. 2.18 were collected right after weld completion with the weld samples being cut in half by a diamond wheel saw and placed in the sample chamber of a FEG-SEM. The fatigue damages shown in the figure were found on the stretched metal surface, which had been in direct contact with the sonotrode. Figure 2.19(a) is a macroscopic view of the weld spot (cut in half) where various surface characteristics exist. It should be noted that the vibration is of out-and-in-of-plane direction and the clamping direction is downward. An "island" feature shown in Fig. 2.19(b) is formed from severely twisted interfacial waves, which is exposed to the surface due to an extensive amount of thinning in the upper sheet. Figure 2.19(c) shows direct evidence of fatigue failure undergone at high frequency of cyclic loading, having evenly spaced, clear fatigue striation marks over the deformed surface. Figure 2.19(d) is another macroscopic view of the weld as a continuous image from Fig. 2.19(a). Visible cracks from large size (50–100 μm) to micro-size (less than 5 μm) are seen in Fig. 2.19(e–f). These surface defects may be the reason for fractures during the tensile test due to the stress concentration, and sometimes to perforations within the given weld time.

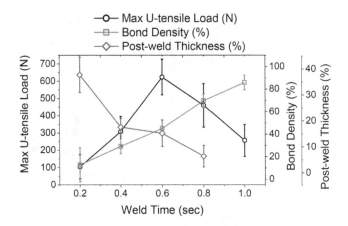

Figure 2.20. Correlation of weld performance with bond density and post-weld thickness.

2.4.5 Summary of Correlation between Weld Attributes and Quality

The relationship between the weld performance and two attributes (i.e., bond density and post-weld thickness) is summarized in Fig. 2.20, plotted against weld time. The bond density is increasing over weld time due to an expansion of the micro-bonds at the weld interface, and the post-weld thickness is decreasing due to material thinning. The highest joint strength is shown in the middle at a weld time of about 0.6 second. This shows that a good quality weld in ultrasonic welding is achieved when the interfacial bond reaches a level of enough metallurgical adhesion and mechanical interlocking, but the material thinning has not progressed to the extent to severely reduce the mechanical strength.

2.5 CONCLUSIONS

A set of measurable weld attributes have been proposed to characterize ultrasonically welded joints of copper and nickel plated copper. The joint characteristics of different quality welds were investigated using those attributes and the relationship between attributes and performance was qualitatively identified. The main conclusions of this chapter are as follows:

1. The bonding strength of ultrasonically welded joints for copper and nickel-plated copper is due to the combined effect of metallurgical adhesion (micro-bonds) and mechanical interlocking.
2. Different levels of weld quality (i.e., under, good, or over weld) are correlated to the combination effect of the bonded area density and the post-weld thickness, which show opposite tendencies.
3. Material flow with extensive plastic deformation occurs at the metal surface in contact with each sonotrode tooth, and causes material thinning or indentation. Indentation of the metal surface intensifies as welding proceeds, and its rate also differs in different quality regions: fast indentation rate in under weld samples, slowing down in good weld and regaining the indentation rate in over weld.
4. Material that has received high ultrasonic energy input show instant work hardening due to the cold working and then softening with continuous temperature increase, which resembles an annealing process (i.e., recovery, recrystallization, and grain growth).

5. Various zones in an ultrasonic metal weld are distinguished by their mechanical properties and micrographs: Weld Nugget (WN), Thermo-Mechanically Affected Zone (TMAZ), and Base Material (BM). The sizes of TMAZ and WN affect the failure type during performance testing and, eventually, weld quality.

A set of well-defined weld attributes help to link welding process variables with weld quality based on an understanding of the characteristics of the weldment. The scientific understanding obtained from this chapter can guide manufacturers in establishing robust process parameter regions to achieve consistent quality. The methodology on identifying these weld attributes will be extended to multi-layer welding in our future work.

Acknowledgment

The work presented here was sponsored by the General Motors Collaborative Research Lab in Advanced Vehicle Manufacturing at the University of Michigan. The authors appreciate the support provided by Dr. Kai Sun at The University of Michigan Electron Microbeam Analysis Laboratory (EMAL).

REFERENCES

[1] Lee, S., Kim, T., Hu, J., Li, J., Cai, W., and Abell, J. A., 2013, "Characterization of Joint Quality in Ultrasonic Welding of Battery Tabs," *ASME Journal of Manufacturing Science and Engineering*, **135**(2), p. 021004.

[2] Lee, S. S., Kim, T. H., Hu, S. J., Cai, W. W., and Abell, J. A., 2010, "Joining Technologies for Automotive Lithium-Ion Battery Manufacturing: A Review," *ASME Conference Proceedings*, **2010**(49460), pp. 541–549.

[3] Hu, S. J., Senkara, J., and Zhang, H., 1996, "Performance Characteristics of Resistance Spot Welds in the Automotive Industry: A Structural Point of View," *Proceedings of IBEC '96 Body & Engineering*, pp. 91–98.

[4] Kong, C., Soar, R., and Dickens, P., 2003, "Characterisation of Aluminium Alloy 6061 for the Ultrasonic Consolidation Process," *Materials Science and Engineering* A, **363**(1–2), pp. 99–106.

[5] Kong, C., Soar, R., and Dickens, P., 2004, "Optimum Process Parameters for Ultrasonic Consolidation of 3003 Aluminium," *Journal of Materials Processing Technology*, **146**(2), pp. 181–187.

[6] Yang, Y., Ram, G. D. J., and Stucker, B. E., 2010, "An Analytical Energy Model for Metal Foil Deposition in Ultrasonic Consolidation," *Rapid Prototyping Journal*, **16**(1), pp. 20–28.

[7] Hetrick, E., Baer, J., Zhu, W., Reatherford, L., Grima, A., Scholl, D., Wilkosz, D., Fatima, S., and Ward, S., 2009, "Ultrasonic Metal Welding Process Robustness in Aluminum Automotive Body Construction Applications," *Welding Journal*, **88**(7).

[8] Bakavos, D., and Prangnell, P. B., 2010, "Mechanisms of Joint and Microstructure Formation in High Power Ultrasonic Spot Welding 6111 Aluminium Automotive Sheet," *Materials Science and Engineering: A*, **527**(23), pp. 6320–6334.

[9] Zhou, B., Thouless, M., and Ward, S., 2006, "Predicting the Failure of Ultrasonic Spot Welds by Pull-out from Sheet Metal," *International Journal of Solids and Structures*, **43**(25–26), pp. 7482–7500.

[10] Zhou, B., Thouless, M. D., and Ward, S., 2005, "Determining Mode-I Cohesive Parameters for Nugget Fracture in Ultrasonic Spot Welds," *International Journal of Fracture*, **136**(1), pp. 309–326.

[11] Kim, T. H., Yum, J., Hu, S. J., Spicer, J. P., and Abell, J. A., 2011, "Process Robustness of Single Lap Ultrasonic Welding of Thin, Dissimilar Materials," *CIRP Annals—Manufacturing Technology*, **60**(1), pp. 17–20.

[12] Zhou, M., Zhang, H., and Hu, S. J., 2003, "Relationships between Quality and Attributes of Spot Welds," *Welding Journal (Miami, Fla)*, **82**(Compendex), pp. 72S–77S.

[13]　Zhang, C., and Li, L., 2009, "A Coupled Thermal-Mechanical Analysis of Ultrasonic Bonding Mechanism," *Metallurgical and Materials Transactions B*, **40**(2), pp. 196–207.

[14]　Ram, G. D. J., Robinson, C., Yang, Y., and Stucker, B., 2007, "Use of Ultrasonic Consolidation for Fabrication of Multi-Material Structures," *Rapid Prototyping Journal*, **13**(4), pp. 226–235.

[15]　Cheng, X., and Li, X., 2007, "Investigation of Heat Generation in Ultrasonic Metal Welding Using Micro Sensor Arrays," *Journal of Micromechanics and Microengineering*, **17**, p. 273.

[16]　Ji, H., Li, M., Kung, A. T., Wang, C., and Li, D., 2005, "The Diffusion of Ni into Al Wire at the Interface of Ultrasonic Wire Bond During High Temperature Storage," *Proc. Electronic Packaging Technology, 6th International Conference on*, pp. 377–381.

[17]　Li, J., Han, L., and Zhong, J., 2008, "Short Circuit Diffusion of Ultrasonic Bonding Interfaces in Microelectronic Packaging," *Surface and Interface Analysis*, **40**(5), pp. 953–957.

[18]　Gunduz, I. E., Ando, T., Shattuck, E., Wong, P. Y., and Doumanidis, C. C., 2005, "Enhanced Diffusion and Phase Transformations During Ultrasonic Welding of Zinc and Aluminum," *Scripta Materialia*, **52**(9), pp. 939–943.

[19]　Kreye, H., 1977, "Melting Phenomena in Solid State Welding Processes," *Welding Journal*, **56**(5), pp. 154–158.

[20]　Joshi, K. C., 1971, "The Formation of Ultrasonic Bonds between Metals," *Welding Journal*, **50**(12), pp. 840–848.

[21]　Zhou, M., Hu, S. J., and Zhang, H., 1999, "Critical Specimen Sizes for Tensile-Shear Testing of Steel Sheets," *Welding Journal (Miami, Fla)*, **78**(9).

[22]　Cáceres, C. H., Griffiths, J. R., Pakdel, A. R., and Davidson, C. J., 2005, "Microhardness Mapping and the Hardness-Yield Strength Relationship in High-Pressure Diecast Magnesium Alloy Az91," *Materials Science and Engineering: A*, **402**(1–2), pp. 258–268.

[23]　Geuser, F. D., Bley, F., Denquin, A., and Deschamps, A., "Mapping the Microstructure of a Friction-Stir Welded (Fsw) Al-Li-Cu Alloy," *Proc. Journal of Physics*, IOP Publishing, p. 012034.

[24]　Prangnell, P. B., and Heason, C. P., 2005, "Grain Structure Formation During Friction Stir Welding Observed by the 'Stop Action Technique'," *Acta Materialia*, **53**(11), pp. 3179–3192.

[25]　Steuwer, A., Dumont, M., Altenkirch, J., Birosca, S., Deschamps, A., Prangnell, P., and Withers, P., 2011, "A Combined Approach to Microstructure Mapping of an Al-Li Aa2199 Friction Stir Weld," *Acta Materialia*, **59**(8), pp. 3002–3011.

Chapter 3

WELDING MECHANISM AND FAILURE OF ULTRASONIC WELDS[1]

Xin Wu[1], Teng Liu[1], and Wayne Cai[2]
[1]Department of Mechanical Engineering, Wayne State University
[2]Manufacturing Systems Research Lab, General Motors Global R&D Center

ABSTRACT

Ultrasonic metal welding has been used widely to join battery cell terminals, or tabs (either Al or Cu), with bus bars (Cu) to form assembled battery packs in battery electric vehicles. However, the mechanism of ultrasonic welding for Al/Cu is still not well understood. In this chapter, the microstructures of the ultrasonic welds between three layers of lithium-ion battery tabs (either Al or Cu) and bus bars were studied. From the microstructure analysis, the weld formation mechanism and failure modes were investigated. It was found that the metal inter-mix or interlocking is the main weld formation mechanism among Al tabs, while metallic bonding is the main mechanism for Cu-Cu or Al-Cu joining. Metallographs also indicated that the weld failure is a combination of the interfacial debonding between the innermost tab (either Cu or Al) and the Cu bus bar and the through-thickness fracture of the tabs. This chapter provides better understanding of weld formation and failure, and hence provides insight into ultrasonic welding process toward weld quality improvement. This understanding and insight can be used to develop science-based design guidelines toward selecting the most appropriate materials (including heat treatment and coating), and welding configurations (such as layers of tabs), and welding process parameters.

Keywords: battery tabs, bonding, failure, fracture, metallography of welds, microstructure, ultrasonic welding, welding mechanism

3.1 INTRODUCTION

In ultrasonic metal welding, a high frequency shear oscillation generated by a piezoelectric system removes surface oxides or contamination by friction. The reciprocating sliding motion under pressure results in metallurgical adhesion at the metal contact interfaces without requirement of melting. Such a solid-state bonding is advantageous for joining dissimilar metals with high electrical/thermal conductivities, such as copper and aluminum, commonly used for lithium-ion batteries. Therefore, in recent years, there are tremendous

---

[1] The content presented in this chapter has previously appeared in Ref. [1].

37

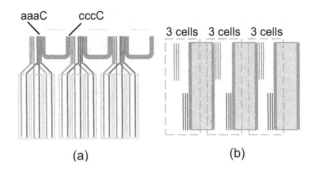

Figure 3.1. Battery cell configuration with three cells grouped in parallel and three groups in series by joining three 0.2-mm tabs to a "U"-shaped 0.9-mm copper bus as shown in (a) front view and (b) top view.

interests in ultrasonic welding of multi-layered battery cell terminals, or tabs, for electrical vehicles. An example of ultrasonic battery tab joining is schematically illustrated in Fig. 3.1. In this configuration, three layers of 0.2-mm-thick Ni-plated pure copper (Cu) or 0.2-mm-thick anodized aluminum (Al), and one layer of 0.9-mm-thick Ni-plated pure Cu are welded in a "cccC" or "aaaC" stacking configuration, where "C" refers to the 0.9 mm Cu, and "c" and "a" refer to the 0.2-mm Cu and Al tabs, respectively.

The performance requirements for the battery tab welds are: mechanical strength (against static load, vibration, crash impact, and fatigue), electrical resistance, and chemical stability (against moisture and corrosion). It is notable that these requirements can conflict with each other. For example, almost all material strengthening mechanisms, such as alloying, grain refinement, cold work, phase-transformation, or second-phase reinforcement, will increase electrical resistivity as well as corrosion reactivity. The soundness of a battery pack highly depends on a sound understanding of the multi-physics process of battery tab joining.

A general description of ultrasonic welding can be found in a number of welding textbooks or handbooks; for example by Potente [2], Staff [3], and Singh [4]. Ultrasonic devices were initially invented for nondestructive evaluation, cleaning, and degreasing during the World War II, and later was used in welding for thermoplastics since 1960s. For polymers, a weld is commonly established at temperatures above glass transition temperature T_g, where the heat is generated by ultrasonic vibration. Upon cooling, the weld is generally stronger than the base materials [5, 6]. The ultrasonic system has experienced a long history of development and significant efforts have been made from academia and industry. For example, the research group led by Tsujuno published a series of papers on various topics of complex vibration weld tip [7], two-vibration system development for multi-spot continuous welding metal plates [8], transverse and torsional complex system with more frequencies besides the fundamental frequency [9–11], the use of large area weld tip [12], and the development of high-powered, stepped complex transverse vibration rods. They also reported research results on high-frequency wire bonding [13], metals/plastics welding [14], aluminum alloys and stainless steel plates welding [15], coated copper wires welding [16], Al/Cu welding [17]. Metals/ceramics ultrasonic joining was studied by Matsuoka [18, 19]. Al/Al welding was studied by Janaki Ram et al. [20]. The ultrasonic welding deformation and microstructure was studied by Bakavos and Prangnell [21] with the use of electron backscatter diffraction (EBSD). They described the Al/Al ultrasonic welding mechanism as a series of progressive processes of micro-welding, expansion, convoluted wavy interface formation, vortices/swirls and ripples, thinning, and shear band formation. Chen et al. [22] reported the formation of heat affected zone in ultrasonic spot welding of aluminum AA6011-T4 with an ageing effect. The measured temperature was as high as 400°C, which caused softening instead of strain hardening. For ultrasonic welding of copper, Elangovan et al. [23] performed experimental study based on a Design of Experiments method, and identified several critical process parameters. The ultrasonic welding of nickel coated Cu/Cu tab was studied by Kim et al. [24]. In the study, a factorial experimental design and peeling test were performed, and three categories of weld quality (cold, good and over-welds) was mapped in the welding time-welding pressure domain. For welding dissimilar materials, Bakavos and Prangnell [21] studied the effect of ultrasonic welding parameters on mechanical properties and micro-structures of dissimilar joints of aluminum and stainless steels, and the results indicated that the maximum tensile strength of the welds is related to the amount of effective bond area, the latter is correlated to and the material thinning. The ultrasonic welding process was modeled by Suresh et al. [25] and by Levy et al. [26] for predicting temperature distribution of polymers using thermomechanical coupled finite element analyses. Other studies for ultrasonic welding of dissimilar metals include welding mild steel/aluminum-magnesium alloy sheets by Watanabe et al. [27] and Al/Mg by Panteli et al. [28].

The ultrasonic welding process may also be used for additive manufacturing from aluminum sheets, as reported by Watanabe and Mori [29], and by Janaki Ram et al. [20]. In the latter case, the substrate was heated/softened to increase effective welding area, and the surface roughening may occur that was caused by sonotrode contacts.

For the present interest of battery tab ultrasonic welding, welding quality affects not only the functionality and energy consumption of a vehicle, but also the durability and reliability. The electrical resistance of the welded tabs typically increases as the welds accumulate micro-damage under a static or fatigue loading when the vehicles are in use. The correlation between fatigue damage and resistance can be recognized from the fact that many researchers have been using this phenomenon as one of the non-destructive evaluation methods for damage monitoring, as reviewed by Ditchburn et al. [30]. The resistance measurement has been used for weld quality inspection or damage evolution, for example by Balle et al. [31] for testing ultrasonically welded aluminum/carbon-reinforced polymer, by Vavouliotis et al. [32] for a carbon nanotube reinforced polymer, by Omarri and Sevostianov [33] for stainless steel, and by Sun and Guo [34] for steel structural damage during high-cycle fatigue.

A review article focused on automotive joining techniques is seen by Barnes and Pashby [35], who listed the advantages and limitations of the selected joining techniques. Another recent review article by Mori et al. [36], also focused on automotive application, summarized the deformation-based joining techniques, including some traditional and non-traditional material forming processes, e.g., rolling, forging, extrusion, hydroforming, electromagnetic forming and incremental forming, impulse welding or electromagnetic welding, friction welding and friction stir welding, and many direct mechanical fastening methods involving plastic deformation (such as self-pierce riveting, mechanical clinching, hemming, seaming and staking).

Currently, ultrasonic welding research as applied to lithium-ion battery tab welding has been very active. The work by Kim et al. [24] studied the ultrasonic welding for battery tabs with like and dissimilar metals. In a follow-up study by Lee et al. [37], the quality of ultrasonically welded battery tab was characterized. Zhao et al. [38] fabricated a micro-scale thin-film thermocouple inserted in the ultrasonic tools 100 m away from the tool/workpiece interface. Such measured temperature rise during ultrasonic welding of Ni-coated Cu was as high as 650°C for Cu/Cu welding. With this technique, Li et al. [39] studied the transient thermal process during ultrasonic welding of battery tabs that provides better understanding of the welding mechanism and resultant microstructure and properties. The high temperature, along with the earlier mentioned high strain rate deformation studied by Panteli on Al/Mg USW [28], results in a special microstructure evolution, including dynamic recrystallization in Cu/Cu ultrasonic welding reported by Lee et al. [37]. The welding process was further modeled by Zhao et al. [40] to predict fatigue life of ultrasonically welded Li-ion battery tabs, and by Lee et al. [41], who simulated the ultrasonic welding process of multiple thin and dissimilar metals. In addition, the system dynamics, stress, and energy transmission in battery tab ultrasonic welding were studied by [42–44, 45].

This chapter focuses on weld formation and failure analyses for ultrasonic welding of multi-layered battery tabs involving a thicker copper to either three thin copper or aluminum tabs, by means of metallographic analyses. The experimental condition is given in Section 3.2. Sections 3.3 and 3.4 study the weld formation and failure mechanisms of Cu and Al tabs, respectively, followed by Conclusions in Section 3.5.

3.2 ULTRASONIC WELDING AND WELD TESTING

Ultrasonic welds were produced from three layers of either Cu or Al tabs and one layer of Cu bus bar (coded as "cccC" and "aaaC," respectively), using a Stapla ultrasonic welder. Each tab is of 45 (length) × 41 (width) × 0.2 (thickness) mm, and each Cu bus bar is a flat coupon of 45 (length) × 41 (width) × 0.9 (thickness) mm, as shown in Fig. 3.2. Note that the flat Cu coupons (shown in Fig. 3.2) were used instead of the "U"-shaped Cu bus bar as in battery pack production (Fig. 3.1) for convenience and cost reasons. Both the Cu tabs and Cu bus bars were electroplated with nickel (Ni). The Ni-coating layer thickness is about 0.75 micron for Cu tabs and 2 microns for the Cu bus bars. The 0.2-mm pure Al tabs were anodized, with about 0.2 micron of oxidation film on the tab surfaces.

As shown in Fig. 3.2, each ultrasonic weld consists of three weld spots with a center-to-center spacing of 12 mm. Each weld spot in cccC is approximately 5 × 3 mm, and in aaaC approximately 10 × 4 mm, both with corner radius of about 1 mm. The three weld spots are collinear along the long axis direction. The ultrasonic vibration direction is along the short axis.

Many parameters can impact the ultrasonic welding quality, ranging from the weld tool design (such as the knurl patterns of the horn and/or anvil) to welding process parameters (e.g., the clamping pressure, the ultrasonic amplitude, and the welding time/energy). In this study, to reduce the sample size of experiments, the clamping pressure, and the ultrasonic amplitude were held constant. Only the welding energies were varied to produce welds at three different quality levels, i.e., under-weld, normal-weld, and over-weld. For cccC welding, the three welding energy levels of 1600 J, 2400 J and 3200 J were used to represent the under-weld, normal-weld and over-weld conditions. For aaaC welding, the three energy levels of 300, 600, and 1200 J were used.

The quality of a weld was evaluated by means of a lap-shear test. Because the most critical bonding quality for either a cccC or aaaC weld is between the innermost tab and the

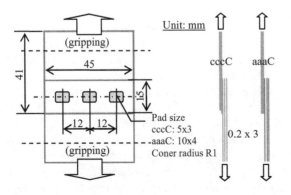

Figure 3.2. Lap shear test setup and specimen dimensions (knurl pattern as shown in the photo on the right hand side is for Al welding).

Cu bus bar [40], a lap-shear test configuration, such as in Fig. 3.2, is used. By clamping the three tabs in one end and the Cu bus bar in another end, the lap-shear tests were performed under a constant speed of 0.5 mm/s on an MTS machine.

3.3 MICROSTRUCTURAL ANALYSIS OF cccC WELDS

Representative cccC weld images are shown in Fig. 3.3 at three different welding conditions. The 5 × 3 array of square biting facets were formed due to the horn knurls. Note the different sizes of the biting facets as well as the differences in residues of the Ni-coating (in silver color) on the weld surfaces in three different welding conditions.

To better understand the bonding between different layers, a cccC normal-weld was sectioned along the long and short axes of the middle spots, respectively, and the optical microscope (OM) micrographs are shown in Fig. 3.4. As can be seen,

- The Ni-coating at the interfaces, or the bond lines, were continuous and essentially intact. No obvious interfacial separation, cracks, or voids existed. The bond line waviness, though, was relatively significant at the interface of the top two tabs. The waviness then decreased substantially to almost nil at the innermost tab and the bus bar interface.
- For both sections, the material flow and deformation occurred mainly at the top Cu tab with thickness reduced to about a half.
- The long-axis section of the metals have been extruded to form complete "valley" area; however, the metal did not fully fill-in the horn grooved regions to form a complete "Λ"-shaped hill, i.e., a complete tool-workpiece surface contact was not

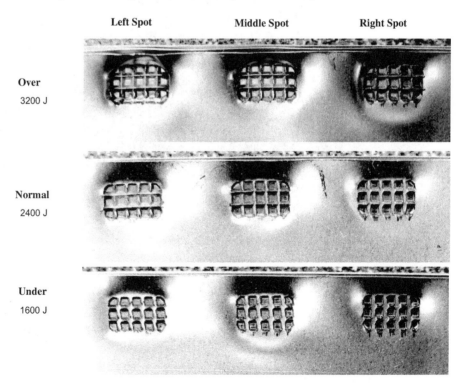

Figure 3.3. Three cccC welds with different levels of welding conditions (produced from three welding energies), as viewed from the Cu tab outside surface.

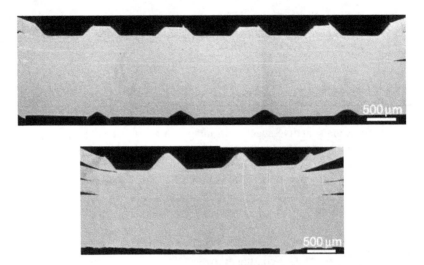

Figure 3.4. Cross-sections of the middle spot of a cccC normal-weld (2400 J): sectioned along the long axis (top), and short axis (bottom).

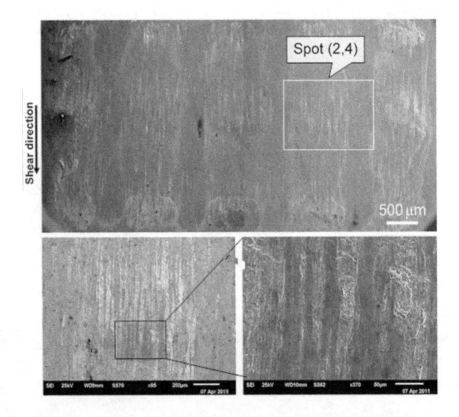

Figure 3.5. SEM micrographs of the fractured ccc|C interface viewed on the 0.9-mm Cu bus bar surface, for the central spot of "normal-weld" specimen and with local enlargements of the area corresponding to the horn knurls at the second row and fourth column.

established. On the short-axis section, which corresponds to the ultrasonic vibration direction, a complete tool-workpiece contact for both "valley" (the horn's teeth) and "hill" (the horn's groove) has been established. This is consistent with Fig. 3.3.

The SEM micrographs of the interface between the innermost tab and the Cu bus bar (ccc|C interface) of the middle spot of a "normal-weld" is shown in Fig. 3.5, after removing all the three tabs away from the Cu bus bar. The 5 × 3 mm teeth impression from the horn was visible, including the contact boundaries. The welded regions showed many long stripes, whose orientation coincided with the ultrasonic shearing directions. Outside the stripe area the surface was relatively flat and smooth, with no sign of interface tearing. This suggests that those stripes areas were strongly bonded, whereas the remaining areas are not bonded or not strongly bonded.

The energy-dispersive x-ray spectroscopy (EDX) chemical analysis by line scanning in the direction perpendicular to the stripe direction is shown in Fig. 3.6. It can be seen that the Cu base metal was exposed on those striped areas, which further confirms the ductile fracture occurred by peeling out of the base Cu metal or the Ni metal within the coating layer. Since the original Cu sheets were coated with Ni and in the Cu-exposed areas the Ni-Ni bonding is stronger than the base metal itself, the bonding strength is controlled by the Cu strength. In the rest of the weld spot, the fractured surfaces are still covered by the

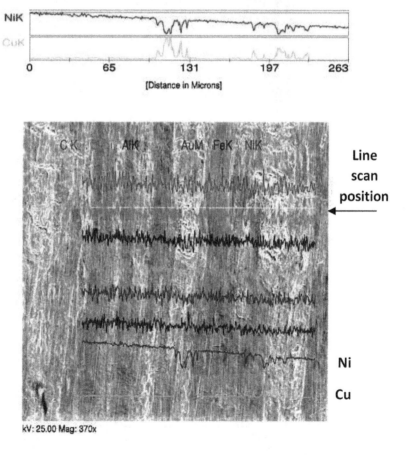

Figure 3.6. The EDX component analysis showing the tearing portion with Cu exposed on the fractured surface, while the rest areas (including weld spot area) being still covered by the Ni coating.

Ni coating layer, which can be either not welded, or weakly welded at lower strength than Ni itself.

Because the weld strength is positively correlated to the total bonding area, it is desirable to determine the actual bonding area or the percentage of Cu-exposed area versus the nominal total bonding area (the knurl area). Hence, a dark field (DF) microscopy technique was used to observe the metal contents at the ccc|C interface, using an optical microscope, as shown in Fig. 3.7. The exposed Cu is shown in brown color, and the Ni is shown in green. As a comparison, under a bright field (BF) mode, this distinction is not possible. With this technique, the DF images for three different welding conditions are shown in Fig. 3.8. A Matlab program was developed to calculate the bonding area by identifying the color code associated with each pixel and then marking the pixels within certain color codes as the bonding area. For example, the brown areas (i.e., the Cu-exposed areas) in Fig. 3.9 correspond to the Cu areas in Fig. 3.8.

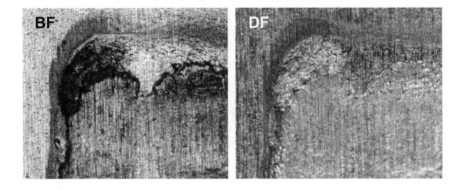

Figure 3.7. Comparison of OM BF and DF images.

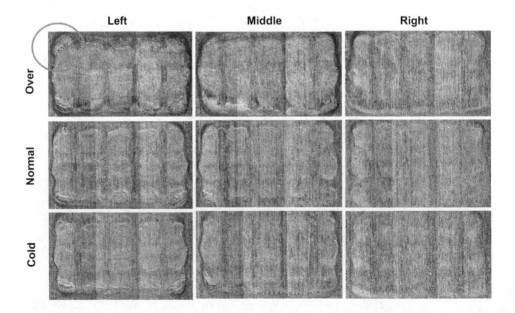

Figure 3.8. Dark field images at the ccc|C interface, where the Cu areas are in bronze and Ni areas are in green. The circled area in the left corner is enlarged and shown in Fig. 3.7.

Figure 3.9. The Cu-Cu torn regions are subtracted from image processing.

Based on the chemical and image analyses of the fractured surfaces shown in Fig. 3.7, it is concluded that:

1. Only a small fraction of the innermost Cu tab (Ni-coated) was bonded with the Cu bus bar (Ni-coated) through a "strong" interfacial Ni-Ni bonding. As shown in Fig. 3.9, the fractions of such bonding ranged from 0.67% (the average of 2.8%, 0.9%, 0.3%) for the under-weld to 2.93% (the average of 4.8%, 2.4%, 1.6%) for the normal-weld, and 4.83% (the average of 8.8%, 4.8%, 0.9%) for the over-weld. It was so determined as "strong" Ni-Ni bonding for these fractions because the weld fractured on the pure Cu (of the innermost tabs) during the shear tests of the welds, knowing that the tensile strength for Ni (450 MPa as annealed) is much higher than that of pure Cu (ranging from 150 to 250 MPa depending on hardness). The rest of such fractions were considered "weak" interfacial Ni-Ni bonding.

2. Although a 100% "strong" Ni-Ni bonding seems to be desirable to achieve the best bonding strength, there exist two limiting factors. First, as discussed in (1) the upper limit of the bonding strength of a weld is determined by the Cu strength. Second, overly strong Ni-Ni bonding requires over-weld conditions, which may cause over-thinning or circumferential fracture at weld perimeters as circled out in the left-upper corner in Fig. 3.8. In such over-weld conditions and other extreme over-weld conditions reported in Zhao et al. [38], the weld strength might be lower than the normal-weld conditions due to severe shear cut of the three Cu tabs by the horn at the weld pad perimeters. Therefore, an optimal welding condition should be at a welding energy level equal to or lower than the "strong" Ni-Ni bonding energy.

3.4 MICROSTRUCTURAL ANALYSIS OF aaaC WELDS

The photo images of representative aaaC welds from three different welding conditions are shown in Fig. 3.10. Note that the finer horn knurl pattern used was different from that of Cu welding.

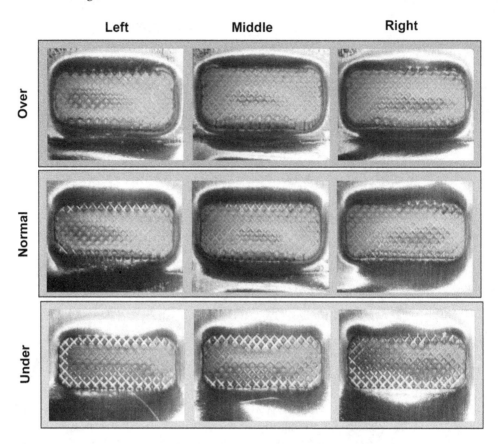

Figure 3.10. The photo images of aaaC welds at three different energy levels (i.e., 1200 J for over-weld, 600 J for normal-weld, and 300 J for under-weld). The ultrasonic vibration is in vertical direction.

A representative cross-sectional view of as-welded samples is shown in Fig. 3.11, sectioned along the central line of long axis and polished without etching. It can be seen that:

- All three 0.2-mm Al layers were severely deformed, and the Al-Al interfaces were in wavy or curly shapes. The amount of deformation decreased from outer to inner tabs. In particular, the Al inter-mixing is observed.
- At the aaa|C interface, the copper surface remained almost straight/flat. This is because Al is much softer and ductile, and thus more deformable than the 0.9-mm Cu.

To view the Al tabs deformation and inter-mixing better, the polished sample in Fig. 3.11 was further electro-polished, as shown in Fig. 3.12 (top). The three tab layers and the interfaces were also schematically drawn in Fig. 3.12 (bottom). It is observed that:

- The grain size of the unwelded Al tab was about 50 to 67 μm because there were about 3 to 4 grains through the 0.2-mm tab thickness (shown in the very left part of Fig. 3.12 (top)). After ultrasonic welding, severe plastic deformation and material flow completely destroyed the original grain structure. Recrystallization did not seem to occur because equiaxed new grains with well-defined grain boundaries were not observed ever in the most severely deformed region.

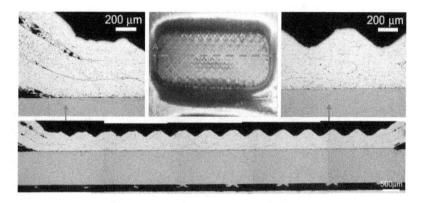

Figure 3.11. Cross-sectional OM view of a "normal-weld" specimen sectioned along the long axis for the middle weld spot.

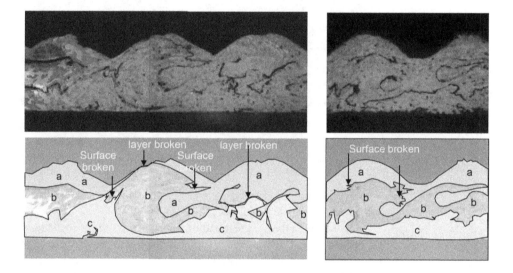

Figure 3.12. Sectioned and etched Al tabs interfaces, observed by OM (1.8% HBF4 in distilled water, 20 vdc for 2 min. with sample at anodic pole, Olympus OMG 3, polarizing light plus sensitive tint lens). Cu sheet is not shown.

- The straight/flat boundaries between the three Al tab layers became highly wavy, curly, and discontinued after welding. Metal flow, inter-mix and interlock were seen.
- The aaa|C interface, however, remained straight/flat. Therefore, the bonding mechanism between the innermost Al and the Cu layer was diffusion bonding.

Figure 3.13 further illustrates two distinct weld failure modes after an aaaC weld was lap-shear tested. The first was the interfacial debonding between the innermost Al and Cu as evidenced by the large areas of the original rolling marks on the Cu sheet in Fig. 3.13(a). This typically represents an under-welding condition due to insufficient welding energy. The second was the Al tab fracture, Fig. 3.13(b) and (c), indicating adequate bonding between the sheets. Note that both normal-welding and over-welding conditions could produce adequate bonding; however, over-welding conditions typically create excessive

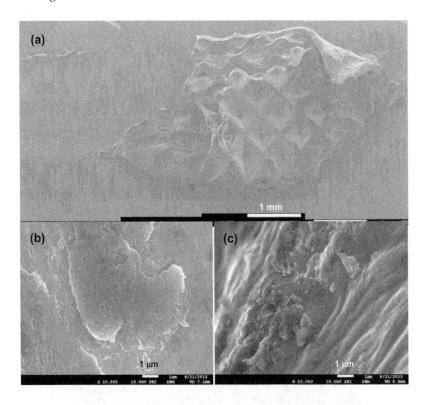

Figure 3.13. (a) A fractured surface of aaaC viewed on 0.9 mm Cu side. (b) The base metal shear fracture of aluminum tab; (c) The torn edge of the first (top) aluminum tab.

circumferential cuts around the perimeters of the weld spots and therefore reduce the weld strength due to circumferential fracture.

To further understand the bonding mechanism, SEM secondary electron images (Fig. 3.14(a)) and back-scattered electron images (Fig. 3.14(b)) were obtained and compared, along with EDX chemical analysis (Fig. 3.14(c) and (d)). The contrast of the secondary electron images was based on sample surface topology as well as atomic weight. The heavier metal reflected more electrons and displays lighter color with stereo surface topology feature, while the contrast of the back-scattered electron images was more sensitive to the atomic weight and gave a better black/white contrast. The two techniques yielded consistent results, and the chemical composition of the two regions was clearly confirmed by the EDX analysis.

The fractured surfaces of all three weld spots and at all three energies are shown in Fig. 3.15 as viewed on the 0.9-mm Cu mating surface. The Al side of the fractured three 0.2-mm Al tabs had a good match to the Cu side, but with severe tearing damage and shape distortion.

The bonding areas between the Al tab and the Cu bus bar were traced at the bonding edges and filled with different colors, and the bonding area fractions over the full spot size were calculated with a user developed Matlab program (Fig. 3.15 bottom). Weld failure occurred as a combination of interfacial debonding between the innermost Al tab (anodized) and the Ni-coated Cu bus bar, and the base Al fracture. The fracture occurred almost at the same spots for all three Al tabs as through-thickness tear. For under-weld, the interface debonding was more predominant than the through-thickness tear. As the welding energy becomes higher, the interfacial bonding area becomes larger, resulting in higher weld

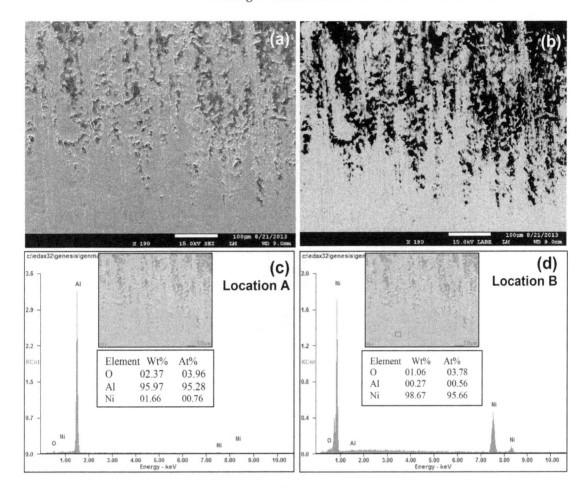

Figure 3.14. Micrographs of a local area of aaa|C fractured surface. (a) Secondary electron image; (b) back-scattered electron image; (c) and (d) EDX chemical analysis at location A of bark black area as Al and location B of grey area as Ni.

strength up to an upper limit that is equivalent to the maximum load carrying capability by through-thickness tear of the circumferences of the three weld pads. Similar to the Cu welding, the welding tool is also slightly misaligned.

3.5 CONCLUSIONS

The purpose of this study is to better understand the mechanism of ultrasonic weld formation and failure to provide insight into welding process for quality improvement. The formation mechanism of ultrasonic welds between three layers of battery tabs (either 0.2 mm thick Ni-coated Cu tabs or 0.2-mm-thick anodized Al tabs) and the bus bar (Ni-coated 0.9 mm thick Cu) were studied, each at three different welding energy levels. Failure modes were examined and analyzed with optical, scanning electron microscope, and energy-dispersive x-ray spectroscopy. It was concluded that although the weld formation mechanisms differ for Al and Cu welding, failure of the welds is always a combination of the interfacial deboning (between the innermost tab, either Cu or Al, and the Cu bus bar) and the through-thickness tear (i.e., Mode III failure as termed in fracture mechanics) of the tabs.

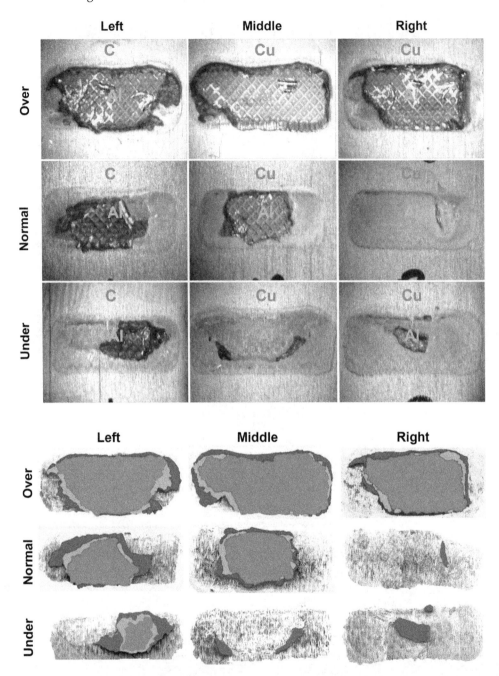

Figure 3.15. (Top) OM observations of fractured specimens, viewed on the 0.9-mm Cu bonding
surface aaa|C; (bottom) The remaining Al tabs from edge tearing for tab from top layer
to the third layer in red, green and blue, respectively, and the remaining Al from interface shearing fracture in dark black spots, obtained from image processing of SEM
micrographs.

More specifically, within the current welding process window, for cccC welds (i.e., three layers of Cu tabs welded onto a Cu bus bar):

1. The primary welding mechanism was the Ni-Ni metallic bonding with little metal inter-mixing at all the interfaces.
2. At the ccc|C interface only a small fraction of the innermost Cu tab (Ni-coated) area was welded with the Cu bus bar (Ni-coated) through a "strong" interfacial Ni-Ni bonding, which is stronger than the Cu base metal, resulting in Cu base metal tearing apart at the fractured surfaces; while the rest of the area was through "weak" interfacial Ni-Ni bonding, with Ni remained over the fractured surface.
3. The maximum local weld strength is limited by the Cu strength, which suggests that an optimal welding condition is at a welding energy level equal to or lower than that required to produce a "strong" Ni-Ni bonding.

For aaaC welds (i.e., three layers of Al tabs welded onto a Cu bus bar):

1. The primary welding mechanism among the three Al tabs is the metal interlocking as evidenced by significant Al inter-mixing.
2. The primary welding mechanism at the aaa|C interface is the metallic bonding.
3. The weld strength is the less of the load carrying capability of the through-thickness shear of the circumferences of the three Al weld pads and that of the aaa|C bonding strength.

REFERENCES

[1] Wu, X., Liu, T., Cai, W., 2015, "Microstructure, Welding Mechanism, and Failure of Al/Cu Ultrasonic Welds," *SME Journal of Manufacturing Processes*, **20**(3), pp. 515–524.
[2] Potente, H., 1984, "Ultrasonic Welding—Principles & theory," *Materials & Design*, **5**(5), pp. 228–234.
[3] Staff, P. D. L., 2008, "Handbook of Plastics Joining: A Practical Guide," Chapter 5, Cambridge University Press.
[4] Singh, R., 2012, "Applied welding engineering: processes, codes, and standards," Section 2, Chapter 2: *Physics of Welding*, Oxford, UK: Butterworth-Heinemann, pp. 115–146.
[5] Matsuoka, S. -I., 1995, "Ultrasonic Welding and Characteristics of Glass-Fiber Reinforced Plastic: Comparison between the Paper-Making Method and the Impregnation Method," *Journal of Materials Processing Technology*, **55**, pp. 427–431.
[6] Takeda, K., Tanaka, H., Tsuchiya, T., and Kaneko, S., 1998, "Molecular Movement During Welding for Engineering Plastics Using Langevin Transducer Equipped with Half-Wave-Length Step Horn," *Ultrasonics*, **36**, pp. 75–78.
[7] Tsujino, J., Furuya, H., and Murayama, Y., 1989, "Detection of Welding Condition and Welding Characteristics of Ultrasonic Wire Bonding Using a Complex Vibration Welding Tip," *Proceedings of IEEE 1989 Ultrasonics Symposium*, Montreal, Quebec, Canada, 3–6 Oct. 1989, 2, pp. 1103–1106.
[8] Tsujino, J., and Ueoka, T., 1996, "Ultrasonic Multi-Spot Continuous Welding of Metal Plate Specimens Using a Two-Vibration-System Welding Equipment," *Ultrasonics*, **34**, pp. 229–233.
[9] Tsujino, J., Uchida, T., Yamano, K., Iwamoto, N., and Ueoka, T., 1998, "Welding Characteristics of Ultrasonic Plastic Welding Using Two-Vibration-System of 90 kHz and 27 or 20 kHz and Complex Vibration Systems," *Ultrasonics*, **36**, pp. 67–74.

[10] Tsujino, J., Ueoka, T., Kashino, T., and Sugahara, F., 2000, "Transverse and Torsional Complex Vibration Systems for Ultrasonic Seam Welding of Metal Plates," *Ultrasonics*, **38**, pp. 67–71.

[11] Tsujino, J., Harada, Y., Ihara, S., Kasahara, K., Shimizu, M., and Ueoka, T., 2004, "Configurations of High-Frequency Ultrasonics Complex Vibration Systems for Packaging in Microelectronics," *Ultrasonics*, **42**, pp. 125–129.

[12] Tsujino, J., Sano, T., Ogata, H., Tanaka, S., and Harada, Y., 2002, "Complex Vibration Ultrasonic Welding Systems with Large Area Welding Tips," *Ultrasonics*, **40**, pp. 361–364.

[13] Tsujino, J., and Hasegawa, K., 1996, "Ultrasonic Wire Bonding Using High Frequency 330, 600 kHz and Complex Vibration 190 kHz Welding Systems," *Ultrasonics*, **34**, pp. 223–228.

[14] Tsujino, J., Ueoka, T., Hasegawa, K., Fujita, Y., Shiraki, T., T. Okada, and Tamura, T., 1996, "New Methods of Ultrasonic Welding of Metal and Plastic Materials," *Ultrasonics*, **34**, pp. 177–185.

[15] Tsujino, J., Hidai, K., Hasegawa, A., Kanai, R., Matsuura, H., Matsushima, K., and Ueoka, T., 2002, "Ultrasonic Butt Welding of Aluminum, Aluminum alloy and Stainless Steel Plate Specimens," *Ultrasonics*, **40**, pp. 371–374.

[16] Tsujino, J., Ihara, S., Harada, Y., Kasahara, K., and Sakamaki, N., 2004, "Characteristics of Coated Copper Wire Specimens Using High Frequency Ultrasonic Complex Vibration Welding Equipments," *Ultrasonics*, **42**, pp. 121–124.

[17] Matsuoka, S. -I., and Imai, H., 2009, "Direct Welding of Different Metals Used Ultrasonic Vibration," *Journal of Materials Processing Technology*, **209**, pp. 954–960.

[18] Matsuoka, S. -I., 1994, "Ultrasonic Welding of Ceramic/Metal," *Journal of Materials Processing Technology*, **47**, pp. 185-196.

[19] Matsuoka, S. -I., 1998, "Ultrasonic Welding of Ceramics/Metals Using Inserts," *Journal of Materials Processing Technology*, **75**, pp. 259–265.

[20] Janaki Ram, G. D., Yang, Y., and Stucker, B. E., 2006, "Effect of Process Parameters on Bond Formation During Ultrasonic Consolidation of Aluminum Alloy 3003," *Journal of Manufacturing Systems*, **25**, pp. 221–238.

[21] Bakavos, D., and Prangnell, P. B., 2010, "Mechanisms of Joint and Microstructure Formation in High Power Ultrasonic Spot Welding 6111 aluminium automotive sheet," *Materials Science and Engineering: A*, **527**, pp. 6320–6334.

[22] Chen, Y. C., Bakavos, D., Gholinia, A., and Prangnell, P. B., 2012, "HAZ Development and Accelerated Post-Weld Natural Ageing in Ultrasonic Spot Welding Aluminium 6111-T4 Automotive Sheet," *Acta Materialia*, **60**, pp. 2816–2828.

[23] Elangovan, S., Prakasan, K., and Jaiganesh, V., 2010, "Optimization of Ultrasonic Welding Parameters for Copper to Copper Joints Using Design of Experiments," *International Journal of Advanced Manufacturing Technology*, **51**, pp. 163–171.

[24] Kim, T. H., Yum, J. S., Hu, J., Spicer, J. P., and Abell, J. A., 2011, "Process Robustness of Single Lap Ultrasonic Welding of Thin, Dissimilar Materials," *CIRP Annals—Manufacturing Technology*, **60**, pp. 17–20.

[25] Suresh, K. S., Rani, M. R., Prakasan, K., and Rudramoorthy, R., 2007, "Modeling of Temperature Distribution in Ultrasonic Welding of Thermoplastics for Various Joint Designs," *Journal of Materials Processing Technology*, **186**, pp. 138–146.

[26] Levy, A., Le Corre, S., Chevaugeon, N., and Poitou, A., 2011, "A Level Set Based Approach for the Finite Element Simulation of a Forming Process Involving Multiphysics Coupling: Ultrasonic Welding of Thermoplastic Composites," *European Journal of Mechanics—A/Solids*, **30**, pp. 501–509.

[27] Watanabe, T., Sakuyama, H., and Yanagisawa, A., 2009, "Ultrasonic Welding between Mild Steel Sheet and Al–Mg Alloy Sheet," *Journal of Materials Processing Technology*, **209**, pp. 5475–5480.

[28] Panteli, A., Robson, J. D., Brough, I., and Prangnell, P. B., 2012, "The Effect of High Strain Rate Deformation on Intermetallic Reaction During Ultrasonic Welding Aluminium to Magnesium," *Materials Science and Engineering: A*, **556**, pp. 31–42.

[29] Watanabe, Y., and Mori, E., 1996, "A Study on a New Flexural-Mode Transducer-Solid Horn System and Its Application to Ultrasonic Plastics Welding," *Ultrasonics*, **34**, pp. 235–238.

[30] Ditchburn, R. J. Burke, S. K., and Scala, C. M., 1996, "NDT of Welds: State of the Art," *NDT & E International*, **29**, pp. 111–117.

[31] Balle, F., Huxhold, S., Wagner, G., and Eifler, D., "Damage Monitoring of Ultrasonically Welded Aluminum/ CFRP-Joints by Electrical Resistance Measurements," *Procedia Engineering*, **10**, pp. 433–438.

[32] Vavouliotis, A., Paipetis, A., and Kostopoulos, V., 2011, "On the Fatigue Life Prediction of CFRP Laminates Using the Electrical Resistance Change Method," *Composites Science and Technology*, **71**, pp. 630–642.

[33] Omari, M. A., and Sevostianov, I., 2013, "Estimation of Changes in the Mechanical Properties of Stainless Steel Subjected to Fatigue Loading via Electrical Resistance Monitoring," International *Journal of Engineering Science*, **65**, pp. 40–48.

[34] Sun, B., and Guo, Y., 2004, "High-Cycle Fatigue Damage Measurement Based on Electrical Resistance Change Considering Variable Electrical Resistivity and Uneven Damage," *International Journal of Fatigue*, **26**, pp. 457–462.

[35] Barnes, T. A., and Pashby, I. R., 2000, "Joining Techniques for Aluminium Spaceframes Used in Automobiles: Part I—Solid and Liquid Phase Welding," *Journal of Materials Processing Technology*, **99**, pp. 62–71.

[36] Mori, K. -I., Bay, N., Fratini, L., Micari, F., and Tekkaya, A. E., 2013, "Joining by Plastic Deformation," *CIRP Annals—Manufacturing Technology*, **62**, pp. 673–694.

[37] Lee, S. S., Kim, T. H., Hu, S. J., Cai, W., Abell, J. A., and Li, J., 2013, "Characterization of joint quality in ultrasonic welding of battery tabs," *ASME Journal of Manufacturing Science and Engineering*, **135**(2), 021004.

[38] Zhao, J., Li, H., Choi, H., Cai, W., Abell, J. A., and Li, X., 2013, "Insertable Thin Film Thermocouples for in Situ Transient Temperature Monitoring in Ultrasonic Metal Welding of Battery Tabs," *Journal of Manufacturing Processes*, **15**(1), pp. 136–140.

[39] Li, H., Choi, H., Ma, C., Zhao, J., Jiang, H., Cai, W., Abell, J. A., and Li, X., 2013, "Transient Temperature and Heat Flux Measurement in Ultrasonic Joining of Battery Tabs Using Thin-Film Microsensors," *ASME Journal of Manufacturing Science and Engineering*, **135**, p. 051015.

[40] Zhao, N., Li, W., Cai, W., and Abell, J. A., 2014, "A Fatigue Life Study of Ultrasonically Welded Lithium-Ion Battery Tab Joints Based on Electrical Resistance," *ASME Journal of Manufacturing Science and Engineering*, **136**(5), p. 051003.

[41] Lee, D. K., Kannatey-Asibu Jr., E., and Cai, W., 2013, "Ultrasonic Welding Simulations for Multiple Layers of Lithium-Ion Battery Tabs," *ASME Journal of Manufacturing Science and Engineering*, **135**(6), p. 061011.

[42] Kang, B., Cai, W., and Tan, C. A., 2013, "Dynamic Response of Battery Tabs Under Ultrasonic Welding," *ASME Journal of Manufacturing Science and Engineering*, **135**(5), p. 051013.

[43] Kang, B., Cai, W., and Tan, C. A., 2014, "Vibrational Energy Loss Analysis of Battery in Ultrasonic Welding," *SME Journal of Manufacturing Processes*, **16**(2), pp. 218–232.

[44] Kang, B., Cai, W., and Tan, C. A., 2014, "Dynamic Stress Analysis of Battery Tabs under Ultrasonic Welding," *ASME Journal of Manufacturing Science and Engineering*, **136**(4), p. 041011.

[45] Lee, S. S., Kim, T. H., Cai, W. W., and Abell, J. A., 2014, "Parasitic Vibration Attenuation in Ultrasonic Welding of Battery Tabs," *International Journal of Advanced Manufacturing Technology*, **71**, Issue 1–4, pp. 181–195.

Chapter 4

TRANSIENT TEMPERATURE AND HEAT FLUX MEASUREMENT USING THIN-FILM MICROSENSORS[1]

Jingzhou Zhao[1], Hang Li[2], Hongseok Choi[3], Chao Ma[1], Wayne Cai[4], Jeffrey A. Abell[4], and Xiaochun Li[1]
[1]*Department of Mechanical Engineering, University of California, Los Angeles*
[2]*Department of Mechanical Engineering, University of Wisconsin, Madison*
[3]*Department of Mechanical Engineering, Clemson University*
[4]*Manufacturing Systems Research Lab, General Motors Global R&D Center*

ABSTRACT

Process physics understanding, real time monitoring, and control of various manufacturing processes, such as battery manufacturing, are crucial for product quality assurance. While ultrasonic welding has been used for joining batteries in electric vehicles (EVs), the welding physics, and process attributes, such as the heat generation and heat flow during the joining process, is still not well understood, leading to time-consuming trial-and-error based process optimization. This study is to investigate thermal phenomena (i.e., transient temperature and heat flux) and to realize production level *in-situ* temperature measurement by using micro thin-film thermocouples (TFTC) and thin-film thermopile (TFTP) arrays (referred to as microsensors in this article) at the very vicinity of the ultrasonic welding spot during joining of three-layered battery tabs and Cu bus bars (i.e., battery interconnect) as in General Motors (GM) Chevy Volt. Microsensors were first fabricated on the bus bars. A series of experiments were then conducted to investigate the dynamic heat generation during the welding process. Experimental results showed that TFTCs enabled the sensing of transient temperatures with much higher spatial and temporal resolutions than conventional thermocouples. It was further found that the TFTPs were more sensitive to the transient heat generation process during welding than TFTCs. More significantly, the heat flux change rate was found to be able to provide better insight for the process. It provided evidence indicating that the ultrasonic welding process involves three distinct stages, i.e., friction heating, plastic work, and diffusion bonding stages. The heat flux change rate thus has significant potential to identify the *in-situ* welding quality, in the context of welding process monitoring, and control of ultrasonic welding process. The weld samples were examined using scanning electron microscopy (SEM) and energy dispersive X-ray spectroscopy (EDS) to study the material interactions at the bonding interface as a function of weld time and have successfully validated the proposed three-stage welding theory. On the other hand, real-time monitoring and control of temperature in ultrasonic joining of battery tabs and coupons are important for the quality improvement and cost reduction of battery assembly. However, there have always been difficulties in accurate and real-time measurement of temperature by conventional sensors for practical implementation. In this study, an innovative method is developed to provide an enabling technology for the *in-situ* transient

---

[1] The content presented in this chapter has previously appeared in Refs. [1, 2].

temperature monitoring, which could provide reliable feedback signals for potential control of ultrasonic joining processes. TFTCs were fabricated on thin silicon substrates, which were then inserted in the welding anvil as a permanent feature so that the sensors were always located about 100 μm directly under the welding spot during joining of multilayer Ni-coated Cu thin sheets for battery assembly. Good repeatability was demonstrated while a temperature rise of up to 650°C was obtained due to the closeness of the sensors to the welding spot. The inserts with thin film sensors remained functional after welding experiments. This method has a great potential for *in-situ* transient temperature monitoring, and thus the control of ultrasonic joining processes to realize a practical smart joining system.

Keywords: lithium-ion battery assembly, ultrasonic metal welding, weld attributes, weld quality

4.1 INTRODUCTION

4.1.1 Background

Battery Electric Vehicles (BEVs) are gaining momentum for automobile industry recently. For their successful commercialization, it is crucial to ensure high quality fabrication and assembly for the battery packs. A battery pack for Electric Vehicles (EVs) typically consists of a large number of battery cells that must be assembled together with robust joints to ensure mechanical and electrical properties. Efforts have been taken to investigate several joining technologies, such as resistance welding, laser welding, ultrasonic welding and mechanical fastening [3, 4]. Among all these techniques, ultrasonic welding, a solid state joining process, is widely regarded as one of the best for battery joining due to its capability of joining dissimilar, multiple, and thin layers at low temperatures [5–11].

Although ultrasonic metal welding (USMW) was invented in 1940s, its bonding mechanism is still not fully understood [12–15]. There are a few different theories proposed so far. Kodama proposed that the ultrasonic bonding process involves two steps [16]. In the first step, friction, as a result of the ultrasonic oscillation, causes mechanical cleaning and smoothing of the interface and initiates point bonding. In the second step, the relative motion between the workpieces induces a sudden plastic flow. In this theory, it is believed that the oxidation at the interface must be removed before bonding can be initiated. Several interrelated phenomena occur during USMW, including plastic friction heating, recrystallization, and inter-diffusion, deformation and fatigue. However, it was suggested that USMW is a heat dependent process by some other investigators [17, 18]. Plastic deformation takes place only when: (1) the relative displacement between the workpieces is sufficient to induce localized slip; (2) the resulting frictional stress is greater than the flow stress of the sublayer. Hazlett and Ambekar observed that bonds can be formed by mechanical mixing at the interface [19]. Moreover, diffusion observed is attributed to grain boundary diffusion as the temperature is not sufficiently high to result in bulk diffusion.

Besides process physics understanding, extensive research has been done to ensure high weld quality and reproducible results for production [17, 20, 21]. A trial-and-error–based welding process optimization is often carried out based on the specific manufacturing conditions. In addition, variations of weld quality persist even with an optimized set of process parameters maintained when successive welds are made [12]. As temperature and heat generation at the welding interfaces are of critical importance to the weld quality, it would be beneficial to monitor the transient temperature at the welding spot to identify the root cause of the variation. With an effective monitoring of the process, problems could be controlled by modulating process parameters in real time. *In-situ* temperature measurement for USMW process is extremely demanding in that any method implemented to measure the interface temperature during USMW must not interfere with the process while offering high spatial and temporal resolutions [22]. Attempts have been made by use of conventional thermocouples, infrared radiation thermometer, meltable inserts and even post processing based on phase transformations or recrystallization, and simulations [10, 23–26]. However, none of these methods can truly meet the requirement of providing *in-situ* data of high spatial and temporal resolutions.

Recently, thermomechanical phenomena were studied by the use of embedded thin film sensors for various manufacturing processes [27–34]. Two types of thin film micro sensors, *K*-type thin film thermocouples (TFTCs) and *K*-type thermocouple-based thermo-piles (TFTPs), were designed and fabricated for *in-situ* temperature measurement of ultra-sonic welding process to better understand the heat generation and temperature field during welding of two layers of materials [27] and explore feasibility of *in-situ* process control [31]. TFTCs are attractive for their small size and fast response. The typical junction size of a TFTC is tens of microns and the typical response time reported for a TFTC is less than a microsecond [29], which is significantly superior to conventional temperature sensors and sufficient for *in-situ* temperature measurement during USMW. Embedding techniques (diffusion bonding [34] and electroplating [30]) that protect the sensors from hostile manu-facturing environments were also explored and successfully developed. These techniques produce "smart" substrates with embedded microsensors to be machined or joined, there-fore are perfect fit for fundamental study. For production level *in-situ* process monitoring and control, on the other hand, sensors need to be separated from the substrates while still located close enough to provide robust and reproducible measurements with high spatial and temporal resolution.

In this chapter, ultrasonic joining will be used to weld a three-layered thin sheet ma-terials (Ni coated Cu battery tab, 0.2-mm thick each layer) with a thicker bottom layer (Ni coated Cu bus bar, 0.9-mm thick). To study the heat generation and bonding mechanism for ultrasonic joining in battery assembly, thin film microsensors (TFTCs and TFTPs) will be fabricated directly on top of the thick Cu bus bar. Closest distance between the fabricated sensing tips and the weld spot is 1 μm. For *in-situ* process monitoring, which could provide reliable feedback signals for potential control of the USMW process, "smart" inserts will be fabricated to be placed into anvil as a permanent feature for the ultrasonic joining system. Micro thin film sensors will be fabricated on Si wafers with a protection layer of polyimide (PI) and then diced and inserted into the anvil as an insertion unit. The anvil will be pre-machined with a slot that can hold the sensor in place. The sensor unit will be designed and placed such that the sensing tip is as close as 100 μm to the bottom of the welding spot.

4.1.2 Ultrasonic Welder and Workpieces

A schematic of a STAPLA ultrasonic metal welder used in this study are shown in Fig. 4.1. There are three main welding parameters, namely, sonotrode vibration amplitude, clamp-ing force and welding time. The nominal operating frequency of the welder is 20 kHz with a maximum output electric power of 3 kW. The clamping force has a range from 311 N to 3536 N. Two different booster units are available to allow a zero-to-peak amplitude output from 10 to 40 μm. The maximum weld duration is 9 seconds, and the resolution is about 0.01 second.

Figure 4.2 shows the workpieces (Ni-coated Cu bus bar and tab) and ultrasonic welded samples being used in General Motors (GM) Chevy Volt battery packs assembly. Three layers of Ni-coated Cu bus tabs (45 mm × 41 mm in size and 0.2-mm thick each layer) are to be welded to the Ni-coated bus bar (49 mm × 35 mm in size) of 0.9-mm thick to serve as an interconnect. A thin nickel coating (~2 μm) offers good corrosion resistance against acids, alkalis, and oxidizing agents.

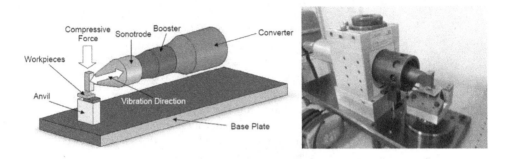

Figure 4.1. Schematic of USMW machine and weld area (left) and the actual machine (right).

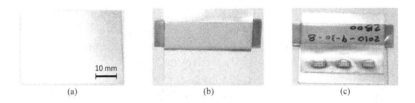

Figure 4.2. USMW workpieces. (a) Ni-coated Cu bus bar, (b) tab, and (c) ultrasonic welded sample.

4.2 DESIGN, FABRICATION, AND CALIBRATION OF THIN-FILM SENSORS

4.2.1 Design of Thin Film Microsensors

Sensor Design on Cu Bus Bars

Two different layouts of thin film microsensor arrays were designed in this study, as illustrated in Fig. 4.3. Figure 4.3(a) shows that two TFTCs are located on the lower side of the welding spot. Two TFTCs ($TFTC_1$ and $TFTC_2$) and one TFTP are placed on the left side of the welding spot. The two TFTCs located in the left of the weld spot can be used to calculate heat flux, which can be compared with the measured heat flux with the TFTP array. Moreover, two more TFTCs ($TFTC_3$ and $TFTC_4$) are placed in the middle but outside the welding zone. Figure 4.3(b) shows four TFTPs designed to investigate the proximity sensitivity of heat flux sensors. Four TFTCs are designed to validate the heat generation during ultrasonic welding. All these 4 TFTCs and 4 TFTPs are placed on the left of the welding zone in the welding vibration direction. In both layouts, the closest distance between the microsensors and edge of the weld zone is 1.5 mm. Neighboring sensors are placed 1.5 mm apart. TFTCs have a sensor junction area (the overlapped area of two sensor legs) of 30 μm by 30 μm. The TFTP consists of 11 pairs of K-type TFTCs on each side to measure the average surface heat flux along the sonotrode vibration direction.

Sensor Design on Insertable Units

Thin film thermocouples (K-type) were fabricated on Si wafers. Si wafers are inexpensive for batch fabrication of multiple sensor units and requires no time-consuming substrate surface preparation. Moreover, silicon offers an excellent thermal diffusivity similar to that of aluminum. The sensor unit can be inserted into a machined slot in the anvil, as shown in Fig. 4.4. Because the sensor top surface would be directly in contact with the metal anvil during measurement, a dielectric film is needed as an insulation and protection layer.

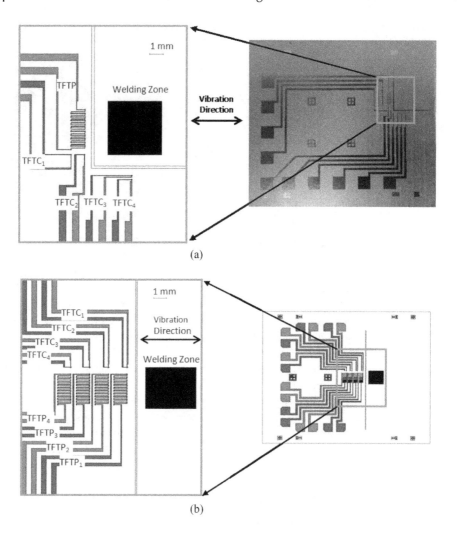

Figure 4.3. Two different thin film micro sensor design layouts. (a) 4 TFTCs and 1 TFTP and (b) 4 TFTCs and 4 TFTPs.

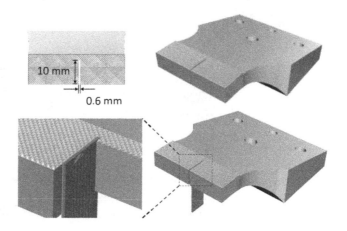

Figure 4.4. Welding anvil with a machined slot and sensor unit inserted.

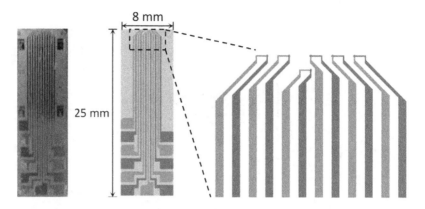

Figure 4.5. Actual sensor unit (left) and the sensor layout with chromel in blue and alumel in red (right).

Spin coated thin film PI was used. An intimate contact between the welding substrate and the top edge of the sensor unit was ensured by careful alignment of the sensor unit top edge and the anvil top surface to a flat solid plane. The sensor units were also accurately diced to ensure a sufficient orthogonality so that the longer edge of the sensor unit fit tightly to the narrow inner wall of the slot machined into the anvil. The slot was done by wire electrical discharge machining (EDM) and its dimension is shown in Fig. 4.4.

Five TFTC sensing tips were placed 0.5 mm apart from each other horizontally with another placed 0.3 mm below, as shown in Fig. 4.5. The sensing tip was located at 0.1 mm below the top edge of the substrate. The center sensing tip was placed directly under the center of the welding spot. With the superior temporal and spatial resolution that the TFTCs array can provide, it is possible to study the temperature gradient and heat flux in different directions during the welding process to obtain insights to the fundamental understanding of the USMW mechanism.

4.2.2 Sensor Fabrication

Sensor Fabrication on Cu Bus Bars

For the microfabrication of thin-film sensors, the substrates should have a good surface finish, preferably with a surface roughness less than 100 nm. Surface topography of the Cu bus bar was evaluated using a white light interferometer. The bus bars typically had a rough surface finish with an Ra of about 0.2 to 0.35 μm and a peak-to-valley (PV) value of 2.7 to 3.3 μm, as shown in Fig. 4.6. To mitigate this problem, a layer of PI with a film thickness of 1 μm was coated on the Cu bus bar with a photoresist spinning machine (spinning for

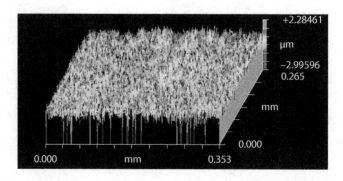

Figure 4.6. Surface finish of as-received Cu bus bar.

10 seconds at 500 rpm, then spinning for 25 seconds at 2500 rpm). The PI film was then cured in a nitrogen-filled oven: heating with a ramp rate of 4°C/minute from room temperature to 200°C, then holding for 30 minutes at 200°C, again heating up to 300°C with a ramp rate of 2.5°C/minute, holding at this temperature for 60 minutes, and finally cooling gradually to room temperature. With the PI film coating on the Cu bus bars, their surface was much smoother with typical surface roughness values of 0.08-μm Ra and 0.8-μm PV, as shown in Fig. 4.7. It should be noted that the thin PI film can also serve as an insulation layer on the Ni-coated Cu bus bar to prevent thin-film sensors from short circuit to the conductive substrates.

Thin film sensor fabrication procedure can be divided into six steps, as shown in Fig. 4.8. Figure 4.8(1) shows the exposure step. After the exposure, the photoresist S1813 was developed in the MF-321 developer. In Step 2, LOR-3A, a non-photosensitive material that dissolves in photo resist developer, was used to generate an undercut beneath S1813 as shown in Fig. 4.8(2). Then, a thin film of chromel was deposited with a CVC 601 DC sputtering system, as shown in Fig. 4.8(3). In Step 4, a subsequent lift-off process removed

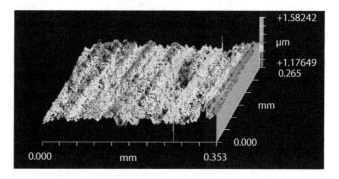

Figure 4.7. Surface finish of Cu bus bar after PI coating.

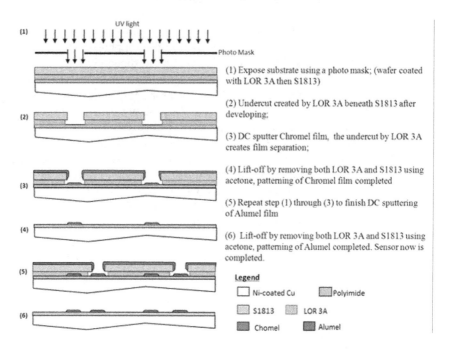

Figure 4.8. Thin film sensor fabrication process.

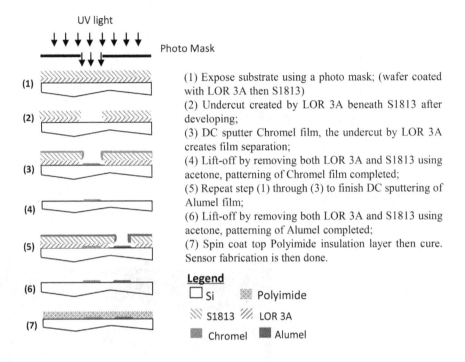

(1) Expose substrate using a photo mask; (wafer coated with LOR 3A then S1813)
(2) Undercut created by LOR 3A beneath S1813 after developing;
(3) DC sputter Chromel film, the undercut by LOR 3A creates film separation;
(4) Lift-off by removing both LOR 3A and S1813 using acetone, patterning of Chromel film completed;
(5) Repeat step (1) through (3) to finish DC sputtering of Alumel film;
(6) Lift-off by removing both LOR 3A and S1813 using acetone, patterning of Alumel completed;
(7) Spin coat top Polyimide insulation layer then cure. Sensor fabrication is then done.

Legend

☐ Si   ▨ Polyimide

▨ S1813 ▨ LOR 3A

▨ Chromel ■ Alumel

Figure 4.9. Sensor fabrication procedure on Si wafers.

S1813 and LOR-3A in acetone, as well as the extra chromel film deposited on S1813, resulting in a structure illustrated in Fig. 4.8(4). The steps were repeated in order to deposit an alumel leg, as shown in Figs. 4.8(5) and 4.8(6), respectively.

Sensor Fabrication on Insertable Unit
The fabrication procedure for thin film sensors on 0.4-mm-thick Si wafers can be divided into seven steps, as shown in Fig. 4.9. Figure 4.9(1) shows the exposure of the spin coated bi-layer resists consisting of S1813 and non-photosensitive LOR-3A (MicroChem) under a photomask. After exposure, wafer was dipped in MF-321 developer for 20 seconds to reveal the photo-defined pattern. Meanwhile, an undercut is created as shown in Fig. 4.9(2) due to the fact that LOR-3A dissolves in MF-321 developer. Then, chromel film of 200 nm was deposited by the DC sputtering, as shown in Fig. 4.9(3). In Step 4, a subsequent lift-off process removed S1813 and LOR-3A in acetone along with the extra chromel film on top of S1813, resulting in   structure illustrated in Fig. 4.9(4). Steps 1 to 3 were then repeated for alumel leg deposition, as shown in Figs. 4.9(5) and 4.9(6). The alumel film was made 50 nm thicker than the just deposited chromel film to ensure the film continuity at the sensor tips where the two materials overlap. A PI (PI-2556) insulation and protection layer (HD Microsystems) was then spun coated and cured to 350°C in a polymer oven with nitrogen flow atmosphere. A final film thickness of 2 μm was obtained. The sensor chip was then carefully diced into the rectangular shape shown in Fig. 4.5. The top and side edges of the diced sensor unit were critical to its precise insertion into the anvil.

4.2.3 Sensor Calibration

Calibration for TFTCs on Cu Bus Bars
To examine the functionality and sensitivity of the fabricated K-type TFTCs, the sensors were calibrated from room temperature to about 700°C in a temperature-controlled tube

furnace. During the calibration process, an argon flow was maintained in the tube furnace. Two commercial K-type thermocouples were attached to the top and bottom of the substrate near the TFTC junction area respectively to serve as references. A NI 6070E data acquisition system from National Instruments (NI) was used to collect data. The furnace was heated up gradually and allowed to stabilize at a number of preset temperatures. The substrate temperature was determined when the temperature difference between two reference thermocouples was smaller than 0.1°C. Calibration results show that TFTC has a linear response and its thermoelectric sensitivity is determined as 41.4 μV/°C, which matches the theoretical value of a standard K-type thermocouple.

Calibration for TFTPs on Cu Bus Bars
The sensitivity of a thermopile, E_{sen}, usually expressed in a voltage output, V_{sen}, per heat flux (W/m²), is related to the substrate material, the number of pairs of thermocouples as well as the distance between two junctions (e.g. ΔX shown in Fig. 4.10). The heat flux can be calculated by

$$Q = V_{sen}/E_{sen} \qquad (4.1)$$

To characterize E_{sen} of the thin film thermopile (TFTP), a sensor unit was fabricated, as shown in Fig. 4.10. The thermopile unit has 11 pairs of K-type thermocouples on each side with a ΔX of 1 mm. Two standard wire thermocouples were attached to the substrate with a large separation distance (ΔL) of 16.5 mm to serve as the reference. The reference heat flux can then be calculated by using the following formula:

$$Q = K(\Delta T/\Delta L) \qquad (4.2)$$

where ΔT is the temperature difference between the two reference thermocouples, and is the thermal conductivity of the copper bus bar. Figure 4.11 shows the calibration setup. A temperature-controlled hot plate was used as the heat source on the hot side. The sensor unit was wrapped with a heat insulation material so that heat flow would be approximately guided in one direction. A large copper plate was attached to the other end of the sensor substrate using a thermal conductive adhesive (LOCTITE 383), serving as a heat sink to dissipate heat to generate a 'cold' end. By controlling the hot plate at different temperatures, different heat flux was obtained. As shown in Fig. 4.12, the voltages from the TFTP are plotted against the reference heat flux Q to determine its sensitivity, E_{sen} to be 9.998 × 10^{-6} mV/(W/m²) whereas the theoretical value was found to be 11.4 × 10^{-6} mV/(W/m²).

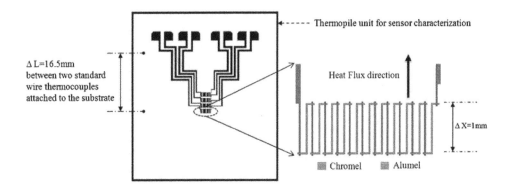

Figure 4.10. TFTP unit for calibration (each sensor junction area: 30 μm × 30 μm).

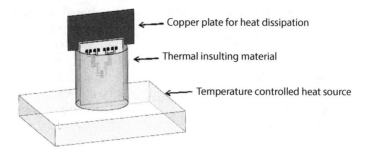

Figure 4.11. TFTP calibration set up.

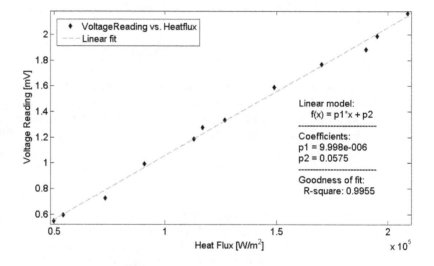

Figure 4.12. Characterization of Thin Film Thermopile (TFTP).

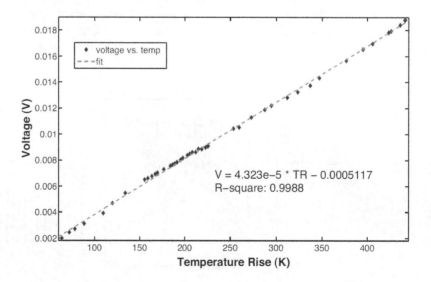

Figure 4.13. Calibration of TFTC fabricated on Si wafer.

Calibration for Sensor Insertion Unit

The sensitivity of the TFTCs on silicon wafers was calibrated from room temperature to about 400°C in a temperature controlled tube furnace. Two commercial K-type thermocouples were attached to the top and bottom of the substrate in the TFTC junction area respectively to serve as references. The data was recorded using the NI 6070E data acquisition system (DAQ) from National Instruments (described in Section 4.2.3). The TFTC sensing signals were recorded when the difference between the two reference temperatures was smaller than 0.1°C. As shown in Fig. 4.13, the TFTCs have a linear response to temperature rises and its thermoelectric sensitivity is about 43.2 μV/°C, which matches the theoretical value for a standard K-type thermocouple well. All sensor chips were batch fabricated on one Si wafer under exactly same process conditions. This measured sensitivity is thus used for all sensor units since little variation in sensitivity for the sensors fabricated together with the calibrated one is expected.

4.3 WELDING EXPERIMENTS AND RESULTS

4.3.1 Temperature Measurement Results on Cu Bus Bars

Ultrasonic welding experiment was conducted using a STAPLA ultrasonic metal welder as previously mentioned in the introduction section. Three layers of Ni-coated Cu tabs (0.2-mm-thick each layer) were welded to the 0.9-mm-thick Ni-coated bus bar. Design of experiments was performed. Welding quality was determined by tension-shear tests. Optimized welding parameters were determined as: welding duration at 1.2 seconds, vibration amplitude at 26 μm, and clamping pressure at 26 MPa. The temperature and/or heat flux data during welding were collected using a NI 6070E DAQ system with a sampling rate of 10 kHz. Figure 4.14 shows the schematic setup for data acquisition, the lead wires that connect the microsensors to the data acquisition system are also K-type thermocouple wires to make sure the cold junction is at room temperature.

Figure 4.15 shows representative measurement results (after noise filtering) from both the thin film thermocouple and the TFTP arrays. The locations of $TFTC_1$, $TFTC_2$ and $TFTC_4$ are shown in Fig. 4.3(a). Temperature rise measured by all TFTCs, as shown in Fig. 4.15(a), showed a similar pattern which indicates a drastic temperature rise at the initial stage and then the temperature rise slows down to reach a peak value. Figure 4.15(b) shows the heat flux measured by TFTPs.

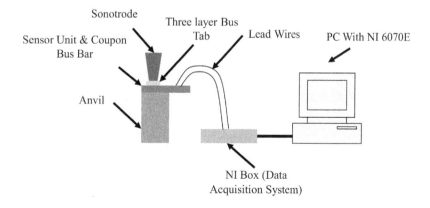

Figure 4.14. Experimental setup for *in-situ* temperature and/or heat flux measurement.

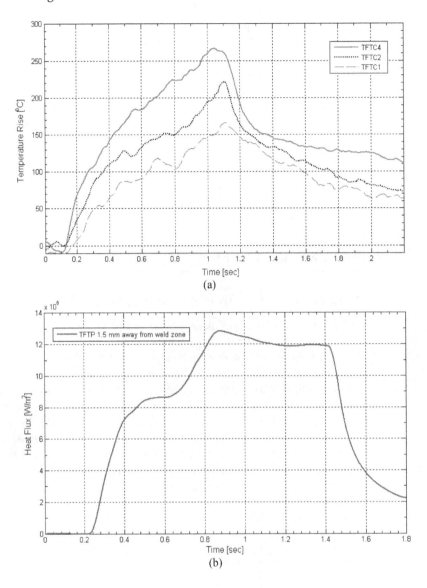

Figure 4.15. *In-situ* temperature and heat flux measurement results during USMW. (a) Temperature measurement results by thin-film thermocouples and (b) Heat flux measurement results by thin-film thermopiles.

4.3.2 Heat Flux Measurement Results on Cu Bus Bars

The design shown in Fig. 4.3(a) was used to compare the heat flux data acquired by TFTP with the heat flux calculated from the temperature difference between $TFTC_1$ and $TFTC_2$. The calculated heat flux matched the measured heat flux by TFTP in general, as shown in Fig. 4.16. However, the calculated heat flux is much noisier because a single TC is too noisy, making it unreliable for process control. Thus only the heat flux signals from TFTPs will be used for process understanding.

The typical heat flux signals, as shown in Figs. 4.15(b) and 4.17(a), have some distinct features. By introducing heat flux change rate, which is the first derivative of heat flux over time, it reveals three distinct regions over time for the welding process, as shown in

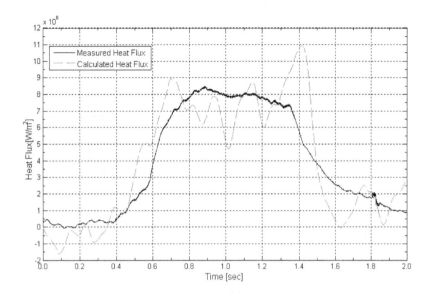

Figure 4.16. Comparison between measured heat flux from TFTPs and the calculated one from two TFTCs.

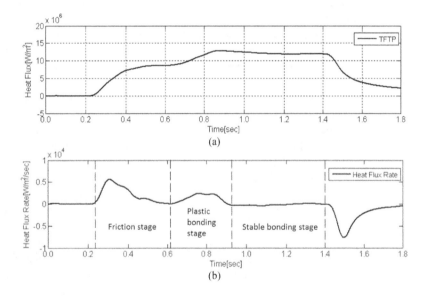

Figure 4.17. Heat flux and heat flux change rate. (a) Typical heat flux signal and (b) First derivative of heat flux signal over time.

Fig. 4.17(b). This significant discovery suggests a three-stage welding mechanism: friction heating, plastic work and diffusion bonding stages.

From the application point of view, further the micro heat flux sensors are placed away from the welding zone, easier the practical implementation can be carried out. Thus a proximity sensitivity of the microsensors during welding was conducted. A typical result is shown in Fig. 4.18. A further study on the heat flux change rates indicates that TFTPs can still effectively capture the three stages even when it is located 4.5 mm away from the welding edge.

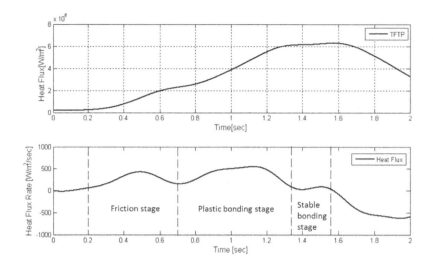

Figure 4.18. Heat flux change rates for different TFTPs with 4.5 mm to welding zone.

4.3.3 Temperature Sensing Results with Inserted Sensor Unit

Design of experiment (DOE) for welding was performed. Welding quality was evaluated by tension-shear tests. Optimized welding parameters were determined as: welding duration at 1.2 second, vibration amplitude at 30 μm, and clamping pressure at 26 MPa. All ultrasonic welding experiments for joining battery assembly were conducted with the optimized parameters except those conducted at lower amplitudes to study its effect on peak temperature. Three layers of Ni-coated Cu tabs (0.2-mm-thick each layer) were welded to the 0.9-mm-thick Ni-coated copper coupon. Chromel and alumel lead wires were bonded to the pads of the sensors by conductive glue. The signals from TFTCs during welding were collected using the NI 6070E DAQ system with sampling rate of 10 kHz. The DAQ box was well shielded to minimize the noise induced by the welding process and lab environment. Figure 4.19 shows the schematic setup for welding and data acquisition.

Two representative sets of temperature sensing data from a single TFTC are shown in Fig. 4.20. Signal processing was performed to average out some of the noise. A total of six samples were welded under the optimized parameters mentioned above. The sensor unit was realigned before each run and sufficient time was given for the anvil to cool down to room temperature. All six sets of data exhibits good consistency. Two were presented here for their even better repeatability at temperature rise greater than 400 K. It suggests that the temperature at the welding spot rises dramatically during the process and reaches its peak at about 1.2 second at the end of the processing time. Because the response time of TFTCs has been reported to be at sub micro second scale, the dynamic temperatures were accurately captured. Unprecedented high temperature rises were detected and the data exhibited good repeatability for *in-situ* sensing during USMW. The reason that the sensor is still functional at temperature higher than 400°C, which is the glass transition temperature of the insulation and protection PI layer, is believed to be the short excursion of the time that the sensor unit experienced. Though it is highly suspected that PI may undergo certain changes in its physical properties, no obvious evidence of degradation of the PI protection layer was observed after the repeated welding cycle.

Three more experiments were also conducted by varying the vibration amplitude while maintaining other parameters to study the effect of amplitude on peak temperature rise. As

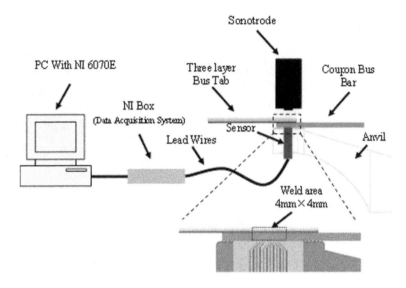

Figure 4.19. Experimental setup for *in-situ* temperature measurement.

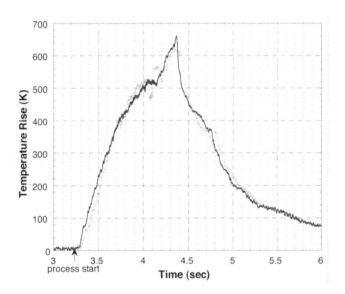

Figure 4.20. Representative temperature rises relative to room temperature during welding experiments.

shown in Fig. 4.21, maximum temperature rise does depend on the vibration amplitude of the welder horn. Higher vibration amplitudes generated faster and higher temperature rises during welding. With the sensor tips located only 100 μm beneath the welded sample, it provides a much more accurate, close-to-true-value monitoring of the process condition than other methods explored. The capability of the inserted sensor unit to capture the dynamic temperatures under various welding parameters suggests that this novel sensor inserts be feasible for *in-situ* process monitoring and control.

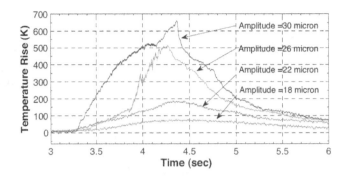

Figure 4.21. Temperature sensing results for experiments under various ultrasonic welding amplitudes.

4.4 VALIDATION OF THE THREE-STAGE BONDING THEORY

To further investigate and validate the theory of three-stage bonding in ultrasonic welding as signaled by the heat flux change rate, weld microstructures were examined by scanning electron microscopy (SEM) and energy dispersive X-ray spectropy (EDS). Samples were prepared with various welding durations of 0.6 second, 0.8 second, 1 second, 1.2 seconds, and 1.5 seconds while maintaining other parameters at the optimized values. An unwelded sample was also used as reference.

The first peak of the heat flux change rate in Fig. 4.17(b) indicated that a large amount of heat was generated at the beginning of the process. This was due to the severe fretting and friction at the interface of two workpieces when the two surfaces are brought into close contact by a large pressure and forced into relative motion of high frequency (~20 kHz). The surface asperities and oxide were removed and dispersed at this stage, which resulted in a smoothened contact interface as shown in Fig. 4.22. Comparison between the interfaces of an unwelded sample (Fig. 4.22(a)) and a welded sample with a duration of 0.6 second (Fig. 4.22(b)) clearly showed the effect of this asperities removal and smoothing process. However, no trace of bonding is found at this stage. Note that Figs. 4.22 through 24 display only the Ni-Ni interfaces, because the bonding of two metals (i.e., 0.2 mm Ni-coated tab and 0.9 mm Ni-coated coupon) occurred between the two Ni coatings only (instead of Cu).

The friction stage ceases at around 0.6 second as shown in Fig. 4.17(b) at which point plastic working stage begins. Partial bonding/seizing develops at this stage as shown in the

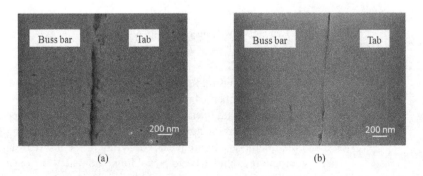

Figure 4.22. SEM pictures of welding interfaces. (a) Non-welded sample and (b) Welded sample (0.6 second).

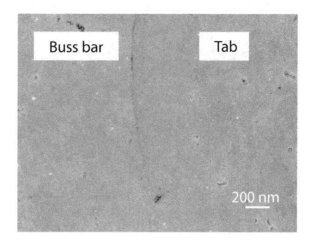

Figure 4.23. SEM pictures of sample welded with a duration of 0.8 second.

SEM picture of the welded sample with duration of 0.8 second (Fig. 4.23). Heat source in this stage is from the plastic deformation at the spots where bonding starts to form.

Plastically deformed interface resulted in even more intimate contact between mating surfaces where the interdiffusion takes place more rapidly. The stable stage in the heat generation curve starts when the transient partial seizing grows to an almost seamless interface as shown in Fig. 4.24. Atomic diffusion then dominates this stage. It is evident that the bonding interface has grown from partial bonding to a full bond throughout the interface and no further change in micro structure can readily be observed in the SEM pictures.

Because it is very difficult to trace the Ni movement during the bonding process at the Ni-Ni interface, we examined the distribution of surface oxygen element (such as in the

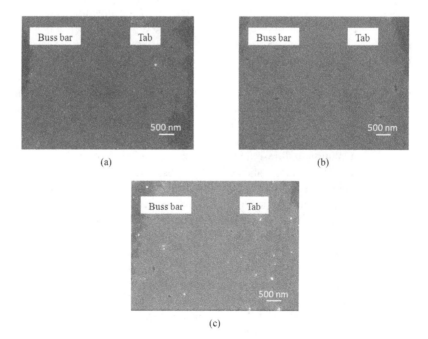

Figure 4.24. SEM pictures of sample welded with duration (a) 1 second, (b) 1.2 second, and (c) 1.5 second.

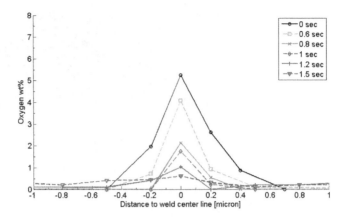

Figure 4.25. Oxygen wt% determined by EDS spot analysis across the welding center line.

forms of Ni oxide) using spot EDS to infer the interfacial Ni mixing/diffusion, as shown in Fig. 4.25. It should be noted that gaps still exist between the tabs and the bus bar in the not-fully-bonded samples (i.e. welding durations of 0 second and 0.6 second) leading to higher concentration of oxygen elements at the interface. It is evident that the diffusion of the oxygen element continues throughout the welding process in a fashion that the oxygen transports further away from the interface and becomes more uniformly distributed normal to the bonding interface line.

4.5 CONCLUSIONS

Thin-film microsensors (TFTCs and TFTPs) were successfully fabricated and utilized to measure transient temperature and heat flux during ultrasonic joining of Cu battery tabs and bus bars. Sensors were either fabricated directly on the Cu bus bar for the study of process physics or on a Si insertion unit for *in-situ* temperature measurement during production. The maximum temperature as measured by the thin-film sensors on the Cu bus bar is 270°C at a location about 1 mm away from the edge of the weld spot. The maximum heat flux is 1.3×10^7 W/m^2 as measured about 2 mm away from the weld spot. The heat flux change rate provides excellent insight to the ultrasonic welding mechanisms. Three distinct welding stages, namely, friction heating, plastic work and diffusion bonding, were found existed during the ultrasonic welding process. Spot EDS was used to study the interfacial bonding evolution in ultrasonic welding process by examining the mixing/diffusion of surface oxide. The method validated our proposed three-stage bonding theory in ultrasonic welding. Thin Film Thermocouples (TFTCs) fabricated on Si wafers for sensor insertion units were successfully inserted into a pre-machined slot in the welding anvil as a temperature sensing device for *in-situ* temperature measurement during production. The top edge of the sensor unit was in intimate contact with the bottom substrate (i.e. Ni-coated copper coupon). Six sensor tips were aligned directly under the welding spot of 4 mm × 4 mm with the closest sensor tip just 100 μm away from the top edge of the insertion unit. A temperature rise of up to 650°C was obtained due to the closeness of the sensors to the welding spot. This TFTC array design may also be utilized for fundamental study of USMW weld forming mechanism in future as well. Dynamic temperature rises were successfully measured with good repeatability for a series of ultrasonic joining experiments on battery electrode assembly. The inserted sensor units were also capable of capturing the peak temperature variations resulted from various welding amplitudes in the welding process.

This study suggests that thin-film sensors are capable of providing insights to the understanding of the welding physics, meanwhile has great potential for real-time monitoring and robust control of the USMW processes to enable a practical smart ultrasonic welding system for battery manufacturing.

Acknowledgment

This work was supported by General Motors and Department of Energy.

REFERENCES

[1] Zhao, J., Li, H., Choi, H., Cai, W., Abell, J. A., and Li, X., 2013, "Insertable thin film thermocouples for *in-situ* transient temperature monitoring in ultrasonic metal welding of battery tabs," *Journal of Manufacturing Processes*, **15**, pp. 136–140.

[2] Li, H., Choi, H., Ma, C., Zhao, J., Cai, W., and Abell, J. A., 2013, "Transient temperature and heat flux measurement in ultrasonic joining of battery tabs using thin-film microsensors," *ASME Journal of Manufacturing Science and Engineering*, **135**, 051015.

[3] Lee, S. S., Kim, T. H., Hu, S. J., Cai, W. W., and Abell, J. A., 2010, "Joining technologies for Automotive Lithium-Ion Battery manufacturing: A review," *ASME Conference Proceedings,* **2010**(49460), pp. 541–549.

[4] Kim, J., Yoo, S., and Kim, J., 2008, "Optimization of welding conditions for sealing of lithium-ion battery by pulsed Nd:YAG laser," *Materials Science Forum,* (0255-5476), pp. 523–526.

[5] Balandin, G. F., Kuznetsov, V. A., and Silin, L. L., 1967, "Fretting action between members in ultrasonic welding of metals," *Welding Production*, **10**, pp. 77–80.

[6] Gao, Y. and Doumanidis, C., 2002, "Mechanical analysis of ultrasonic bonding for rapid prototyping," *ASME Journal of Manufacturing Science and Engineering*, **124**(2), pp. 426–434.

[7] Neville, S. W., 1961, "Ultrasonic welding," *British Weld. J.*, **8**, pp. 177–187.

[8] Friswell, M. I. and Inman, D. J., 2000, "Sensor validation for smart structures," *Journal of Intelligent Material Systems and Structures*, **10**(12), pp. 973–982.

[9] Lee, S. S., Kim, T. H., Hu, S. J., Cai, W., Abell, J. A., and Li, J., 2013, "Characterization of joint quality in ultrasonic welding of battery tabs," *ASME Journal of Manufacturing Science & Engineering*, **135**(2).

[10] Lee, D., Kannatey-Asibu, Jr., E., and Cai, W., 2012, "Ultrasonic welding simulations for multiple layers of lithium-ion battery tabs," *ASME Journal of Manufacturing Science & Engineering*, **135**(6), 061011.

[11] Kim, T., Yum, J., Hu, S. J., Spicer, J. P., and Abell, J. A., 2011, "Process robustness of single lap ultrasonic welding of thin, dissimilar materials," *CIRP Annals—Manufacturing Technology*, **60**(1), pp. 17–20.

[12] De Vries, E., 2004, "Mechanics and mechanisms of ultrasonic metal welding," Ph.D. Thesis, The Ohio State University.

[13] Du, H. and Klamecki, B. E., 1999, "Force sensors embedded in surfaces for manufacturing and other tribological process monitoring," *ASME Journal of Manufacturing Science and Engineering*, **121**(4), pp. 739–748.

[14] Edelman, F., Gutmanas, E., and Brener, R., 1988, "Interfacial processes and diffusion in the metal/Si3N4Si thin-film systems," *Israel Journal of Technology*, **24**(4), pp. 447–451.

[15] Foedinger, R., Rea, D., Sirkis, J., Wagreich, R., Troll, J., Grande, R., Davis, C., and Vandiver, T. L., 1998, "Structural health monitoring of filament wound composite pressure vessels with embedded optical fiber sensors," *International SAMPE Symposium and Exhibition—Proceeding, Anaheim,* Part 1 (of 2), **43**(1), pp. 444–457.

[16] Kodama, M., 1989, "Ultrasonic welding of non-ferrous metals," *Welding International*, **3**(10), pp. 853–860.

[17] Chang, U. I. and Frisch, J., 1974, "On optimization of some parameters in ultrasonic metal welding," *Welding Journal*, **53**(1), pp. 24s–35s.

[18] Pfluger, A. R. and Sideris, X. N., 1975, "New developments in ultrasonic welding," *SAMPE Quarterly*, **7**(1), pp. 9–19.

[19] Hazlett, T. H. and Ambekar, S. M., 1970, "Additional studies on interface temperatures and bonding mechanisms of ultrasonic welds," *Welding Journal*, **49**(5), pp. 196s–200s.

[20] Neppiras, E. A., 1965, "Ultrasonic welding of metals," *Ultrasonics*, **3**(3), pp. 128–135.

[21] Neville, S. W., 1961, "Ultrasonic welding," *British Welding Journal*, **8**, pp. 177–187.

[22] Wagner, J., Schlicker, U., and Kaiserslautern, D. E., 1998, "Bond formation during the ultrasonic welding of ceramic with metal," *Welding and Cutting*, **50**(10), pp. E199–E202.

[23] Harman, G. and Albers, J., 1977, "The ultrasonic welding mechanism as applied to aluminum- and gold-wire bonding in microelectronics," *IEEE Transactions on Parts, Hybrids, and Packaging*, PHP-**13**(4), pp. 406–412.

[24] Jones, J. B., Maropis, N., Thomas, J. G., and Bancroft, D., 1961, "Phenomenological considerations in ultrasonic welding," *Welding Journal*, **46**(7), pp. 289-s–305-s.

[25] Okada, M., Shin, A., Miyagi, M., and Matsuda, H., 1963, "Joint mechanism of ultrasonic welding," *Japan Institute of Metals*, **4**, pp. 250–256.

[26] Tsujino, J., Ueoka, T., Fujita, Y., and Watanabe, I., 1994, "Ultrasonic butt welding of aluminum, copper and steel plate specimens," *Japanese Journal of Applied Physics Part 1*, **33**(5B), pp. 3058–3064.

[27] Cheng, X. and Li, X. C., 2007, "Investigation of heat generation in ultrasonic metal welding using micro sensor arrays," *Journal of Micromechanics and Microengineering*, **17**(2), pp. 273–282.

[28] Cheng, X., Datta, A., Choi, H., Zhang, X., and Li, X. C., 2007, "Study on embedding and integration of micro sensors into metal structures for manufacturing applications," *ASME Journal of Manufacturing Science and Engineering*, **129**(2), pp. 416–424.

[29] Zhang, X., Choi, H., Datta, A., and Li, X. C., 2006, "Design, fabrication and characterization of metal embedded thin-film thermocouples with various film thicknesses and junction sizes," *Journal of Micromechanics and Microengineering*, **16**(5), pp. 900–905.

[30] Choi, H., Datta, A., Cheng, X., and Li, X. C., 2006, "Microfabrication and characterization of metal-embedded thin-film thermomechanical microsensors for applications in hostile manufacturing environments," *Journal of Microelectromechanical Systems*, **15**(2), pp. 322–329.

[31] Cheng, X., Choi, H., Schwieso, P., Datta, A., and Li, X. C., 2005, "Micro thin-film sensor embedded in metal structures for *in-situ* process monitoring during ultrasonic welding," *North American Manufacturing Research Conference, NAMRC*, **33**, pp. 267–272.

[32] Choi, H. and Li, X. C., 2007, "Fabrication and application of micro thin-film thermocouples for transient temperature measurement in nanosecond pulsed laser micromachining of nickel," *Sensors and Actuators A: Phys.*, **136**(1), pp. 118–124.

[33] Datta, D., Choi, H., and Li, X. C., 2006, "Batch fabrication and characterization of embedded thin-film thermocouples in metal," *Journal of The Electrochemistry Society*, **153**(5), pp. H89–H93.

[34] Choi, H., Konishi, H., Xu, H., and Li, X. C., 2007, "Embedding of micro thin film strain sensors in sapphire by diffusion bonding," *Journal of Micromechanics and Microengineering*, **17**(11), p. 2248.

Chapter 5

MOTION ANALYSIS FOR MULTILAYER SHEETS[1]

S. Shawn Lee[1], Tae Hyung Kim[2], S. Jack Hu[2], Wayne Cai[3], and Jeffrey A. Abell[3]
[1]*Intellectual Property Prosecution, McDermott Will & Emery LLP*
[2]*Department of Mechanical Engineering, The University of Michigan*
[3]*Manufacturing Systems Research Lab, General Motors Global R&D Center*

ABSTRACT

One of the biggest challenges in manufacturing automotive lithium-ion batteries is to achieve consistent weld quality in joining multiple layers of dissimilar materials. Although most fusion welding processes face difficulties in such joining, ultrasonic welding overcomes those difficulties due to its solid-state process characteristics. However, inconsistency of weld quality still exists because of limited knowledge on the weld formation through the multiple interfaces. This chapter aims to establish real-time phenomenological observation on the multilayer ultrasonic welding process by analyzing the vibration behavior of metal layers. Such behavior is characterized by a direct measurement of the lateral displacement of each metal layer using high-speed images. Two different weld tools are used in order to investigate the effect of tool geometry on the weld formation mechanism and the overall joint quality. A series of bond density measurements is carried out to validate the observations and hypotheses of those phenomena in multilayer ultrasonic welding. The results of this research enhance the understanding of the ultrasonic welding process of multiple metal sheets and provide insights for optimum tool design to improve the quality of multilayer joints.

Keywords: high speed images, multilayer ultrasonic welding, weld propagation mechanism

5.1 INTRODUCTION

Ultrasonic metal welding creates a solid-state bond between metals using oscillating shears generated by a high-frequency ultrasonic energy. It has recently been applied to joining lithium-ion batteries for hybrid and electric vehicles. This process is well suited for such applications because of its ability in joining multiple layers of dissimilar materials [1].

In the battery assembly, a large number of battery cells are connected through bus-bars to meet the desired power and capacity requirement [2]. In such configuration, multiple layers of dissimilar metals, mostly of copper, nickel or aluminum as typical materials of anodes, cathodes, and bus-bars, are welded together. Achieving consistent weld quality in those multiple weld interfaces is critical for good battery performances.

Although extensive research has been done on the weld formation of two metal sheets in ultrasonic welding [3–8], only limited research has been carried out on multilayer welding. Ram et al. [9] presented layer-by-layer fabrication between multiple foils of Al 3000 series using ultrasonic consolidation process in additive manufacturing. They described the effects of process parameters on product quality in fabricating multiple layers of similar materials and further investigated the weldability between multiple, dissimilar materials,

---

[1] The content presented in this chapter has previously appeared in Ref. [10].

especially of Al alloys to brass or to stainless steel [11]. Obielodan et al. [12] examined ultrasonic welding of several other multi-material combinations, such as silver/copper/nickel, molybdenum/aluminum/copper, aluminum/titanium, and nickel/stainless steel. However, most of these studies were limited to demonstrating the ability of ultrasonic welding in joining multilayer dissimilar materials. Recently, some research has been carried out on the ultrasonic welding of multi-stacked batteries. Kang et al. [13, 14] presented the effect of structural vibration that is generated from the ultrasonic welding process on weld quality in the multilayer battery tab configuration. Lee et al. [15] conducted research on the ultrasonic welding of multiple, dissimilar metals by developing a mechanical-thermal coupled finite element model. In their study, the temperature distribution within the multi-material stack-up was obtained for a considerable amount of weld time (500 ms) by the numerical simulation model. Nonetheless, there is still a lack of understanding on the oscillating behavior of each metal sheet in multi-stacked configurations during the ultrasonic welding process. Little effort has been made to identify how and in what order the weld is created through multiple interfaces.

Several researchers investigated how the weld is developed at the interface during the ultrasonic welding process by experiments and numerical simulations. Ji et al. [16] examined the cross-section of Al+1%Si wire-bonded on the Au/Ni/Cu pad using scanning electron microscopy with energy dispersive X-ray spectroscopy, and observed a large number of vacancies and dislocations that can be fast diffusion paths across the weld interface. Zhang and Li [17] developed a dynamic temperature displacement finite element model to correlate process parameters with the weld development, whereas Elangovan et al. [18] introduced friction as a heat source to the workpiece in their numerical model. Siddiq and Ghassemieh [19] developed a theoretical as well as a numerical model [20] to investigate the effect of friction and material softening behaviors on the temperature change at the interface. However, most of these studies lack real-time phenomenological observation on weld development during the process.

In this chapter, the weld formation mechanism through the multiple interfaces is investigated experimentally using high-speed images. High-speed imaging has been widely used by many researchers for analyzing various welding techniques, for example, laser welding [21, 22] or arc welding [23–26], but never been attempted for ultrasonic metal welding due to its high speed process characteristics. However, recent developments in high-speed imaging technology [27] enable the observation of high-frequency oscillations of the metal sheets in ultrasonic welding.

The goal of this study is to characterize weld development in multilayer ultrasonic welding through in-depth understanding of the vibration behavior of the metals. Such behavior is analyzed by processing high-speed images obtained during the welding process and measuring the lateral displacement of the workpiece. Different weld tools are introduced to investigate their impact on the vibration behaviors, and ultimately on the weld propagation mechanism. Furthermore, microscopic analyses and bond density measurements provide additional information on weld development in multilayer ultrasonic welding.

The remainder of this chapter is organized as follows: Section 5.2 describes experimental setups and procedures; Section 5.3 discusses the results from high-speed imaging and post-weld experiments; and Section 5.4 summarizes and concludes the chapter.

5.2 EXPERIMENT

5.2.1 Ultrasonic Welding Process

Figure 5.1 describes a typical ultrasonic metal welding system. A piezoelectric transducer converts a low frequency electrical signal to a high-frequency, 20 kHz or above, mechanical

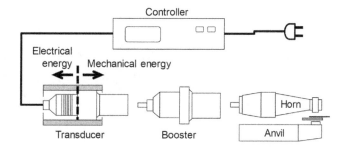

Figure 5.1. Ultrasonic metal welding system.

vibration. This mechanical vibration is amplified by a booster and then transferred to a horn. The metal sheets to be joined are placed and clamped under pressure between the horn and anvil. As welding begins, oscillating shears generated by the welder breaks the oxide layers or contaminants and finally creates a solid-state bond between the exposed metals. Because of such bonding characteristics, a wide range of multiple, dissimilar metal sheets or thin foils can be joined by ultrasonic welding despite the thickness limitation of workpiece to 3 mm [2].

5.2.2 High-Speed Imaging

In this study, the Phantom v1610 digital high-speed camera with a telescope lens was used to record the dynamics of the metal workpiece during ultrasonic welding, as described in Fig. 5.2(a). Three layers of 0.2-mm nickel-plated C11000 copper (top) and one layer of the same material but 1.0 mm (bottom) were placed on an anvil, as seen in Fig. 5.2(b). Figure 5.2(c) shows the front view of the workpiece as shown in the camera screen. To measure displacement, the group of metal layers was marked with a straight line. Figure 5.3(a) illustrates the side view of the camera setup showing the workpiece aligned with the horn. This alignment was intended for observing the vibration behavior of the horn and workpiece together.

The images were taken at 100,000 frames per second with an exposure time of 9 μs, which provides five images per one vibration cycle. The size of the image was 256×256 pixels. The small vibration motion of a metal layer, tens of microns, was able to be recorded

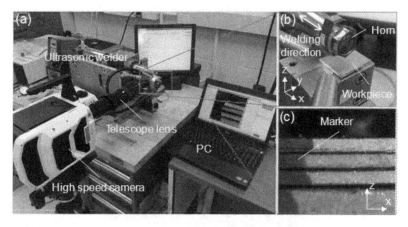

Figure 5.2. High-speed camera setup: (a) entire view of setup; (b) focused view on welding part; and (c) workpiece in PC screen view.

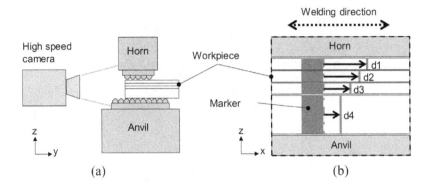

Figure 5.3. Schematic of high-speed camera setup: (a) workpiece stack-up aligned with horn (side view); and (b) displacement measurement of metal layer (front view).

owing to a 35× zoom capability of the telescope lens together with the CCD. Light was provided by a 150-W Dolan-Jenner illuminator through fiber optic light-guides for high-speed imaging. Finally, the images were digitally obtained and processed by Phantom camera control application software. The lateral displacement of each metal layer was measured in the consecutive high-speed images as illustrated in Fig. 5.3(b).

5.2.3 Multilayer Welding Experiment

The multiple layers of nickel plated copper with different thicknesses were welded by a 20-kHz, 3.6 kW, AmTech lateral-drive ultrasonic spot welder. Table 5.1 shows the input parameters and their levels. The clamping pressure and the horn vibration amplitude were fixed at 50 psi and 60 μm, respectively. The weld time was varied to analyze the weld formation through multiple interfaces during the welding process. The input range of weld time was pre-determined by a screening test. Replication of each parameter was ten: nine for T-peel testing and one for cross-sectioning. Two anvil types with different knurl patterns ("fine" and "coarse") were used to study the effect of the anvil roughness on the weld formation in multilayer ultrasonic welding. Figure 5.4 describes the knurl patterns and their

TABLE 5.1. Factors and levels for experimental design.

Factor	Level
Weld time (sec), T	0.1, 0.2, 0.3, 0.4, 0.5, 0.6
Anvil type	Fine, coarse

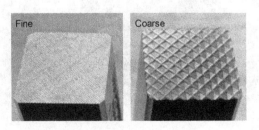

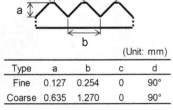

(Unit: mm)

Type	a	b	c	d
Fine	0.127	0.254	0	90°
Coarse	0.635	1.270	0	90°

Figure 5.4. Two anvil types and their knurl dimensions.

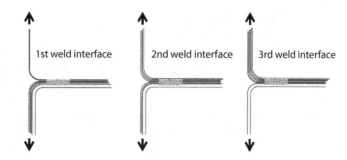

Figure 5.5. T-peel test for multi-joint welds.

dimensions. It is expected that the difference in anvil teeth geometry will cause different levels of material deformation, which eventually affect the weld development at the bottom interface.

5.2.4 Post-Weld Performance Testing/Microscopy/Bond Density Measurement

As a multi-joint configuration, each weld sample has three interfaces: first, second, and third. To evaluate the mechanical strength of multilayer joints, a T-peel test [28] per sample, as illustrated in Fig. 5.5, was performed by an Instron testing machine with a pulling speed of 10 mm/min. Of the nine T-peel samples, three are tested for each interface. The maximum tensile load during the T-peel test was recorded. The remaining one weld sample was cross-sectioned, mounted, polished, and applied to light surface etching for further optical micrographs and bond density measurement. The details of sample preparation and post-west measurement for ultrasonic metal welds were fully described in the previous study [1].

5.3 RESULTS AND DISCUSSION

This section presents the results from high-speed imaging and post-weld experiments. Based on these results, we discuss the weld formation mechanism in multilayer welding as well as the effect of anvil geometry on the vibration behaviors of the metal sheets and the weld development.

5.3.1 Observation of Vibration Development in Multiple Layers

Figure 5.6 shows an example of how the lateral displacement of one metal layer varies in a single weld cycle of 5×10^{-5} second. As the horn vibrates with constant amplitude, the workpiece also vibrates with it. The displacement of each layer is measured from the high-speed images as seen in Fig. 5.6(a), which shows six consecutive images taken at 0.00001-second intervals. These six images constitute a vibration cycle as described in Fig. 5.6(b).

Figure 5.7 describes the development of vibration cycles for each metal layer during the initial 0.1-second weld time. Each plot in Fig. 5.7 shows two vibration cycles of four metal layers at a weld time of 0.005, 0.02, 0.04, 0.06, 0.08, and 0.1 second. Each data point in the plots is obtained by using the image processing algorithm in the Phantom application

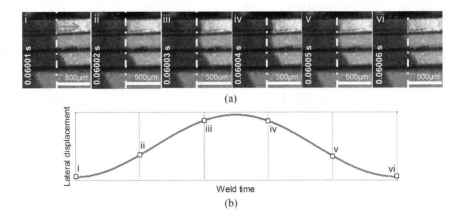

Figure 5.6. Example of displacement variation in one weld cycle (5×10^{-5} second): (a) consecutive high-speed images showing single vibration cycle of a metal layer; (b) an illustration of displacement curve measured from (a).

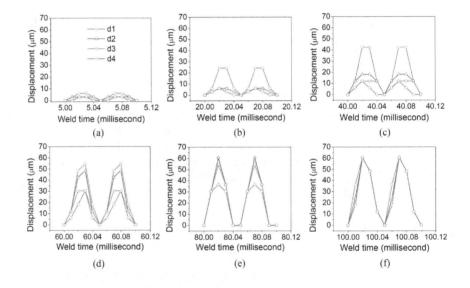

Figure 5.7. Development of vibration cycles of multiple layers with fine anvil: (a) 0.005 second, (b) 0.020 second, (c) 0.040 second, (d) 0.060 second, (e) 0.080 second, and (f) 0.100 second weld time.

software. The resolution of this measurement is approximately 3 μm. Despite the limitation of focal length of the telescope lens used in this experiment, the variation cycles and their developing trends are clearly shown. The weld time 0.005 second in Fig. 5.7(a) represents the vibration cycles at the very beginning of the welding process, and the rest of the figures (Figs. 5.7[b]–[f]) show the progress of the vibrations with increment of 0.02 second weld time. The following observations can be made from the figure.

- In two consecutive cycles, very little difference in the vibration magnitude exists.
- When the observations are made sufficiently apart from each other, then a clear increase in the vibration magnitude can be seen. Each layer experiences an increase in vibration amplitude during the initial 0.1 second of weld time, which can be called "growth" of the vibration of the layers.

- The vibration magnitude is highest in the top layer, but the vibration of the other layers increases over time and finally reaches that of the top layer.

We confirmed that the results in Fig. 5.7 were repeatable based on multiple measurements from the same images, and were not subject to operator reproducibility.

5.3.2 Weld Formation Mechanism in Multilayer Welding

Many previous studies agreed that an intensive frictional behavior between the metals is crucial for forming a pure metallurgical bond at the interface [8, 17, 24, 30]. Gao and Doumanidis [31] introduced, a slippage and stick (i.e., bonding) phenomenon, which is accompanied by a frictional coefficient that varies throughout the welding process. Gilbert et al. [33] further confirmed this. They argued that the friction force induced by the shear motion of the horn led to a slippage between workpiece resulting in plastic deformation thorough dislocations and finally a weld at the joint. Therefore, the slippage or rubbing action also plays a key role in weld formation in multilayer configuration.

To characterize the variations of lateral movements of the metal layers during the initial stages of the welding process, the vibration magnitudes at different weld times are extracted from Fig. 5.7 and plotted against time as described in Fig. 5.8. The following observations can be made from the figure.

- The top metal layer (d1) increases its vibration amplitude exactly with the vibration amplitude of the horn. Then, the vibration of the rest of the layers is developed sequentially, i.e., in the order of d2, d3, and d4.
- The amplitude of the vibration for the fine anvil converges to 60 μm while that for the course anvil converges to 30 μm.
- The third and fourth layers (d3 and d4) for the course anvil show less vibration than those for the fine anvil.

To understand the trend of amplitude change of the multiple layers for the entire welding process, Fig. 5.8 is extended further to 0.4 second weld time, as seen in Fig. 5.5. Figure 5.9(a) shows the variation of vibration amplitude for the horn and four nickel-plated copper sheets when using the fine type anvil whereas Fig. 5.9(b) is the result from the coarse type anvil. The following observations can be made from the figure.

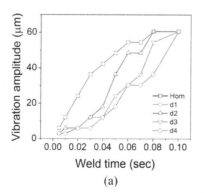 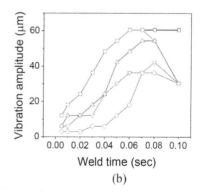

(a)   (b)

Figure 5.8. Progress of vibration amplitude of horn and four metal layers during initial stages (0 ~ 0.1 sec) of welding process when using (a) fine anvil; and (b) coarse anvil.

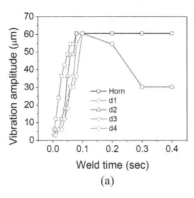 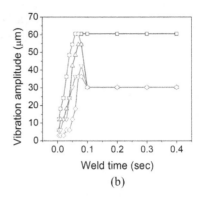

(a)   (b)

Figure 5.9. Progress of vibration amplitude of horn and four metal layers during the entire welding process when using (a) fine anvil and (b) coarse anvil.

Both results in Fig. 5.9 show that the vibration amplitude of each metal layer initially changes over time and then merges into uniform amplitude for the rest of the welding process.

As weld time reaches 0.1 second, the vibration amplitudes of all four layers when using the fine type anvil converge at approximately 60 μm, the same magnitude as the horn, and decrease to 30 μm, while those with the coarse type converge at 30 μm and stay until the end of the process.

After 0.1 second weld time, slippage is observed between the tool (both horn and anvil) and workpiece.

These indicate that the average vibration in multilayer welding is bigger with the fine type anvil than with the coarse type. This is mainly because the lower layers in the stack-up experience more slippage during the initial welding process (< 0.1 second) due to the smaller engagement between the material and the tool when using the fine knurl. In contrast, the bigger teeth of the coarse knurl allows the tool to penetrate the material more and provides a tighter engagement, which leads to less vibration in the lower metal layers. In addition, the extra slippage between the tool and metal workpiece imply possible tool wear.

Figure 5.10 shows the relative displacement between the two metal layers that face each other, which represents the amplitude difference between two adjacent layers in Fig. 8.8. The following observations can be made from the figure.

- As described in Fig. 5.10(a), the maximum difference in vibration amplitude between d1 and d2 occurs at around 0.03 to 0.04 second whereas those maximum points for the second and third weld interface were at 0.06 and 0.08 second, respectively. Therefore, the relative motion between layers is maximal first at the 1st weld interface, and then followed by the second and third interface.
- The relative motion between layers in Fig. 5.10(b) is developed in the order of the first (~ 0.04 second), third (~ 0.05 second) and second weld interface (~ 0.07 second).

These different trends indicate that, when the fine anvil is used, a larger amount of slippage occurs between the bottom layer and the anvil so that the rubbing action between the 3rd and 4th layer is relatively low compared to that of the coarse anvil case. This difference in mobility of the bottom layer between those anvils may result in the different sequence of weld formation in multi-interfaces.

Figure 5.11 shows the progression of the vibration amplitude of the fourth layer which interfaces with the anvil during the welding process. A clear distinction in mobility between

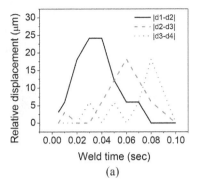 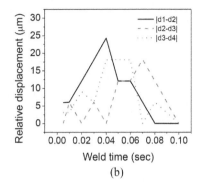

Figure 5.10. Progress of relative displacement between metal layers during initial stages (0–0.1 sec) of welding process when using (a) fine anvil, and (b) coarse anvil.

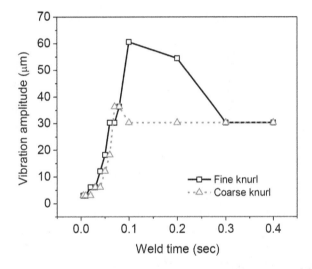

Figure 5.11. Progress of vibration amplitude of the fourth layer (anvil side) during the entire welding process with different anvil types.

the fine and coarse anvil is shown due to the different frictional conditions induced by different knurl patterns. The difference in relative movement between the fourth layer and the anvil is also evidenced by the difference in the amount of tool wear between fine and coarse anvils.

5.3.3 Effect of Weld Tool Geometry on Bond Density and Joint Strength

The bond density is one of the key weld attributes that defines quality in an ultrasonic metal weld in a quantitative way [1]. Figure 5.12 shows how the bond densities in multiple weld interfaces are developed throughout the welding process. For the fine anvil case, the bond densities in second and third interface are very low (less than 10%) in the beginning of the welding process (~ 0.2 second). As welding proceeds, the bond density in the second interface remarkably increases up to almost the same level as the first interface, 80%, whereas that in the third interface increases only up to 40%. This slow development of bond density in the third interface is mainly caused by a large amount of slippage between the

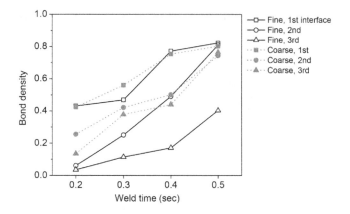

Figure 5.12. Bond density development at multiple weld interfaces for different anvil types.

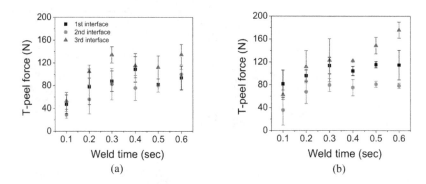

Figure 5.13. Mechanical performance of multiple joints (three weld interfaces) obtained by T-peel test for: (a) fine anvil type; and (b) coarse anvil type.

bottom metal layer and the anvil, especially during the middle stage of the welding process, as discussed in Section 5.3.2. However, when using the coarse anvil, the bond densities in the second and third interface begin with relatively higher levels than the fine anvil case (approximately 25% and 15%, respectively), and increase rapidly with time: both are over 70%. This faster growing trend of weld formation in the third interface results from the higher relative motion between the last two sheets due to reduced slippage of the bottom.

This high bond density development is supported by the T-peel test result in which the joint of the third interface with course anvil is stronger than the joint with fine anvil, as shown in the later welding process in Fig. 5.13. It should be noted that the reason of higher performance of the third interface in most regions is a bigger weld thickness or diffusion layer that may be formed between the thicker materials (total, 1.2 mm) than other interfaces (total, 0.4 mm). The effect of the ultrasonic weld thickness on the ultrasonic weld strength can be further investigated.

5.4 CONCLUSIONS

This chapter proposes a new methodology of high-speed imaging for characterizing the ultrasonic metal welding process and reveals insights for optimum tool design to improve the quality of multilayer joints. To analyze the weld formation in multilayer ultrasonic welding, a high-speed camera is used to record the vibration of the metal sheets. The vibrating profiles of the multiple layers and their relative motions are obtained by high-speed images. The results from this high-speed imaging and the subsequent microscopic analyses provide in-depth understanding of the propagation mechanism in multilayer ultrasonic welding. Two anvil types are used to investigate the impact of tool geometry on the weld formation in the multiple interfaces. This study provides valuable insights on tool wear that can result from the extensive amount of slippage during the ultrasonic welding process. Notable findings are summarized as follows:

1. The vibration cycles of the multiple layers develop with increasing magnitude in the initial period of the welding process. Each layer oscillates with different amplitude but in phase, meaning that there are relative differences in amplitude but no out-of-phase motions between the layers.
2. The maximum difference in vibration magnitude between the interfacing layers occurs in the order of first, second, and third weld interface when using the fine anvil, whereas the order is first, third, and second when using the coarse anvil.
3. The weld with the fine anvil propagates from top to bottom interface, i.e., "uni-directional," while the weld with the coarse anvil is developed from both ends, i.e., "bi-directional." These different propagation mechanisms between two anvil types are mainly caused by different amounts of slippage between the bottom layer and the anvil due to the distinction in tool engagement with materials.
4. The coarse anvil design performs better than the fine anvil in terms of higher bond density and higher mechanical strength over the multiple weld interfaces.
5. The coarse anvil provides longer tool life since relative movement between the 4th layer and the tool is smaller compared with the anvil with fine geometry.

REFERENCES

[1] Lee, S. S., Kim, T. H., Hu, S. J., Cai, W., Abell, J. A., and Li, J., 2013, "Characterization of Joint Quality in Ultrasonic Welding of Battery Tabs," *Journal of Manufacturing Science and Engineering*, **135**(2), 021004.
[2] Lee, S. S., Kim, T. H., Hu, S. J., Cai, W. W., and Abell, J. A., 2010, "Joining Technologies for Automotive Lithium-Ion Battery Manufacturing—A Review," *Proceedings of the ASME 2010 International Manufacturing Science and Engineering Conference*, Erie, PA, Paper No. MSEC2010-34168, October 12–15.
[3] Joshi, K. C., 1971, "The Formation of Ultrasonic Bonds Between Metals," *Welding Journal*, **50**(12), pp. 840–848.
[4] Harthoorn, J., 1973, "Joint Formation in Ultrasonic Welding Compared With Fretting Phenomena for Aluminium," *Ultrasonics international*, *1973*, 43–51.
[5] Kreye, H., 1977, "Melting Phenomena in Solid State Welding Processes," *Welding Journal*, **56**(5), pp. 154–158.
[6] Tucker, J. C., 2002, "Ultrasonic Welding of Copper to Laminate Circuit Board," M.S. Thesis, Worchester Polytechnic Institute.
[7] De Vries, E., 2004, "Mechanics and Mechanisms of Ultrasonic Metal Welding," Ph.D. Thesis, The Ohio State University.
[8] Zhang, C. and Li, L., 2009, "A Coupled Thermal-Mechanical Analysis of Ultrasonic Bonding Mechanism," *Metallurgical and Materials Transactions B*, **40**(2), pp. 196–207.
[9] Ram, G. D. J., Yang, Y., and Stucker, B., 2006, "Effect of Process Parameters on Bond Formation During Ultrasonic Consolidation of Aluminum Alloy 3003," *Journal of Manufacturing Systems*, **25**(3), pp. 221–238.
[10] Lee, S., Kim, T., Hu, S. J., Cai, W., and Abell, J. A., 2015, "Analysis of Weld Formation in Multilayer Ultrasonic Metal Welding Using High-Speed Images," *ASME Journal of Manufacturing Science and Engineering*, **137**(3), 031016.
[11] Ram, G. D. J., Robinson, C., Yang, Y., and Stucker, B., 2007, "Use of Ultrasonic Consolidation for Fabrication of Multi-Material Structures," *Rapid Prototyping Journal*, **13**(4), pp. 226–235.

[12] Obielodan, J., Ceylan, A., Murr, L., and Stucker, B., 2010, "Multi-Material Bonding in Ultrasonic Consolidation," *Rapid Prototyping Journal*, **16**(3), pp. 180–188.

[13] Kang, B., Cai, W., and Tan, C. A., 2014, "Vibrational Energy Loss Analysis in Battery Tab Ultrasonic Welding," *Journal of Manufacturing Processes*, **16**(2), pp. 218–232.

[14] Kang, B., Cai, W., and Tan, C. A., 2013, "Dynamic Response of Battery Tabs Under Ultrasonic Welding," *Journal of Manufacturing Science & Engineering*, **135**(5): 051013.

[15] Lee, D., Kannatey-Asibu, E., and Cai, W., 2013, "Ultrasonic Welding Simulations for Multiple, Thin and Dissimilar Metals," *ASME Journal of Manufacturing Science & Engineering, 135(6), 061011.*

[16] Ji, H., Li, M., Kung, A. T., Wang, C., and Li, D., 2005, "The Diffusion of Ni Into Al Wire at the Interface of Ultrasonic Wire Bond During High Temperature Storage," *6th International Conference on Electronic Packaging Technology*, doi: 10.1109/ICEPT.2005.1564652.

[17] Zhang, C. and Li, L., 2009, "A Coupled Thermal-Mechanical Analysis of Ultrasonic Bonding Mechanism," *Metallurgical and Materials Transactions B*, **40**(2), pp. 196–20.

[18] Elangovan, S., Semeer, S., and Prakasan, K., 2009, "Temperature and Stress Distribution in Ultrasonic Metal Welding—An FEA-Based Study," *Journal of Materials Processing Technology*, **209**(3), pp. 1143–1150.

[19] Siddiq, A. and Ghassemieh, E., 2009, "Theoretical and Fe Analysis of Ultrasonic Welding of Aluminum Alloy 3003," *Journal of Manufacturing Science and Engineering* **131**(4), 041007.

[20] Siddiq, A. and Ghassemieh, E., 2008, "Thermomechanical Analyses of Ultrasonic Welding Process Using Thermal and Acoustic Softening Effects," *Mechanics of Materials* **40**(12), pp. 982–1000.

[21] Eriksson, I., Gren, P., Powell, J., and Kaplan, A. F., 2010, "New High-Speed Photography Technique for Observation of Fluid Flow in Laser Welding," *Optical Engineering* **49**(10), 100503.

[22] Eriksson, I., Powell, J., and Kaplan, A. F., 2010, Ultra High Speed Camera Investigations of Laser Beam Welding. *International Congress on Applications of Lasers & Electro-Optics (ICALEO)*, Anaheim (CA), USA.

[23] Zaal, J., van Driel, W., Kessels, F., and Zhang, G., 2008, "Correlating Drop Impact Simulations with Drop Impact Testing Using High-Speed Camera Measurements," *IEEE International Conference on Thermal, Mechanical and Multi-Physics Simulation and Experiments in Microelectronics and Micro-Systems, EuroSimE 2008.*

[24] Ogawa, Y., 2011, "High Speed Imaging Technique Part 1; High Speed Imaging of Arc Welding Phenomena," *Science and Technology of Welding & Joining* **16**(1), pp. 33–43.

[25] Wen, Y. M., Huang, S. S., and Liu, G. X., 2011, "Testing and Analysis of High-Speed Camera for Droplet Transition," *Advanced Materials Research,* **271**, pp. 79–83.

[26] Wen, Y. M., Huang, S. S., and Liu, G. X., 2012, "Testing and Analysis of High-Speed Camera for Pulse Mig/Mag Welding Droplet Transition," *Applied Mechanics and Materials* **103**, pp. 134–137.

[27] AmeTek, 2013, Phantom V1610 Digital High-Speed Camera Data Sheet.

[28] Kim, T. H., Yum, J., Hu, S. J., Spicer, J. P., and Abell, J. A., 2011, "Process Robustness of Single Lap Ultrasonic Welding of Thin, Dissimilar Materials," *CIRP Annals—Manufacturing Technology* **60**(1), pp. 17–20.

[29] Zhang, C., Zhu, X., and Li, L., 2006, "A Study of Friction Behavior in Ultrasonic Welding (Consolidation) of Aluminum," *87th FABTECH International and AWS Welding Show Professional Program.*

[30] Yang, Y., Ram, G. D. J., and Stucker, B. E., 2010, "An Analytical Energy Model for Metal Foil Deposition in Ultrasonic Consolidation," *Rapid Prototyping Journal* **16**(1), pp. 20–28.

[31] Gao, Y. and Doumanidis, C., 2002, "Mechanical Analysis of Ultrasonic Bonding for Rapid Prototyping," *Journal of Manufacturing Science and Engineering* **124**(2), pp. 426–434.

[32] Gibert, J. M., McCullough, D. T., Fadel, G. M., Martin, G. K. M., and Austin, E. M., 2010, "Stick-Slip Dynamics in Ultrasonic Consolidation," *2009 ASME International Design Engineering Technical Conferences and Computers and Information in Engineering Conference*, Aug. 30–Sept. 2, 2009, San Diego, CA, USA.

Chapter 6

COUPLED THERMO-MECHANICAL SIMULATION[1]

Dongkyun Lee[1], Elijah Kannatey-Asibu Jr[1], and Wayne Cai[2]
[1]Department of Mechanical Engineering, University of Michigan, Ann Arbor
[2]Manufacturing Systems Lab, General Motors Global R&D Center

ABSTRACT

Ultrasonic welding is a solid-state bond created using ultrasonic energy. It has been used in the semiconductor industry for several decades, and more recently, in the automotive industry such as for battery welding. Even though there existed several numerical simulations on ultrasonic welding, the models were too simplistic, in both theory and welding configuration, to present the multiple sheet, dissimilar metal ultrasonic welding. In this study, theories and a finite element procedure for the ultrasonic welding process are developed. The procedure invokes both Abaqus/Standard and Abaqus/Explicit to simulate the mechanical-thermal coupled phenomena over the entire weld duration with moderate computational cost. The procedure is verified and used to simulate selected specific cases involving multiple sheets and dissimilar materials, i.e., copper and aluminum. The simulation procedure demonstrates its capability to predict welding energy, temperature distribution, and fracture/distortion of the workpieces toward the goal of improving welding quality.

Keywords: battery, finite element analysis, plasticity, thermo-mechanical analysis, ultrasonic welding, vibration

6.1 INTRODUCTION

Ultrasonic welding creates a solid-state bond using ultrasonic energy. It is capable of creating a joint not only between similar metals but also between dissimilar metals or even between metals and plastics. It has the advantage of requiring no melting of the workpieces, no atmospheric control or adhesives to create a joint, low-energy consumption, and being environmentally friendly [1].

Ultrasonic welding has been widely used in the semiconductor industry for micro-wire joining over several decades. There have been several experimental investigations for the process in an effort to enhance joint quality. Tsujino et al. [2] investigated the ultrasonic weld joint strength of aluminum wire on a copper substrate for different ultrasonic welding frequencies ranging from 40 to 780 kHz. They concluded that higher frequencies require shorter welding time for a quality weld joint. Gao and Doumanidis [3] investigated application of ultrasonic welding for layer-by-layer rapid prototyping technology using aluminum

---

[1] The content presented in this chapter has previously appeared in Ref. [4].

foils. They obtained an analytical solution for a simplified case, conducted a numerical analysis, and measured friction coefficient history during the process. Imai and Matsuoka [1] studied optimal clamping pressure and welding time for high-quality ultrasonic welding of aluminum alloys. Born et al. [5] investigated the feasibility of ultrasonic welding for joining $AlMg_3$ with aluminum foam sandwich, considering that ultrasonic welding involves less degradation of workpieces than any other welding technique. Numerical analyses of ultrasonic welding have also been conducted by several researchers. Viswanath et al. [6] studied stress distribution during the ultrasonic welding process for gold wire on a copper substrate using Abaqus. Liu et al. [7] conducted numerical analyses on stress distribution and its development during cooling of ultrasonic welding for gold wire using Ansys. Siddiq and Ghassemieh [8] investigated ultrasonic welding of one sheet of aluminum on an aluminum substrate using Abaqus. They adopted the isotropic-kinematic combined hardening model with their extension for temperature dependence of the hardening model. Elangovan et al. [9] conducted numerical simulations on ultrasonic welding of two aluminum sheets to investigate effects of ultrasonic welding parameters on temperatures of the workpieces, a horn and anvil of an ultrasonic welding machine. They introduced a heat source at the interface between the workpieces that results from the frictional slipping motion of the workpieces over a weld duration of the order of 100 ms, rather than considering the dynamic temperature-displacement analysis for the process. On the other hand, Zhang and Li [10] conducted a dynamic temperature-displacement coupled analysis for ultrasonic welding of one sheet of aluminum on an aluminum substrate, and correlated weld area measurements with von Mises plastic strain calculations. They conducted the analysis only up to 50 cycles at 20 kHz ultrasonic welding frequency, i.e., a period of 2.5 milliseconds. However, it should be noted that no ultimate numerical analysis model for ultrasonic welding process has yet been established, even though there have been several numerical analysis models proposed for the process.

The fundamental mechanism of joining workpieces with ultrasonic welding is not clearly understood yet. A significant amount of research indicates that ultrasonic energy applied to workpieces removes oxide layers of the workpieces and reveals clean surfaces at the interface of the workpieces. Ultrasonic softening of the workpieces that helps in forming a joint then occurs [11]. It should also be noted that several results also indicate that thermal conditions such as temperature play important role in achieving a successful ultrasonic weld [12, 13]. Thus, it is clear that the ultrasonic welding process needs to be investigated considering both mechanical and thermal aspects of the process. It should farther be noted that the published numerical simulations only consider simple geometric configurations, which are not realistic for applications in the automotive industry.

In this study, theories and finite element procedures are constructed with a commercial FEA (Finite Element Analysis) package, Abaqus, to analyze the mechanical-thermal coupled ultrasonic welding process. The simulation is designed for complex realistic geometry configurations involving multiple sheets of dissimilar materials with moderate computational cost, and to provide scientific understanding of the impact of ultrasonic welding parameters on weld quality.

6.2 THEORY

Ultrasonic metal welding produces a joint by applying clamping pressure and tangential vibration to the workpieces. The process involves compression loading in the workpiece normal direction, cyclic loading in the tangential direction, and consequently heat generation due to friction between workpieces. Thus, the ultrasonic welding process should be considered as a coupled mechanical-thermal problem.

6.2.1 Mechanical Model

Mechanical aspects of the workpieces under ultrasonic welding include tangential cyclic and normal clamping loading on the workpieces. Chaboche [14] summarized the constitutive model that is appropriate for analyzing metal plasticity under cyclic loading. The model is briefly discussed here. Its basic assumption is that the total strain rate ($\dot{\varepsilon}$) can be decomposed as [15]:

$$\dot{\varepsilon} = \dot{\varepsilon}^{el} + \dot{\varepsilon}^{pl} \tag{6.1}$$

where $\dot{\varepsilon}^{el}$ and $\dot{\varepsilon}^{pl}$ are the elastic and plastic components of the total strain rate, respectively. The elastic behavior is modeled as [15]:

$$\sigma = D^{el} : \varepsilon \tag{6.2}$$

where, D^{el} is the fourth-order elasticity tensor, and σ and ε are the second-order stress and strain tensors, respectively. The operator ":" in Eq. (6.2) represents the scalar product that can be written in the Einstein notation as $a : b = a_{\alpha\beta}b^{\beta\alpha}$, where a and b are tensors, and α and β are indices for components of both tensors. The plastic behavior in the model assumes the associated flow rule [15]:

$$\dot{\varepsilon}^{pl} = \frac{\partial f(\sigma - \alpha)}{\partial \sigma} \dot{\bar{\varepsilon}}^{pl} \tag{6.3}$$

where $f(\sigma - \alpha) = \sigma_0$ is the yield surface for the yield stress σ_0 with respect to the backstress α, and $\dot{\bar{\varepsilon}}^{pl} = \sqrt{\dfrac{2}{3}\dot{\varepsilon}^{pl} : \dot{\varepsilon}^{pl}}$ is the equivalent plastic strain rate. In this study, the von Mises yield criterion is used for the yield surface. Stress evolution in the model is described by a combination of the isotropic hardening and kinematic hardening models to describe material plastic behavior under cyclic loading. The isotropic hardening model relates the evolved yield stress, σ^0, with the initial yield stress, $\sigma|_0$, as [15]:

$$\sigma^0 = \sigma|_0 + Q_\infty(1 - Exp(-b\bar{\varepsilon}^{pl})) \tag{6.4}$$

where Q_∞ and b are material related constants, Fig. 6.1(a). And the kinematic hardening model describes the evolution of backstress, α, as [15]:

$$\dot{\alpha} = \frac{C}{\sigma^0}(\sigma - \alpha)\dot{\bar{\varepsilon}}^{pl} - \gamma\alpha\dot{\bar{\varepsilon}}^{pl} \tag{6.5}$$

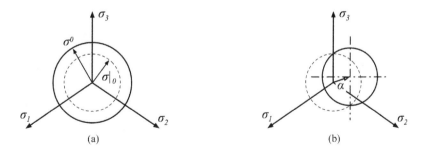

Figure 6.1. Illustrations of the hardening models in stress space for (a) the isotropic and (b) the kinematic hardening model, respectively [15].

where C and γ are material related constants, Fig. 6.1(b). This model has been used for numerical analysis of ultrasonic welding of aluminum foil on a substrate, with an extension to model temperature dependency for Eqs. (6.4) and (6.5) as [8]:

$$\sigma^0(T) = [\sigma|_0 + Q_\infty(1 - Exp(-b\bar{\varepsilon}^{pl}))]f(T) \tag{6.6}$$

for the isotropic hardening model, and

$$\dot{\alpha}(T) = \left[\frac{C}{\sigma^0(T)}(\sigma - \alpha(T))\dot{\bar{\varepsilon}}^{pl} - \gamma\alpha(T)\dot{\bar{\varepsilon}}^{pl}\right]f(T) \tag{6.7}$$

for the kinematic hardening model, where $f(T)$ is a scaling function that can be obtained from temperature-dependent initial yield stress of a material. Eqs. (6.6) and (6.7) are used in this study.

6.2.2 Thermal Model

Thermal aspects of the workpieces under ultrasonic welding should be seriously considered because significant amount of heat is generated during ultrasonic welding due to friction between the workpieces. For this, the conduction equation should be solved simultaneously with the mechanical constitutive equations, where the conduction equation is given as:

$$\rho c(T)\frac{\partial T}{\partial t} = -\vec{\nabla}\cdot(-k(T)\vec{\nabla}T) + S \tag{6.8}$$

where ρ, $c(T)$ and $k(T)$ are density, specific heat and thermal conductivity of the material, respectively. The term S in Eq. (6.8) represents the volumetric heat generation, and it is neglected in this study. Temperature-dependent thermal and mechanical material properties are considered in this study. Materials of interest for the workpieces in this study are aluminum and copper. Temperature-dependent specific heats [16], $c(T)$, and thermal conductivities [17], $k(T)$, of aluminum and copper for Eq. (6.8) are shown in Fig. 6.2. There are several temperature-independent material properties used in this study. They include the

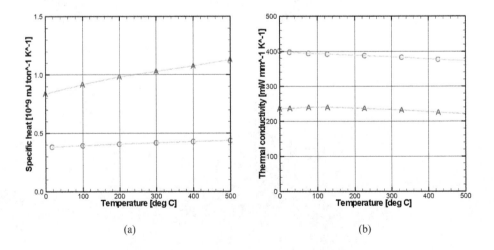

(a)   (b)

Figure 6.2. Temperature-dependent thermal properties of aluminum and copper: (a) specific heat and (b) thermal conductivity. In the figures, "C" and "A" represent copper and aluminum, respectively.

density of aluminum and copper, and material properties of steel for the ultrasonic welding machine parts that contact with the workpieces, such as horn and anvil. The density of aluminum and copper are set as 2.7×10^{-9} ton mm^{-3} and 8.94×10^{-9} ton mm^{-3}, respectively. Material properties of steel used in this study are summarized in Table 6.1.

The main heat source during ultrasonic welding is friction between two adjacent workpieces, i.e., frictional heat dissipation. Thus friction and frictional heat dissipation models are required to analyze thermal behavior of the workpieces during the process. The Coulomb friction model is used in this study, Fig. 6.3(a). In Coulomb friction, slipping motion between the two workpieces occurs when the equivalent shear stress $\tau_{eq} = \sqrt{\tau_1^2 + \tau_2^2}$ for 2D interface shear stress as τ_1 and τ_2 becomes larger than the critical shear stress $\tau_{crit} = \mu p$, where μ is the friction coefficient and p is contact pressure. When slipping occurs between the two workpieces, the corresponding frictional heat dissipation, q_f, can be obtained as [15]:

$$q_f = \eta \mu \dot{s} \tag{6.9}$$

where η is a fraction of frictional heat dissipation that ranges between 0 and 1, and $\dot{s}$ is the speed of slipping motion. It should be noted that η is not an explicitly known parameter, but it can be indirectly obtained from experimental results. Another thermal aspect to be considered in the ultrasonic welding process is a factor that introduces temperature discontinuity between two workpieces contacting to each other, namely gap conductance, Fig. 6.3(b). Gap conductance, κ, is defined as [15]:

$$q_g = \kappa \Delta T \tag{6.10}$$

where q_g is heat flux across the two adjacent surfaces of the workpieces in contact, and ΔT is temperature difference between the two surfaces. The gap conductance becomes important especially in an ultrasonic welding process that involves multiple sheets simultaneously, which is a case of interest in this study. Unfortunately, the gap conductance κ is neither an explicitly known parameter, nor a material property such as thermal conductivity. However, it can be estimated from a model, for example, one proposed by Song et al. [18]. They proposed a model to estimate the gap conductance for a given contact condition and surface

TABLE 6.1. Material properties of steel [8].

Property	Value
Density	7.8×10^{-9} ton mm^{-3}
Specific heat	4.4×10^8 mJ ton^{-1} °C^{-1}
Thermal conductivity	80 mW mm^{-1} °C^{-1}
Elastic modulus	2.0×10^5 MPa

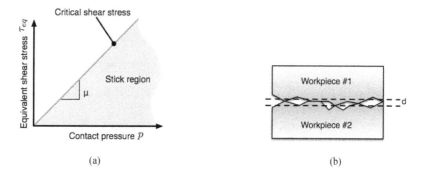

(a)   (b)

Figure 6.3. Illustrations for (a) Coulomb friction and (b) the gap resistance, respectively.

roughness, based on their experimental data. In the model, κ is related to the dimensionless gap resistance, G, as [18]:

$$G = \frac{k_g}{\kappa d} \qquad (6.11)$$

where k_g is thermal conductivity of gas between the two workpieces, and d is an effective gap distance that is determined by surface roughness and clamping pressure. Thus, the gap conductance can be roughly estimated using this equation with assumption for the effective gap distance and thermal conductivity of air, and their result indicated $G \approx 1$ when the gas pressure is atmospheric.

Thermal expansion of the material should also be considered in investigating mechanical-thermal coupled behavior of materials in ultrasonic welding because it directly couples mechanical and thermal behavior in terms of thermal strain, ε^{th}, as [15]:

$$\varepsilon^{th} = \alpha(T)(T - T^0) - \alpha(T^I)(T^I - T^0) \qquad (6.12)$$

where $\alpha(T)$ is the temperature-dependent thermal expansion coefficient, and T^I and T^0 are initial and thermal expansion coefficient reference temperatures, respectively. Temperature-dependent thermal expansion coefficients of aluminum and copper for Eq. (6.12) are shown in Fig. 6.4 [19].

Temperature-dependent elastic modulus and the initial yield stress of aluminum [20] and copper [21] for Eqs. (6.2), (6.6), and (6.7) are shown in Fig. 6.5. As can be seen in Fig. 6.5(a), the elastic modulus data points of copper are more scattered with respect to the trend curve than aluminum. The trend curve of copper is a second-order polynomial curve obtained from the data points. In this study, the polynomial curve is selected as the elastic modulus value of copper, rather than the actual data points to avoid any possible numerical instability that may happen due to the scattered data points. It should also be noted from Fig. 6.5(b) that the trend curves in the figure provide the information on the temperature-dependent scaling function $f(T)$ in Eqs. (6.6) and (6.7). In a manner similar to Siddiq and Ghassemieh [8], the scaling function is assumed to have a form of

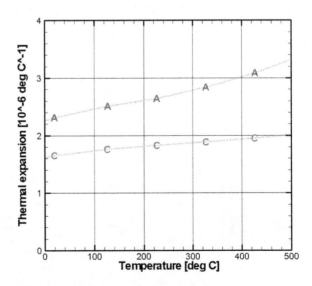

Figure 6.4. Temperature-dependent thermal expansion coefficients of aluminum and copper. In the figure, "C" and "A" represent copper and aluminum, respectively.

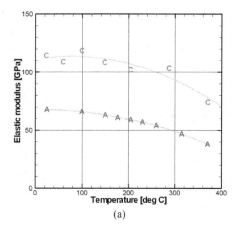
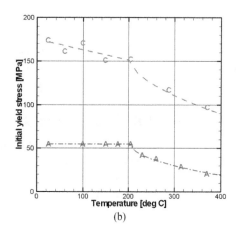

Figure 6.5. Temperature-dependent mechanical properties of aluminum and copper: (a) elastic modulus and (b) initial yield stress. In the figures, "C" and "A" represent copper and aluminum, respectively.

TABLE 6.2. Constants related to Eqs. (6.6), (6.7), (6.13), and (6.14) for aluminum and copper.

Term	Aluminum	Copper	Notes
Q_∞	100*	40	Eq. (6.6)
b	20*	11	Eq. (6.6)
C	15000*	22300	Eq. (6.7)
γ	60*	340	Eq. (6.7)
T_1	205°C	200°C	Eq. (6.13)
T_m	660°C	1085°C	Eq. (6.13), melting point
n	0.5027	0.4599	Eq. (6.13)
a	0	-6.86×10^{-4}	Eq. (6.14)
b_0	1	1.004	Eq. (6.14)

* Data taken from Siddiq and Ghassemieh [8].

$$f(T) = 1 - \left(\frac{T - T_1}{T_m - T_1} \right)^n, \quad if \ T > T_1 \qquad (6.13)$$

where T_m and T_1 are melting point and a transition temperature of a material, respectively. The exponent η in the equation is a material constant. The function $f(T)$ is assumed to be a linear function for temperatures lower than the transition temperature T_1, i.e.

$$f(T) = a_0 T + b_0, \quad if \ T \le T_1 \qquad (6.14)$$

where a_0 and b_0 are material constants. The constants are summarized in Table 6.2. The parameter values of aluminum for Eqs. (6.6) and (6.7) are taken from Siddiq and Ghassemieh [8]. On the other hand, the parameter values of copper for the equations are estimated by comparing Abaqus results for different parameters with a cyclic loading experimental result for copper taken from Bower [22].

6.3 FINITE ELEMENT ANALYSIS PROCEDURE

In this study, a general purpose FEM package, Abaqus, is used to analyze mechanical-thermal coupled behavior of materials during ultrasonic welding. The goal of the study is to establish numerical analysis models and procedures for ultrasonic welding simulations to be used for investigating energy, temperature distribution and weld distortion of workpiece during the process. The simulation model will provide scientific understanding of the impact of product/process designs on weld quality.

6.3.1 Basic Units Selected for This Study

Abaqus has no implemented unit system, thus users can select basic units to be used in their problem for their convenience. It is the user's responsibility to keep consistency for material property database that is used in Abaqus, when the database is constructed by the user. In this study, the metric ton (= 1000 kg), millimeter, second, and degree Celsius are selected as basic units for mass, length, time, and temperature. Corresponding units for several properties and quantities are summarized in Table 6.3.

6.3.2 Finite Element Procedures Using Abaqus

To construct finite element procedures for ultrasonic welding simulation, the welding process should be divided into several steps to enable the entire process to be implemented in Abaqus. The multi-step division of the entire ultrasonic welding process is shown in Fig. 6.6. Figure 6.6(a) illustrates a clamping step, in which clamping pressure is applied to the workpieces via the horn and anvil of an ultrasonic welding machine over a time period. The step can be modeled as a mechanical process without any thermal behavior in Abaqus. In addition, it is modeled as a quasi static process, which involves negligible dynamic effect on the workpieces during the step. It seems feasible because the clamping step is not intended to deform the workpieces severely, unlike the forming process.

At the same time, it should be noted that the clamping time for the step is the time period from the moment of contact between the horn and workpiece to the moment when the clamping pressure reaches its final value. The clamping time is defined in such a manner to reduce calculation time for the step. Figure 6.6(b) illustrates the welding step that

TABLE 6.3. Summary of units for select material properties and quantities.

Material property or quantity	Unit
Elastic modulus, stress	MPa
Thermal conductivity	mW mm^{-1} °C^{-1}
Specific heat	mJ ton^{-1} °C^{-1}
Thermal expansion coefficient	°C^{-1}
Energy	mJ
Heat flux	mW mm^{-2}

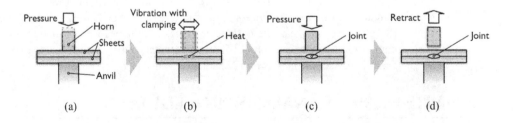

(a)   (b)   (c)   (d)

Figure 6.6. The ultrasonic welding process divided into four steps: (a) clamping, (b) welding, (c) holding, and (d) unloading steps.

involves cyclic motion of the horn and corresponding frictional heat generation. It means that this step should be modeled as a coupled mechanical-thermal case in Abaqus, and it should incorporate frictional heat generation during the step. One option for the frictional heat generation is to evaluate it directly from slipping motion, clamping pressure and frictional work by simulating the step as a dynamic process. However, this demands extremely high computational cost, i.e., impractically long simulation time, if this is conducted for the entire welding time which generally varies from several hundred milliseconds to up to a couple of seconds. An alternative option is to introduce frictional heat generation boundary condition between the workpieces without the cyclic motion of the horn. This will enable the entire welding process to be simulated with moderate computational cost. However, this requires information on the frictional heat generation between the workpieces, and no dynamic effect will be simulated. Figures 6.6(c) and 6.6(d) illustrate holding and unloading steps, respectively. They should also be modeled as a mechanical-thermal coupled case in a manner similar to the welding step, but there is no cyclic motion of the horn during the steps.

Abaqus provides two types of solvers, Abaqus/Standard and Abaqus/Explicit. Abaqus/Standard uses the implicit time marching scheme. It is capable of conducting simulation with relatively large time step, thus suitable for a case that requires numerous time increments due to the length of the period to be simulated. However, it requires a relatively large amount of memory, and it may experience difficulties in finding a solution for a case with severe contact conditions in a dynamics problem. On the other hand, Abaqus/Explicit uses the explicit time marching scheme. This solver is recommended for analyzing a complex dynamic case with relatively short simulation period. Unfortunately, the ultrasonic welding process involves a dynamic process with severe contact conditions as illustrated in Fig. 6.6, which is unfavorable for Abaqus/Standard, while the welding time of the order of 100 ms is a relatively long simulation period to be evaluated by Abaqus/Explicit. It should also be noted that such a severe contact condition barely allows constructing a multi-step Abaqus analysis procedure using both solvers sequentially, mainly due to incompatibility of contact algorithms used in each solver. In this study, Abaqus/Explicit is chosen to predict heat flux due to frictional motion between workpieces by simulating the initial 100 cycles of the welding process, while Abaqus/Standard is selected to analyze the coupled mechanical-thermal process for the entire ultrasonic welding process. The Abaqus/Explicit result is supplied to Abaqus/Standard using Python script that extracts the heat flux data from the output file of Abaqus/Explicit calculation for the initial 100 cycles, as illustrated in Fig. 6.7.

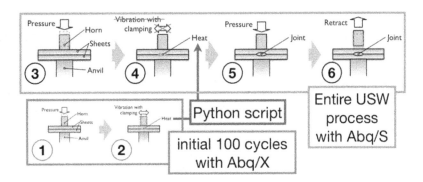

Figure 6.7. Schematic diagram of ultrasonic welding analysis using Abaqus. The numbers in circles represent the order of executing simulation for each step with corresponding solvers, Abaqus/Explicit or Abaqus/Standard. "Abq/X" and "Abq/S" represent Abaqus/Explicit and Abaqus/Standard, respectively.

6.4 FEA PROCEDURE VERIFICATION AND CASE STUDIES

6.4.1 Verification Test for Abaqus/Explicit

An ultrasonic welding configuration with two thin sheets, or foils, is considered to examine the feasibility of the Abaqus procedure illustrated in Fig. 6.7. The configuration is shown in Fig. 6.8(a).

The size of the foil is set as 20×20 mm with 0.2 mm thickness. Sizes of the horn and the anvil are set as 8×8 mm with 8 mm height and 9×9 mm with 9 mm height, respectively. The foils are meshed in such a manner as to have two elements in the thickness direction as shown in Fig. 6.8(b), to avoid shear locking. An Abaqus element C3D8RT is used for the horn, anvil and foils, which has three degrees of freedom in deformation, and one degree of freedom in temperature. The horn and anvil are modeled with 512 elements, whereas the foil is modeled with 4856 elements. The C3D8RT element is an eight-node brick element with reduced integration scheme. It is selected to evaluate deformation in the thickness direction, i.e., indentation, and at the same time to reduce calculation cost. The hourglass prevention mechanism for the reduced integration of Abaqus is used in this study. Rigid body constraint is applied to the mesh of the horn and anvil to define them as non-deformable rigid bodies, while the foils are modeled as deformable. Aluminum and steel are selected as materials of the foils, and of the anvil and horn, respectively. The combined isotropic and kinematic hardening rule, i.e., Eqs. (6.6) and (6.7), are used for Abaqus/Explicit solver. The contact conditions for the horn and the foil, between foils, and for the anvil and the foil are defined using the Abaqus functionality "contact pair." The contact pair between foils is defined using the center square area of 10×10 mm, Fig. 6.8(b), to reduce computational cost.

The Abaqus/Explicit solver is used to analyze the clamping and welding steps that are shown in Fig. 6.7. Boundary conditions for the steps are illustrated in Fig. 6.9. For the clamping step, a clamping pressure of 100 MPa is applied on the top surface of the foil with a clamping time of 2.5 ms, Fig. 6.9(a). The pressure is linearly increased from zero to the peak value over the clamping period. Analysis for the welding step starts from the end of the clamping step. The clamping pressure is kept as constant during the welding step, whereas sinusoidal displacement is applied to the horn (Fig. 6.9(b)). The sinusoidal displacement is defined as:

$$U_1(t) = u_0 \sin(2\pi f t) \tag{6.15}$$

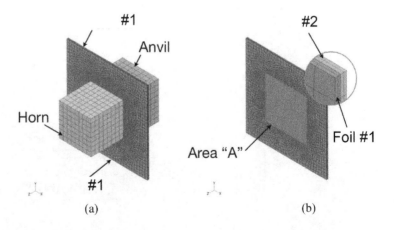

Figure 6.8. (a) Geometry configuration with horn, anvil and two foils. (b) Two foils have a center square area (Area "A", 10×10 mm) for defining contact in Abaqus. Each foil is meshed to have two elements in the thickness direction.

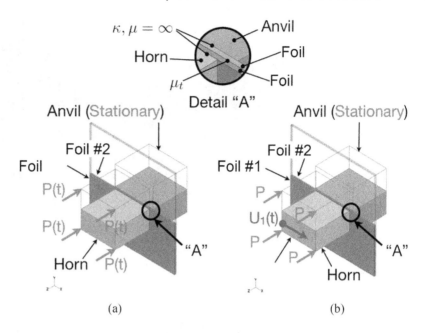

Figure 6.9. Boundary conditions for (a) clamping and (b) welding steps. In the figures, "P" and "U_1" represent pressure and displacement, respectively. "P(t)" and "$U_1(t)$" represent their respective changes over time. The top middle figure, Detail "A", is a zoomed-in view for the portion "A" marked in the figures.

where u_0 and f are amplitude and frequency of the sinusoidal motion of the horn, respectively. The amplitude and frequency are selected as 25 μm and 20 kHz, respectively. The welding step analysis is conducted for the initial 100 cycles using Abaqus/Explicit. For both steps, the friction coefficients between the horn and the foil, and between the anvil and the foil are set as infinite, whereas the friction coefficient between the foils is set as 0.3. The fraction of heat generation due to frictional slipping motion, η in Eq. (6.9), is selected as 1.0. The gap conductance κ is assumed to be 235 mW mm^{-2} °C^{-1}.

Deformation and normal stress of the aluminum foils in the thickness direction and corresponding equivalent plastic strain and contact pressure distribution are shown in Fig. 6.10. The dynamic explicit procedure of the Abaqus/Explicit solver is selected for the clamping step analysis. It can be seen from Figs. 6.10(a) and 6.10(b) that deformation and normal stress in the thickness direction show feasible values, because the values of the deformation and the normal stress at the center, -520×10^{-6} mm and -117 MPa, respectively, correspond to values above the elastic deformation limit for the combined sheet thickness of the two foils of 0.4 mm, -323.5×10^{-6} mm, and a value similar to the given clamping pressure, 100 MPa, respectively. Figure 6.10(c) shows feasible nonzero equivalent plastic strain at the center square, noting that the clamping pressure of 100 MPa is beyond the initial yield stress of aluminum, which is about 55 MPa. Finally, from the fact that there is a region with zero contact pressure around the center square area in Fig. 6.10(d), it can be deduced that the center square for the contact pair definition shown in Fig. 6.8(b) is large enough for this study.

The Abaqus/Explicit solver was designed to analyze high speed dynamic systems for short time periods, for example the forming process. Such dynamic behavior of the workpieces will occur if the clamping pressure is applied to the workpieces within a short time period. In other words, the clamping time should be long enough to avoid such extreme dynamic behavior of the workpieces. However, an unnecessarily long clamping time will result in a very long calculation time. Thus, the clamping time should be carefully selected. To evaluate the dynamic behavior of the workpieces, kinetic energy, and internal energy of

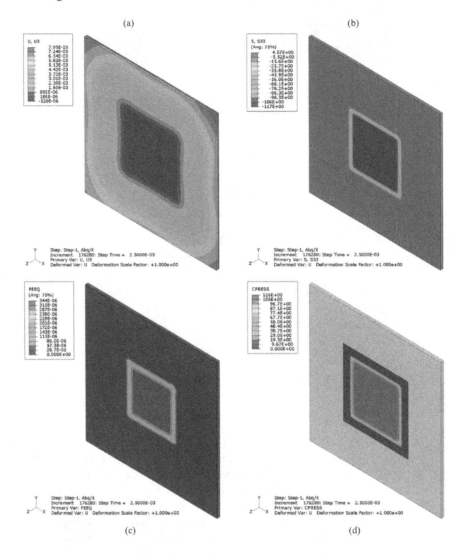

Figure 6.10. Abaqus/Explicit results on (a) displacement (U3) and (b) normal stress component (S33) in the thickness direction, (c) corresponding plastic equivalent strain and (d) contact pressure distribution for the clamping step.

the entire domain is examined, as shown in Fig. 6.11. It is generally accepted that the dynamic behavior is negligible if the fraction of kinetic energy with respect to internal energy is less than, or of the order of 1% (Simulia Co, 2008). As can be seen from the figure, the clamping time of 2.5 ms results in a fraction less than 1%. Thus, the clamping time is long enough to neglect the dynamic behavior for the clamping step.

As shown in Fig. 6.7, the Abaqus/Explicit solver was also used for the welding step to obtain information on frictional heat generation, after the simulation for the clamping step is complete. To check the verification of Abaqus/Explicit setup for the welding process, two different friction coefficients were selected, $\mu = 0$ and 0.3. Dynamic explicit procedure for mechanical-thermal coupled case of Abaqus/Explicit solver was selected to analyze the welding step. Two simulations were conducted for 3 cycles using the coefficients, and the results are shown in Fig. 6.12. The fraction of heat generation in Eq. (6.9) was set as 1.0 in this case. It can be seen from the figure that there is no numerical error induced during the simulation, i.e., there is no heat generation due to friction for the case of $\mu = 0$. However, as Fig. 6.12(b) shows,

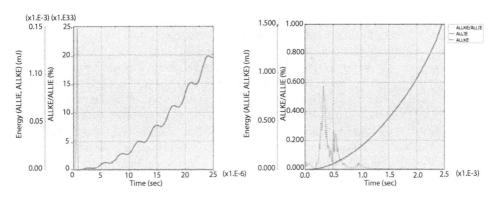

Figure 6.11. Kinetic energy (ALLKE), internal energy (ALLIE) and the fraction of kinetic energy with respect to internal energy of the entire domain for different clamping times of (a) 0.025 ms and (b) 2.5 ms.

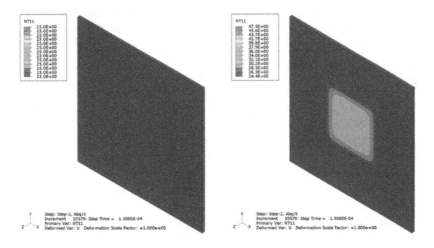

Figure 6.12. Temperature distribution obtained from Abaqus/Explicit, after three cycles with (a) $\mu = 0$ and (b) $\mu = 0.3$.

the temperature increment over just three cycles is about 22.5°C. The increment appears to be too high, considering that the maximum temperature at the end of ultrasonic welding process is usually about 40% of the melting point of a material, and the entire ultrasonic welding process has the order of 10,000 cycles. This implies that the fraction may need to be adjusted to correct such an extreme temperature rise obtained for $\eta = 1$. However, it should be noted that accurate values can only be clearly determined from experimentally measured temperatures.

6.4.2 Verification Test for Abaqus/Standard

The geometry used for the previous verification test for Abaqus/Explicit, Fig. 6.8, is also used in this verification test for Abaqus/Standard. Corresponding boundary conditions are the same for the clamping step with Abaqus/Explicit, Fig. 6.9(a). However, the boundary conditions for the welding step with Abaqus/Standard are slightly modified from the ones with Abaqus/Explicit, Fig. 6.9(b). One modification is that the sinusoidal horn motion of Eq. (6.15) is replaced with $U_1(t) = 0$. Another modification is that a heat flux boundary condition is applied to the center square of 8×8 mm at the interface of foil #1 and #2 of Fig. 6.9. The 8×8 mm center square is defined in a manner similar to the center square shown in Fig. 6.8(b). The heat flux distribution due to friction between foils is assumed to be constant over the 8 × 8 mm center square in this verification study. In addition, the heat flux data is read from the output of Abaqus/Explicit, and written to Abaqus/Standard input script in this verification study. The hardening rule is also modified for Abaqus/Standard because the combined isotropic kinematic hardening rule is not available for Abaqus/Standard. At the same time, it should be noted that the Abaqus/Standard solver is set to solve the static case in this study, in which the combined hardening rule has no significance. Thus, the isotropic hardening rule, Eq. (6.16), is used for Abaqus/Standard.

Abaqus/Standard results for the clamping step are shown in Fig. 6.13. The static procedure of Abaqus/Standard solver was used for this analysis. It can be seen from the figure that both displacement and normal stress in thickness direction show feasible values, considering that the values of the deformation and the normal stress at the center, -466×10^{-6} mm and -103 MPa, respectively. This corresponds to a value above the elastic deformation limit for the combined sheet thickness of the two foils of 0.4 mm, -323.5×10^{-6} mm, and a value similar to the given clamping pressure, 100 MPa, respectively. These trends were also observed from the results of Abaqus/Explicit, Fig. 6.10.

The Abaqus/Standard solver was then used to analyze the welding process after the heat flux data was obtained from the Abaqus/Explicit results, which is 3.4 W mm^{-2}. For both solvers, $\mu = 0.3$ and $\mu = 0.1$ were used for Eq. (6.9) in this case. The displacement (in the thickness direction) and temperature histories of the bottom center point of foil #1 in Fig. 6.8 were obtained from both solvers, Fig. 6.14. Figure 6.14(a) shows that each solver predicts different displacement values for the center point. This is because Abaqus/Explicit uses a dynamic temperature-displacement coupled procedure while Abaqus/Standard involves a static coupled procedure, i.e., dynamic effect is missing in the Abaqus/Standard results. However, Abaqus/Standard and Abaqus/Explicit show similar temperature results at the point for the initial cycles, as shown in Fig. 6.14(b), and Abaqus/Standard demonstrates its ability to solve for the temperature history over the entire ultrasonic welding process time, which was set as 500 ms in this case. Thus the verification of the strategy illustrated in Fig. 6.7 is successfully demonstrated, considering that the main output of interest in this study is temperature at the end of the ultrasonic welding process.

The fraction of heat generation due to frictional slipping motion, η in Eq. (6.9), is a parameter which can only be obtained indirectly from experimental data. In other words, repetitive simulation should be conducted for different values and the results compared

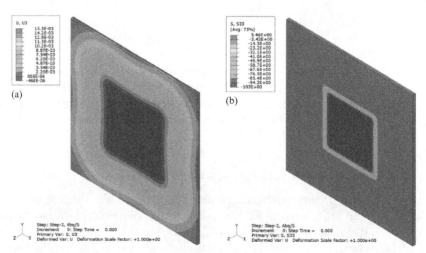

Figure 6.13. Abaqus/Standard results for the clamping step. (a) Displacement (U_3) and (b) Normal stress component (S_{33}) in thickness direction.

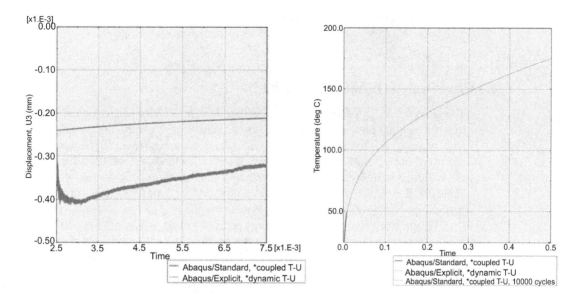

Figure 6.14. Comparison of the results obtained from Abaqus/Explicit and Abaqus/Standard on (a) displacement and (b) temperature histories of the bottom center point of foil #1 shown in Fig. 6.8.

with corresponding experimentally measured temperature. To demonstrate the procedure, it is assumed that the final temperature for two aluminum foils after ultrasonic welding with a clamping pressure of 100 MPa and an ultrasonic vibration amplitude u_0 of 25 μm, for an ultrasonic welding time of 200 ms becomes 200°C. The friction coefficient is assumed to be 0.3, and the fraction is varied in the range between 0.1 and 0.2. Abaqus/Standard results for the final temperature are shown in Fig. 6.15. The figure illustrates that the repetitive

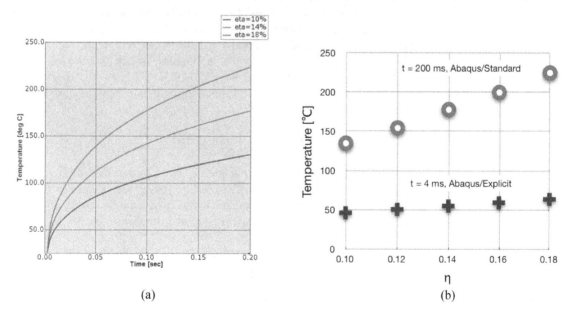

Figure 6.15. (a) Temperature histories for different fraction, η, over 200 ms of ultrasonic welding time, calculated with Abaqus/Standard. (b) Temperatures at the end of Abaqus/Explicit simulations for 4 ms of welding time and Abaqus/Standard for 200 ms, with respect to η.

calculation procedure can be applied to obtain a realistic fraction value, provided that a corresponding experimentally measured temperature data is available.

6.4.3 Case Study (1): Abaqus/Explicit

The setup for Abaqus/Explicit solver was used to conduct case studies on the effect of ultrasonic welding parameters such as clamping pressure (P_c), ultrasonic welding vibration amplitude (u_0) and frequency (f) of Eq. (6.1), the friction coefficient (μ) between two foils, and the clamping time (t_c). The geometry setup and boundary conditions are identical to those illustrated in Figs. 6.8 and 6.9. Parameters used in this case study are summarized in Table 6.4. The ultrasonic welding process is analyzed for 2 ms for the cases in the table. The fraction η of Eq. (6.9) was set as 0.16 for all the cases.

Temperature histories of the bottom center of foil #1 in Fig. 6.8 for different clamping pressures, ultrasonic welding amplitudes and frequencies, and friction coefficients are shown in Fig. 6.16. It can be seen from the figure that those parameters have significant impact on the temperature of the workpieces. This temperature rise occurs because those parameters are directly related to the frictional heat generation, Eq. (6.9), in terms of the shear stress term for the clamping pressure and friction coefficient, and slipping velocity and distance for the ultrasonic welding amplitude and frequency. On the other hand, the clamping time does not have significant impact on temperature of the workpieces, Fig. 6.17. As the figure shows, the two histories are offset from each other by the difference in the clamping time, but the curves are almost identical to each other. This implies that the clamping time does not need to be set too long, because it will merely result in a high computational cost. All the results for displacement in the thickness direction after the clamping step and temperature after 2 ms of the ultrasonic welding step are compared with respect to the default setup in Table 6.4 and summarized in Table 6.5.

Because Abaqus/Explicit solves a dynamic temperature-displacement coupled case, it can also be used to analyze the dynamic aspect of workpiece behavior, such as misalignment, occurring during the welding process. To demonstrate such capability of the Abaqus/Explicit solver, a geometry configuration with three copper foils (0.2-mm thick) and a copper coupon (1.0-mm thick) was considered, Fig. 6.18. Mesh configuration for the horn, anvil, and foils are identical to the one illustrated in Fig. 6.8. The coupon has a size of 20 × 20 mm with 1.0-mm thickness, and meshed using 7254 C3D8RT elements. The boundary conditions are almost identical to the one illustrated in Fig. 6.9, except the motion of the horn. Equation (6.1) was replaced with

$$U_1(t) = u_0 \left(\frac{t}{t_r} \right) \sin(2\pi f t) \tag{6.16}$$

where t_r is a transient rising time of the horn motion from the initial standstill status to the steady sinusoidal motion, and 200 cycles at 20 kHz, i.e., 10 ms, was selected as the rising time in this case study. Abaqus/Explicit simulation was conducted for 10 ms of welding step duration. For this case study, clamping pressure and time were selected as 80 MPa

TABLE 6.4. Parameters used in case studies with Abaqus/Explicit.

Cases	P_c [MPa]	$u_0[\mu m]$	f[kHz]	μ	t_c [ms]
Default	100	25	20	0.3	2.5
1	**150**	25	20	0.3	2.5
2	100	**50**	20	0.3	2.5
3	100	25	**40**	0.3	2.5
4	100	25	20	**0.1**	2.5
5	100	25	20	0.3	**5.0**

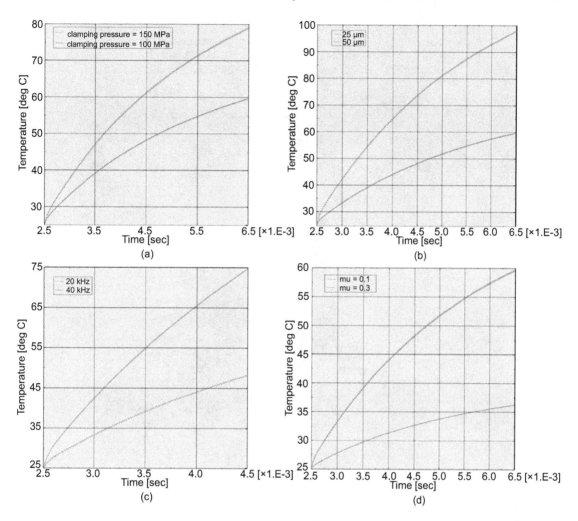

Figure 6.16. Temperature histories at the bottom center of foil #1 in Fig. 6.8 for different (a) clamping pressures, (b) amplitudes, (c) frequencies, and (d) friction coefficients, calculated using Abaqus/Explicit.

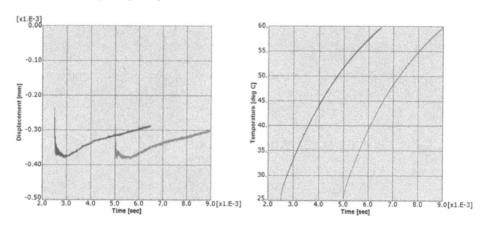

Figure 6.17. Histories of the bottom center of foil #1 in Fig. 6.8 with different clamping times of 2.5 and 5.0 ms for (a) displacement in thickness direction and (b) temperature.

TABLE 6.5. Comparison of displacement in thickness direction (U_{3c}) after the clamping step (U_{3c}), and temperature after 2 ms of the ultrasonic welding step (T(2 ms)) at the bottom center of foil #1 in Fig. 6.8 with respect to the default configuration listed in Table 6.4.

Case	Varying input	U_{3c}	T(2 ms)
1	P_c 50% up	73% up	57% up
2	u_0 100% up	0%	10% up
3	f 100 % up	0%	37% up
4	μ 66% down	7% up	61% down
5	t_c 100 % up	0%	3% up

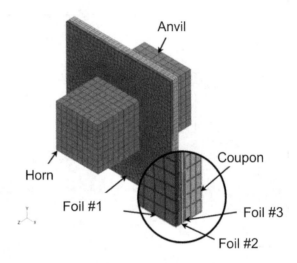

Figure 6.18. Geometry configuration with a horn, anvil, three 0.2-mm-thick foils and one 1.0-mm-thick coupon.

and 2.5 ms, respectively. The ultrasonic welding amplitude u_0 and frequency were set as 24 μm and 20 kHz, respectively, and friction coefficient and the fraction η set as 0.3 and 0.2, respectively. Displacement and temperature histories at the top center of the foils are shown in Fig. 6.19. It can be seen from Fig. 6.19(a) that foils #2 and #3 show drifting from the initially aligned position. However, it should be noted that the direction drift does not depend on the initial starting direction of the horn motion, and a more detailed study is required to get a better understanding of the drifting behavior. The temperature histories of the top center points in Fig. 6.19(b) indicate that most of the frictional heat is generated between foil #1 and #2. It is interesting to note that the workpiece misalignment occurs in a different manner for an ultrasonic welding with a different number of foils (Fig. 6.20).

6.4.4 Case Study (2): Abaqus/Standard

There are two model parameters which are important to predict realistic workpiece temperatures using the Abaqus procedure analysis process illustrated in Fig. 6.7. These are the friction coefficient, μ, and the fraction of heat generation due to frictional slipping motion, η. Their importance can be seen from Eq. (6.9) that describes the heat source of the ultrasonic welding process implemented in Abaqus. Unfortunately, they are not explicitly known, and they, especially η, can only be estimated from experimentally measured temperature data obtained for a given set of ultrasonic welding parameters. Their estimations are done

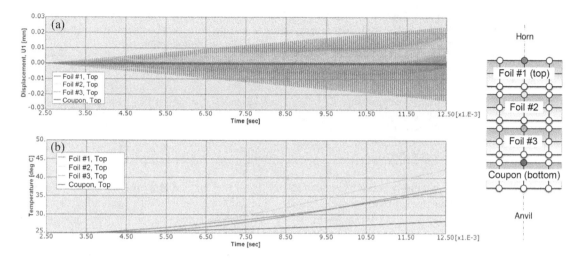

Figure 6.19. (a) Displacement histories in the horn motion direction and (b) temperature histories, at the top center of the foils for 200 cycles of welding step analysis with Abaqus/Explicit.

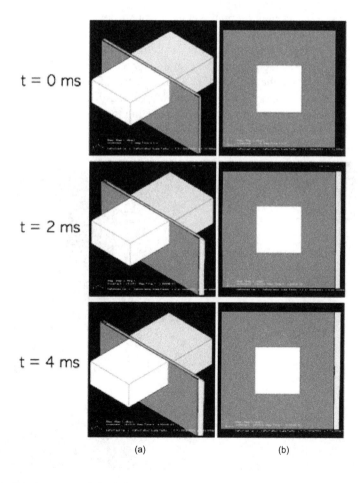

Figure 6.20. Displacement of the foils at select times for 80 cycles of welding step analysis with Abaqus/Explicit in case of three foils and no coupon: (a) isometric and (b) top views. The displacement is scaled up by 20 in the horn motion direction.

TABLE 6.6. Experimentally measured final temperatures, corresponding ultrasonic welding conditions, and friction coefficient and the fraction η of Eq. (6.9) for two ultrasonic welding configurations.

	3 Cu foils + 1 Coupon	3 Al foils + 1 Coupon
Clamping pressure	80 MPa	30 MPa
Welding amplitude, u_0	24 μm	12 μm
Welding time	500 ms	500 ms
Final temperature	400°C	300°C
Friction coefficient, μ	0.30	0.73
Fraction, η	0.65	1.00

using a geometry setup illustrated in Fig. 6.18, with available temperature measurements. The data and estimations are summarized in Table 6.6. In the table, foil and coupon thicknesses are 0.2 and 1.0 mm, respectively. It should be noted that the fraction for copper foil is lower than the value for aluminum foil. It may be due to an oxide layer on the copper foil, i.e., a greater portion of the frictional work is consumed in breaking the copper oxide layer than for the aluminum oxide layer. However, this is not conclusive because the values are just estimations. Noting that the friction coefficient can be experimentally obtained, a more realistic fraction value needs to be obtained if such experimentally measured friction coefficients are available.

Different thermal conditions of workpieces illustrated in Fig. 6.18 are considered in this case study. Parameters listed in Table 6.6 are used in this study, and they are assumed to be precise. The conditions include ultrasonic welding processes with insulated anvil, preheated coupon, and a coupon thinner than 1.0 mm. The insulated anvil is implemented by reducing the gap conductance by a factor of 10,000. The preheated coupon is implemented by assigning an initial temperature condition of 100°C to the anvil. Finally, the thinner coupon is implemented by remodeling the coupon thickness as 0.4 mm. Temperature contours and histories at the end of 500 ms ultrasonic welding process are shown in Figs. 6.21

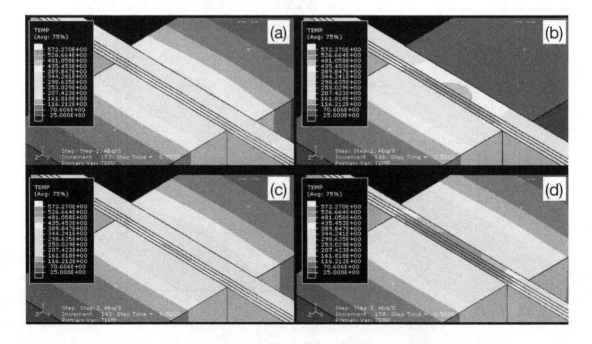

Figure 6.21. Temperature contours at the end of a 500-ms ultrasonic welding step for (a) default configuration, (b) insulated anvil, (c) preheated coupon, and (d) thin coupon.

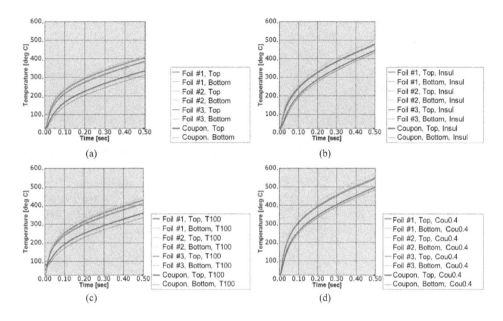

Figure 6.22. Temperature histories at the end of a 500-ms ultrasonic welding step for (a) default configuration, (b) insulated anvil, (c) preheated coupon, and (d) thin coupon.

and 6.22. It can be seen from the figures that the thin coupon case results in the highest final temperature. It can be also seen from Fig. 6.21(b) that the gap conductance reduction effectively implemented the insulated condition for the anvil. However, it should be noted that such an extremely low gap conductance may be hard to obtain in a real situation.

6.5 CONCLUSIONS

In this study, theories and a finite element simulation procedure for ultrasonic welding are developed. The procedure invokes both Abaqus/Standard and Abaqus/Explicit to simulate the coupled mechanical-thermal phenomena. Abaqus/Explicit is used to obtain heat flux information due to frictional heat. The heat flux information is extracted from the Abaqus/Explicit output to Abaqus/Standard to simulate the entire ultrasonic welding process.

The finite element simulations presented in this study can predict the energy and temperature distribution associated with the ultrasonic welding process, as well as distortion. They provide scientific understanding of the impact of product/process design on ultrasonic welding quality.

REFERENCES

[1] Imai, H. and Matuoka, S., 2005, "Finding The Optimum Parameters for Ultrasonic Welding of Aluminum Alloys," *JSME international Journal Series A*, **48**(4), pp. 311–316.

[2] Tsujino, J., Hasegawa, K., Sone, Y. and Nozaki, K., 1996, "Frequency Characteristics of Ultrasonic Wire Bonding Using High Frequency Vibration Systems of 40 kHz to 780 kHz," *Proceedings of the IEEE Ultrasonics Symposium*, 2, San Antonio, TX, USA, pp. 1021–1026.

[3] Gao, Y. and Doumanidis, C., 2002, "Mechanical Analysis of Ultrasonic Bonding for Rapid Prototyping," *ASME, Journal of Manufacturing Science and Engineering*, **124**, pp. 426–434.

[4] Lee, D., Kannatey-Asibu, E. and Cai, W., 2013, "Ultrasonic Welding Simulations for Multiple Layers of Lithium-Ion Battery Tabs," *ASME, Journal of Manufacturing Science and Engineering*, **135**(6), 061011.

[5] Born, C., Wagner, G. and Eifler, D., 2006, "Ultrasonically Welded Aluminum Foams/Sheet Metal—Joints," *Advanced Engineering Materials*, **8**(9), pp. 816–820.

[6] Viswanath, A.G.K., Zhang, X., Ganesh, V.P. and Chun, L., 2007, "Numerical Study of Gold Wire Bonding Process on Cu/Low-K Structures," *IEEE Transactions on Advanced Packaging*, **30**(3), pp. 448–456.

[7] Liu, Y., Irving, S. and Luk, T., 2008, "Thermosonic Wire Bonding Process Simulation and Bond Pad Over Active Stress Analysis," *IEEE Transactions on Electronics Packaging Manufacturing*, **31**(1), pp. 61–71.

[8] Siddiq, A. and Ghassemieh, E., 2008, "Thermomechanical Analyses of Ultrasonic Welding Process Using Thermal and Acoustic Softening Effects," *Mechanics of Materials*, **40**, pp. 982–1000.

[9] Elangovan, S., Semeer, S. and Prakasan, K., 2009, "Temperature and Stress Distribution in Ultrasonic Metal Welding—An FEA-Based Study," *Journal of Material Processing Technology*, **209**, pp. 1143–1150.

[10] Zhang, C. and Li, L., 2009, "A Coupled Thermal-Mechanical Analysis of Ultrasonic Bonding Mechanism," *Metallurgical and Materials Transactions B*, **40B**, pp. 196–207.

[11] Tian, Y., Wang, W., Lum, I., Mayer, M, Jung, J.P. and Zhou, Y., 2008, "Investigation of Ultrasonic Copper Wire Wedge Bonding on Au/Ni Plated Cu Substrates at Ambient Temperature," *Journal of Material Processing Technology*, **208**, pp. 179–186.

[12] Chan, Y.H., Kim, J.K., Liu, D., Liu, P.C.K., Cheung, Y.M. and Ng, M.W., 2006, "Comparative Performance of Gold Wire Bonding on Rigid and Flexible substrates," *Journal of Materials Science: Materials in Electronics*, **17**, pp. 597–606.

[13] Ding, Y. and Kim, J.K., 2008, "Numerical Analysis of Ultrasonic Wire Bonding: Part 2. Effects of Bonding Parameters on Temperature Rise," *Microelectronics Reliability*, **48**, pp. 149–157.

[14] Chaboche, J.L., 2008, "A Review of Some Plasticity and Viscoplasticity Constitutive Theories," *International Journal of Plasticity*, **24**, pp. 1642–1693.

[15] Simulia Co., 2008, *Abaqus Manuals* (v. 6.8), Providence, RI.

[16] Touloukian, Y.S. and Buyco, E.H., 1970, *Thermophysical Properties of Matter*, Vol. 4, IFI/Plenum, New York, NY.

[17] Touloukian, Y.S., Powell, R.W., Ho, C.Y. and Klemens, P.G., 1970, *Thermophysical Properties of Matter*, Vol. 1, IFI/Plenum, New York, NY.

[18] Song, S., Yovanovich, M.M. and Goodman, F.O., 1993, "Thermal Gap Conductance of Conforming Surfaces in Contact," *ASME, Journal of Heat Transfer*, **115**, pp. 533–540.

[19] Touloukian, Y.S., Kirby, R.K., Taylor, R.E. and Desai, P.D., 1975, *Thermophysical Properties of Matter*, Vol. 12, IFI/Plenum, New York, NY.

[20] Kaufman, J.G., 1999, *Properties of Aluminum Alloys*, ASM International, Material Park, OH.

[21] Upthegrove, C. and Burghoff, H.L., 1956, *Elevated-Temperature Properties of Coppers and Copper-Base Alloys*, ASTM, Philadelphia, PA.

[22] Bower, A.F., 1989, "Cyclic Hardening Properties of Hard-Drawn Copper and Rail Steel," *Journal of the Mechanics and Physics of Solids*, **37**, pp. 455–470.

Chapter 7

MICROSTRUCTURE EVOLUTION AND PHYSICS-BASED MODELING[1]

Hongtao Ding[1], Ninggang Shen[1], Avik Samanta[1], and Wayne Cai[2]
[1]Department of Mechanical & Industrial Engineering, University of Iowa
[2]Manufacturing Systems Lab, General Motors Global R&D Center

ABSTRACT

Ultrasonic welding offers ability to weld thin layers of malleable metals at low temperature and low power consumption. During ultrasonic welding, intensive material interactions occur due to the severe plastic deformation (SPD) and frictional heat generation, which leads to the microstructural change. Different grain microstructures have been observed after different ultrasonic welding conditions. Theory of the microstructural evolution was for the first time hypothesized as three regimes, namely SPD, dynamic recrystallization (DRX) and grain growth according to the material thermomechanical loading conditions.

A novel metallo-thermo-mechanically coupled model was developed to model the temperature-dependent mechanical deformation and microstructural evolution during the ultrasonic spot welding process. The numerical analysis was carried out with a three-dimensional (3D) finite element model using DEFORM 11.0. The material constitutive model considered cyclic plasticity, thermal softening, and acoustic softening. Dynamic recrystallization and grain growth kinetics laws were applied to simulate the microstructural evolution under different welding time durations. The simulation results demonstrated that the essential characteristics of the deformation field and microstructure evolution during ultrasonic welding were well captured by the metallo-thermo-mechanically coupled model. The numerical framework developed in this study has been shown to be a powerful tool to optimize the ultrasonic welding process for its mechanical properties and microstructures.

Keywords: dynamic recrystallization, grain growth, microstructure, modeling, ultrasonic welding

7.1 INTRODUCTION

Battery electric vehicles have drawn great attentions in recent years. The battery pack for a battery electric vehicle is assembled from a large amount of battery cells. Due to the virtues of low power consumption, rapid solid-state joining, and environment friendliness, ultrasonic spot welding has been applied as a practical and efficient solution for joining of metallic battery tabs to a bus [1]. Ultrasonic welding is often used to create a joint between thin malleable metals, such as aluminum (Al), copper (Cu) and nickel (Ni) [2]. It is also applied to join multi-layer dissimilar metals with varying sheet thicknesses.

---

[1] The content presented in this chapter has previously appeared in Ref. [3].

The performance of ultrasonic spot welding has been extensively studied for battery tab joining in recent years. Lee et al. [1] conducted a thorough experimental analysis of ultrasonic spot welding of copper battery tabs and defined several key weld attributes, i.e., bond density, post-weld thickness, weld nugget size, and thermomechanically affected zone size, to determine the weld quality. Their study revealed that the resultant microstructure and material strength of the weld high depended on the welding process parameters. They also experimentally investigated the performance of multi-layer ultrasonic weld by joining four coupons of Cu with various thicknesses [4]. A high-speed imaging technique was used to capture the displacement of horn and different coupons for ultrasonic welding using different knurling tools. The effect of vibration on weld formation from top to bottom layers was investigated from the analysis, which concluded that weld quality deteriorates from top to bottom layers due to less heat generation at the interfaces of bottom layers. Wu et al. [5] investigated the welding and failure mechanism of the Al/Cu ultrasonic welding using the mechanical testing and microstructural analysis. Online monitoring system was developed using welding power and horn displacement [6]. The weld quality was evaluated in terms of post-weld thickness and bond density based on the online signals for process control. Zhao et al. [7] developed a fatigue life cycle model to predict the life of Al/Cu ultrasonic weld tab joints by monitoring electrical resistance. The dynamic response of battery tabs under ultrasonic welding was studied to understand its effects on weld quality and to reduce energy loss [8, 9].

Considerable research efforts have also been devoted to characterize the thermal field in the weld zone. The thermal contact conductance between thin metal sheets was determined as a function of contact pressure [10]. The real-time temperature and heat flux change have been measured and monitored near the weld zone using thin-film thermocouples [11] and thin-film micro-sensors [12]. Different weld formations were studied for various welding time durations from 0.6 to 1.5 second. Based on the history of heat flux change rate, Li et al. [12] proposed a bonding mechanism for ultrasonic welding consisting of three continuous stages within one operation, which were firstly friction heating, then bonding by plastic work, and finally diffusion bonding.

Materials often demonstrate a significant softening phenomenon under ultrasonic loading. The softening effect during ultrasonic spot welding is considered in two main mechanisms of thermal softening and acoustic softening. Thermal softening is attributed to the frictional heat generation from the high frequency vibration. The thermal energy is uniformly absorbed by the metal material. The acoustic softening contributes more on the flow stress reduction. The acoustic energy generated by ultrasonic sonotrode is transmitted to the metal and locally absorbed at defected crystal lattice, e.g., vacancies, dislocations, and grain boundaries [13]. As a result, the activation energy of the dislocation line movement is considerably reduced [14]. The increased mobility of dislocations drastically attenuates the work-hardening, so flow stress can be extremely reduced.

Numerical modeling studies have been attempted to model the thermomechanical coupling effect during ultrasonic spot welding. Elangovan et al. [15] developed a two-dimensional (2D) finite element (FE) model for ultrasonic welding of dissimilar materials. In their model, the effective heat generation terms were adopted from a previous study [16] for modeling heat generation due to deformation and friction under ultrasonic vibration. Lee et al. [17] developed a three-dimensional (3D) thermomechanical FE model and used a combined explicit/implicit multi-step numerical approach to predict ultrasonic spot welding of multi-sheet dissimilar materials (Al and Cu). However, the acoustic softening effect on material flow stress under ultrasonic loading was not considered in these aforementioned studies.

Siddiq and Ghassemieh [18] developed a material phenomenological constitutive model to consider the acoustic softening effect in the combined isotropic/kinematic hardening model under cyclic loading. This model was successfully implemented in a 3D thermomechanical FE model for an ultrasonic seam welding process of Al alloy 6061 using a sonotrode with smooth cylindrical surface. The temperature-dependent friction coefficient was calibrated and applied to predict the frictional heat generation under ultrasonic vibration. Siddiq et al. [19] applied this numerical approach to model ultrasonic seam welding of Al alloy 3003 and investigated the effects of various process parameters, such as applied load, ultrasonic vibration amplitude, and tool velocity, on weld material response. Siddiq and Sayed [20] further proposed a micromechanics-based crystal plasticity model by incorporating the phenomenological acoustic softening term and simulated the ultrasonic assisted deformation of both single crystalline and polycrystalline Al materials. With this model development, the workpiece material textural change was simulated for ultrasonic consolidation at sub-micron scale [21].

Different from ultrasonic seam welding using a smooth cylindrical sonotrode, for ultrasonic spot welding of battery tabs, a sonotrode and an anvil with diamond knurl patterns are used to significantly enhance the welding process capability. During the process, weld forms from compression and ultrasonic in-plane sliding of the diamond knurling tool, which induces severe plastic deformation (SPD) in the workpiece material. Experimental results of ultrasonic spot welding obtained by Lee et al. [1] showed complex coupling effects among mechanical deformation, heat transfer, and microstructure change for various welding time durations. Their study revealed the material microstructure underwent different evolution routes with varying thermal and deformation histories. There is a great challenge in modeling such a metallo-thermo-mechanical coupled process under ultrasonic vibration. The available numerical approaches in literature are not capable to simulate the complex weld formation and microstructural evolution for the ultrasonic spot welding process.

Our present study developed a predictive metallo-thermo-mechanically coupled model to simulate SPD and microstructural change during the ultrasonic spot welding process for battery tabs. Multiple 3D-coupled thermomechanical FE simulations are conducted with DEFORM 11.0 to simulate the deformed weld shape and temperature change after different process durations. The microstructural evolution and the microhardness change are predicted using a post-processing user routine.

7.2 MICROSTRUCTURE EVOLUTION IN ULTRASONIC WELDING

The principle of ultrasonic welding is discussed based on a systematic experimental study carried out at General Motors [1]. In their experimental study of ultrasonic welding for tab-bus joining in automotive battery cell, two C11000 Cu sheets (99.9% pure) were joined by an AmTech Ultraweld® L-20 high power welder with a maximum output electric power of 3.3 kW. The top and bottom sheets were 0.4 and 1 mm in thickness, respectively. The bottom sheet was plated by a thin Ni layer (~3 μm thick). The ultrasonic vibration was implemented in the workpiece transverse direction with an amplitude of 30 μm at 20 kHz frequency. The clamping force was applied along the vertical direction and varied from 40 to 60 psi. Multiple experiments were performed for different welding time from 0.2 to 1.0 second. Different knurl and anvil patterns were applied in their experiments. All the experimental parameters were listed in Table 7.1.

The weld joint microstructure was examined near the joint interface. The as-received sheets were rolled and annealed before the welding experiments, which had strain-free grains for both top and bottom coupons as shown in Fig. 7.1a. Figures 7.1b–f examine the microstructures obtained after ultrasonic spot welding under a clamping pressure of 50 psi with varying welding time durations observed by Lee et al. [1]. It can be recognized that the material microstructure underwent different evolution routs as the welding time increased. For a short welding time of 0.2 second, a great amount of elongated grains can be seen in Fig. 7.1b on both side of the joint interface. As the welding time increased to

TABLE 7.1. Experimental conditions [1].

Tool design	Coarse design and fine design
Materials	C11000 Cu (tab) and Ni-plated C11000 Cu (bus)
Coupon thickness (mm)	0.4 mm (tab) and 1 mm (bus)
Load (psi)	40, 50, 60
Vibration amplitude (μm)	30
Frequency (kHz)	20
Welding time (sec)	0.2, 0.4, 0.6, 0.8, 1.0

Original microstructure

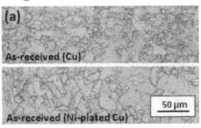

Regime I: Grain Elongation due to SPD

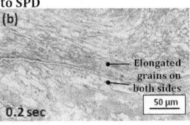

Regime II: Recrystallized Grains from DRX

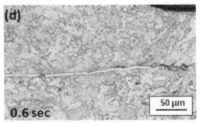

Regime III: Grain Growth with Longer Welding Time

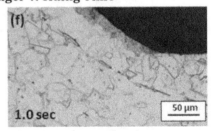

Figure 7.1. Microstructure after various welding time durations: (a) original microstructure before welding; (b) 0.2 sec; (c) 0.4 sec; (d) 0.6 sec; (e) 0.8 sec; (f) 1.0 sec. The original images were adopted from [1].

0.4 second, the elongated grains became dissolved, and newly formed strain-free–like fine grains can be seen in Fig. 7.1c. Similar microstructure with newly formed fine grains near the weld interface was also observed after a 0.3-second ultrasonic spot welding of Al alloy 6111 under a similar ultrasonic loading condition [22]. In Fig. 7.1d, fine equiaxed recrystallized grains were formed with very clear grain boundaries in most area of the specimen cross-section after a 0.6-second welding. As the welding time increased to 0.8 to 1.0 second, coarse grains were mainly seen in the specimens as shown in Figs. 7.1e–f.

In addition, a uniform microstructure was formed under these two conditions, whereas the difference across the weld interface was obvious for the shorter welding durations.

The grain size was measured separately for the top and bottom coupons using the optical micrographs for all the specimens. Figure 7.2 shows the measured grain size from both sides of the weld line, i.e., from the top and bottom coupons. The grain size of the as-received material was also measured: finer grains of 7.5 μm were observed in the thinner top coupon, whereas the thicker bottom coupon had a greater grain size of 12.5 μm. Significant grain refinement was observed after a 0.2-second welding. After a welding time of 0.4 to 0.6 second, the grain size of about 10 μm was obtained. As the welding time increased to above 0.8 second, significant grain growth to 30 μm occurred. After welding time of 0.4 second, a small grain size of about 7.6 μm was measured in the top coupon, whereas a big grain size of 11.6 μm was found in the bottom coupon. However, this difference in grain size between the top and bottom coupons started to diminish during grain growth under a longer welding time duration.

Figure 7.3 shows the microhardness at different locations on the cross-sectioned of weld joints from these experiments. The micro-indentation hardness tests were performed on the yellow spots. As labeled in Fig. 7.3, valley is denoted as the more plastically deformed domain under the tip of the knurling tool, whereas the peak is the less deformed

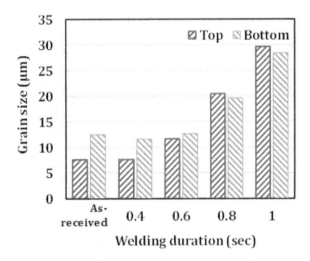

Figure 7.2. Grain size measurement.

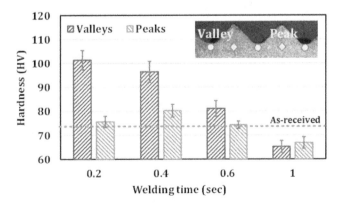

Figure 7.3. Hardness measurement of the joints: (a) effect of welding time; (b) effect of deformation.

domain. Significant hardness increases can be observed for specimens made from a short welding time duration of 0.2 second, especially at the valleys. As welding time duration increased from 0.2 to 1 second, the microhardness at the valleys drastically decreased. It became even lower than the original value, when welding time duration increased to 1 second. Figure 7.3 also shows the microhardness of weld joint varied at different locations due to different plastic deformation. For a short welding time duration (less than 0.4 second), the more deformed valley has a much higher microhardness than that of the peaks. However, as the welding time increased, the difference in microhardness between the more and less deformed domains was significantly reduced or even diminished. The microhardness change was caused by the combined effect of the welding time, SPD as well as microstructural evolution during ultrasonic welding.

The changes of microstructure and microhardness as shown in Figs. 7.1–3 highly depend on the process time duration. The main effect of increasing welding time duration is the increase of process temperature. After the welding time duration, the knurling tools were disengaged from the joints and coupons and a workpiece cooling process took place in air. For a high process temperature with a long welding time duration, it also takes a longer time for the joint to cool down. For a short welding time less than 0.2 second, the process temperature was most likely low. Work hardening and grain refinement were significant under SPD at a low temperature condition, whereas dynamic recovery was relatively slow [23, 24]. A more severe deformation would lead to a finer grain size and a higher mechanical strength. As the welding time duration increased to 0.4 to 0.6 second, more heat was generated and the processing temperature would likely reach the recrystallization temperature range. Sufficient strain energy was stored to enable dynamic recrystallization (DRX) due to deformation. As DRX took place, it provided a softening mechanism after a certain level of strain and resulted in a significant drop of the flow stress to a steady-state level. As the welding time duration increased to 0.8–1.0 second, the processing temperature would become even higher. As the completion of recrystallization, grain growth took place to reduce the grain boundary area. Given a high processing temperature condition, grain growth would continue even after the welding process. Eventually, the material would be softened and had a uniform coarse-grained structure across the weld interface after grain growth.

Different welding time durations also led to different levels of plastic deformation within the weld zone. During the recrystallization process, the extent of deformation affected the final grain size. A more severe deformation had a higher rate of nucleation than the rate of growth [25]. So, the final grain size was reduced by the increased deformation. This explains that a finer grain size existed in the top coupon under more plastic deformation and a coarser grain size existed in the less deformed bottom coupon before grain growth.

Based on the above analysis, the microstructural evolution during ultrasonic spot welding can be classified into three regimes:

- For regime I under a low processing temperature, SPD is hypothesized as the major mechanism to govern the material response and microstructural evolution.
- For regime II under a medium processing temperature, DRX is hypothesized as the dominate mechanism for microstructural evolution as well as material flow stress response.
- For regime III under a high processing temperature, DRX and subsequent grain growth are hypothesized as the dominate mechanisms for microstructural evolution as well as material flow stress response.

The final microstructure is determined by the coupled metallo-thermo-mechanical histories during ultrasonic welding. Therefore, modeling of different mechanisms under different regimes is critically needed to better understand the process of ultrasonic spot welding.

7.3 MODELING

To study the microstructural evolution during the ultrasonic welding and subsequent cooling process, a 3D metallo-thermo-mechanically coupled model was developed with a commercial FE software package of DEFORM 11.0. A material constitutive model was implemented to calculate the flow stress during high frequency ultrasonic vibration. The microstructural evolution and hardness change due to DRX and the subsequent grain growth were simulated with a post-processing user routine.

7.3.1 Flow Stress Model under Ultrasonic Vibration

Ultrasonic welding involves high-frequency cyclic loading, thermal effect at the interface and ultrasonic effect due to ultrasonic vibration. Therefore, flow stress should be expressed in combined effect of all three phenomena [18]. The basic constitutive equations for cyclic plasticity model were adopted from uniaxial loading. The total strain is the sum of elastic and plastic strain tensor:

$$\underline{\varepsilon} = \underline{\varepsilon}^{el} + \underline{\varepsilon}^{pl} \tag{7.1}$$

Flow stresses at any step of the simulation are calculated using the elastic stress strain relation:

$$\underline{\sigma} = \boldsymbol{D}_{el}\underline{\varepsilon}^{el} = \boldsymbol{D}_{el}\left(\underline{\varepsilon} - \underline{\varepsilon}^{pl}\right) \tag{7.2}$$

where $\boldsymbol{D}_{el}$ is the elasticity tensor. The yield surface is defined by modified Chaboche model, which is considered more accurate for cyclic loading condition [26].

$$\mathrm{F} = |\underline{\sigma} - \underline{\alpha}| = \sigma_0 + R \tag{7.3}$$

where σ_0 is initial yield stress, $\underline{\alpha}$ is the term related to back stress tensor due to kinematic hardening, and R is the term related to isotropic hardening. The plastic strain during any deformation process is given by

$$d\underline{\varepsilon}^{pl} = d\lambda \frac{\partial F}{\partial \underline{\sigma}} \tag{7.4}$$

where $d\lambda$ is the plastic multiplier which satisfies the following Kuhn-Tucker type consistency conditions.

$$F \leq 0; \ d\lambda \geq 0; \ d\lambda. \ F \cong 0 \tag{7.5}$$

The expansion of yield surface due to isotropic hardening can be expressed as an exponential function of accumulated plastic strain [21]:

$$R = Q(1 - \exp(-b\bar{\varepsilon}^{pl})) \tag{7.6}$$

where Q and b are material constants. Q is the maximum change of yield surface due to isotropic hardening and b is the rate at which yield surface changes with accumulated plastic strain ε^{pl}. For nonlinear kinematic hardening, the rate of back stress ($\dot{\underline{\alpha}}$) is given by

$$\dot{\underline{\alpha}} = C \frac{1}{\sigma_0}(\underline{\sigma} - \underline{\alpha})\dot{\bar{\varepsilon}}^{pl} - \gamma \underline{\alpha} \dot{\bar{\varepsilon}}^{pl} \tag{7.7}$$

TABLE 7.2. Material parameters in the flow stress model [17, 27].

Q (MPa)	b	C (MPa)	γ	m	T_m (°C)	T_r (°C)	d_u (m²/W)	E_u (W/m²)	e
40	11	22300	340	1.09	1083	25	1.3e-6	3.5e5 for Top 8.1e4 for Bottom	2

where C and γ are material constants from cyclic testing. C stands for the kinematic shift of yield surface and γ stands for the rate at which saturation value of kinematic hardening decreases with increasing plastic strain. $\sigma_0 = \sigma_y + R$ with σ_y is the yield stress for zero plastic strain. The back stress α can be integrated from Eq. (7.7) for uniaxial case:

$$\alpha = C \frac{1}{\gamma}\left[1 - \exp\left(-\gamma \varepsilon^{pl}\right)\right] + \alpha_1 \exp\left(-\gamma \varepsilon^{pl}\right) \tag{7.8}$$

where α_1 is obtained from stabilized cycle and is given by $\alpha_1 = \sigma_1 - \sigma_s$ with σ_1 is the stress at the start of the stabilized cycle, and σ_s is the yield stress at stabilized cycle:

$$\sigma_s = \frac{\sigma_1 + \sigma_n}{2} \tag{7.9}$$

where σ_1 and σ_n are the stress at the start and end of stabilized cycle.

A phenomenological softening term $[(1 - d_u E_u)^e]$ dependent on the ultrasonic energy density per unit time has been introduced in the relations of isotropic and kinematic hardening terms to demonstrate the acoustic softening effect on yield stress [18]. The thermal softening is included in the flow stress model by embedding the temperature term of $[1 - ((T - T_r)/(T_m - T_r))^m]$ [27]. Including both thermal softening and acoustic softening, the modified equations of isotropic and kinematic hardening are given by [21]

$$R_{ultrasonic} = \left[Q(1 - e^{-b\varepsilon^{pl}})\right]\left[1 - \left(\frac{T - T_r}{T_m - T_r}\right)^m\right][(1 - d_u E_u)^e] \tag{7.10}$$

$$\alpha_{ultrasonic} = \left[\frac{C}{\gamma}\left(1 - e^{-\gamma \varepsilon^{pl}}\right) + \alpha_1 e^{-\gamma \varepsilon^{pl}}\right]\left[1 - \left(\frac{T - T_r}{T_m - T_r}\right)^m\right][(1 - d_u E_u)^e] \tag{7.11}$$

where d_u and e the material constants related to ultrasonic softening and E_u is the ultrasonic energy density per unit time transferred from ultrasonic vibrator to the material. The constant values of copper are given in Table 7.2. These values were calibrated from experimental work for cyclic loading on copper [28], except the value of e was adopted from the previous simulation work for ultrasonic seam welding [18]. E_u was adopted as 3.5×10^5 W/m² for the top coupon, whereas a smaller E_u of 8.1×10^4 W/m² was accessed for the bottom coupon subjected to less acoustic softening. The bottom coupon was relatively far away from the knurling tool, which was mounted on the ultrasonic horn. Based on the literature search and observations in Lee et al. [4], the amplitude of ultrasonic vibrations decreased for the bottom coupon.

7.3.2 Modeling for Microstructural Evolution

To predict the microstructural evolution correctly, modeling approach must comprehend the process physics under different regimes during ultrasonic spot welding. For grain refinement by SPD under regime I, a dislocation density-based computational approach has been established by the authors to model the microstructural evolution and strength enhancement during various SPD processes, such as multi-pass cold rolling [23] and large strain orthogonal cutting [24, 29]. The nucleation of dislocations due to deformation, annihilation of dislocations due to dynamic recovery, and interaction of dislocations between the dislocation cell interiors and cell walls can be evaluated based on the deformation process state variables [30, 31]. The dislocation density-based material plasticity model was compatible with the material constitutive models developed under various conditions of strain, strain rate, and temperature. With the developed dislocation density-based numerical solution, the modeling effort for regime I is omitted in this work. Modeling of microstructural evolution under regimes II and III are described as follows.

As the rise of regime II, the refined grain structure from SPD is rapidly replaced by DRX. The strain hardened weld is softened by DRX and subsequent grain growth during regimes II and III. The DRX and grain growth were coupled together in this analysis. The model for either regime would be enabled if specific conditions were fulfilled. As the increase of welding time duration, the DRX-dominated regime II would arise first. The microstructural evolution of copper by DRX has been studied by researchers for a wide range of temperatures [32, 33]. A critical temperature is required for the onset of DRX. In this study, the starting temperature of DRX was assumed as $0.4\ T_m$, which is about 270°C for Cu. When this starting temperature is reached, the onset of DRX occurs at a critical equivalent plastic strain. As soon as DRX occurs, the softening effect induced by DRX becomes noticeable, and the flow stress increase rate becomes slower until the peak stress value is reached [34]. After reaching the peak value, the flow stress curve drops rapidly to a steady-state region as strain further increases.

A kinetic model was developed to capture the microstructural evolution during a warm/hot deformation process. The progress of DRX is characterized as the change of the volume fraction of DRX [35]. The DRX kinetic model is defined by [36]:

$$\varepsilon_c = a_2 \varepsilon_p \tag{7.12}$$

$$\varepsilon_p = a_1 d_0^{n1} \dot{\varepsilon}^{m1} \exp\left(\frac{Q_1}{RT}\right) \tag{7.13}$$

$$\varepsilon_{0.5} = a_5 d_0 \dot{\varepsilon}^{m5} \exp\left(\frac{Q_5}{RT}\right) \tag{7.14}$$

$$X_{DRX} = 1 - \exp\left[-\beta_d \left(\frac{\varepsilon}{\varepsilon_{0.5}}\right)^{k_d}\right] \tag{7.15}$$

where ε_c is the critical strain for the onsite of DRX, ε_p is the peak stress strain corresponding to the maximum flow stress, $\varepsilon_{0.5}$ denotes the strain at 50% recrystallization, d_0 is the initial grain size, T is the process temperature in K, and X_{DRX} is the volume fraction of DRX. R is the ideal gas constant of 8.314 J/mol·K. β_d, and k_d are material constants. a_i, n_i, and m_i ($i = 1, 2, \ldots, 9$) are material constants in each equation, and Q_i is a modified activation energy. During the recrystallization, the averaged grain size (d) after DRX can be predicted by a mixture rule:

$$d = d_0 - (d_0 - d_{DRX}) X_{DRX} \tag{7.16}$$

$$d_{DRX} = a_8 d_0 \dot{\varepsilon}^{m8} \exp\left(\frac{Q_8}{RT}\right) \tag{7.17}$$

where d_{DRX} is the predicted grain size after DRX. The initial grain size d_0 was assumed uniformly distributed in the coupons.

As recrystallization completes, grain growth would take place to reduce the grain boundary area per unit volume if the temperature is higher than the grain growth starting

TABLE 7.3. Model parameters to predict grain growth and microhardness.

β_d	k_d	a_1	n_1	m_1	a_2	Q_1 (kJ/mol)	Q_5 (kJ/mol)	Q_8 (kJ/mol)
0.72	4.1	0.0003	1	0.1029	0.81	20.27	15.39	−44.33

a_5	m_5	a_5	m_8	a_9	m_9	H_0(HV)	Q_9 (kJ/mol)	k (HV√m)
0.0011	0.0781	711.45	0.15	25.29	−0.225	56.1	4.027	0.0487

TABLE 7.4. Mechanical and physical properties for pure Cu [38].

Property	Value	Property	Value
Density (kg/m³)	8890	Thermal conductivity (W/m·°C)	391
Young's modulus (GPa)	115	Heat Capacity (J/Kg/°C)	385
Poisson's ratio	0.33	Thermal expansion (μm/m·°C)	17
Melting point (°C)	1083	–	–

temperature [25]. In this study, the grain growth starting temperature was assumed as 0.5 T_m, which is 406°C for Cu. Grain growth was considered to end as temperature dropped below 406°C during the cooling step. The final grain size due to grain growth, d_g, is given by:

$$d_g = \left[d_0^{m_9} + a_9 t \cdot \exp\left(\frac{Q_9}{RT} \right) \right]^{1/m} \tag{7.18}$$

where t is the time duration for temperature above grain growth starting temperature, which also includes the time duration during the cooling stage.

The microhardness after welding is determined by average grain size using Hall-Petch equation [37]:

$$H = H_o + kd^{-\frac{1}{2}} \tag{7.19}$$

where H is the microhardness of the material, H_o and k are material constants determined from the relationship of measured grain size and hardness. All the aforementioned material constants were calibrated based on the previously reported experimental results [1, 33]. These values are listed in Table 7.3. Other necessary mechanical and physical properties of copper are given in Table 7.4.

7.3.3 Process Modeling

Figure 7.4a shows the 3D modeling configuration in DEFORM 11.0 for the ultrasonic spot welding experiment. The typical knurl and anvil pattern designs are shown in Figs. 7.4b–c, respectively. For the modeled condition, both knurl and anvil had the diamond pattern with 4 × 4 knurling tips to treat an area of 5 × 5 mm². Both knurl and anvil were treated as rigid bodies in this model. The top and bottom sheets were 0.4 and 1 mm in thickness, respectively. The thin Ni layer of 3 μm was not considered in this model. Clamping force was applied at the back of the knurling tools along the vertical direction. The knurl can move along the vertical direction, whereas the anvil was fixed in all the degree of freedoms. Multiple simulations were conducted with varying welding time durations from 0.2 to 1.0 second. After the welding step simulation, the tools were disengaged from the joints and coupons, and a cooling step was simulated for the workpiece using a natural convection (20 W/m²-K) condition. The modified Chaboche yield criterion was applied effectively by defining kinematic and isotropic hardening rule separately. The hardening rule was specified as kinematic with the back stress defined within the whole coupon domain. The sum of

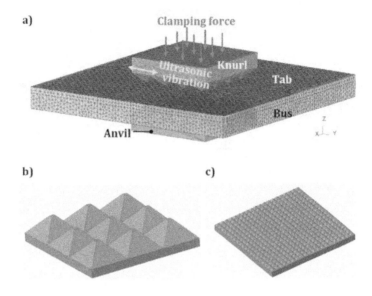

Figure 7.4. FE modeling setup for ultrasonic welding: (a) FE configuration; (b) knurl pattern; (c) anvil pattern.

isotropic hardening term R and initial yield stress σ_0 was given as tabular data in DEFORM, which were calculated from various strains and temperatures.

Ultrasonic vibration was not directly modeled for the horn in this work to save computational cost. When ultrasonic vibration was implemented for the knurling tool, computational cost was too high to complete even a very short period of welding process. In this study, the effect of ultrasonic vibration was considered as acoustic softening on flow stress and frictional heat generation. The acoustic softening effect by ultrasonic vibration was modeled as in Section 7.3.1. The effect on frictional heat generation was considered for both friction coefficient and heat generation.

During ultrasonic welding, heat generation mainly occurs at the interface between the two sheets from both mechanical deformation and friction [15]. Thus, a constant surface heat flux was applied in this model at the interface between the top and bottom copper sheets. The applied surface heat flux was 18.15 W/mm^2 in this model, which was calibrated by comparing the simulated temperature histories at different locations to the measurement [12]. The friction coefficients between the knurling tools and workpieces were considered to be temperature-dependent. The friction coefficient was reported to increase with temperature up to a certain temperature then start to decrease [39]. The temperature dependency of friction coefficient was given by:

$$\mu = \mu_0(8.485\times10^{-10}T^4 - 8.842\times10^{-7}T^3 + 1.969\times10^{-4}T^2 - 9.762\times10^{-3}T + 1.12)$$

(7.20)

where, $\mu_0 = 0.39$, the kinetic friction coefficient between copper and steel at room temperature [40].

To predict the continuous grain growth after ultrasonic welding, a cooling step was simulated with a natural convection (20 W/m^2-K) applied after the welding step. For the experiments with longer welding time durations of 0.8 and 1.0 second, the simulated thermal history for both welding and cooling steps was used to predict the final grain size due to grain growth. A post-processing user routine programmed in FORTRAN was implemented to predict the microstructural evolution and microhardness change as given in

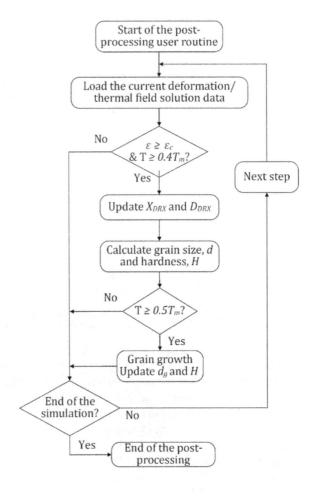

Figure 7.5. Flowchart for post-processing user routine.

Section 7.3.2. Figure 7.5 shows the flow chart of the post-processing user routine. As afore-mentioned, the starting temperature of DRX and grain growth were adopted as 0.4 T_m and 0.5 T_m, respectively, i.e., 270°C and 406°C for Cu. If the temperature was higher than 406°C, the grain growth would continue through the cooling step after the welding step until the temperature dropped below 406°C.

7.4 SIMULATION RESULTS AND DISCUSSIONS

Figure 7.6 shows the simulated 3D Von Mises stress distributions on both top and bottom coupons at the welding time of 1.0 second. A 4 × 4 array of indents can be seen in the weld zone on the top sheet. The stress in the top sheet was lower than that of the bottom sheet. This was resulted from different magnitudes of acoustic softening. More acoustic softening was applied in the top sheet because significantly more ultrasonic energy was absorbed in the top sheet.

Simulated temperature distributions are shown in Fig. 7.7 for both welding step (1.0 second welding time duration) and cooling step. The weld joint area was predicted to have a relative uniform temperature distribution of about 500°C at the end of 1.0 second welding duration. This average temperature was determined for welding processes with various welding time durations. Figure 7.7b shows the temperature prediction during the

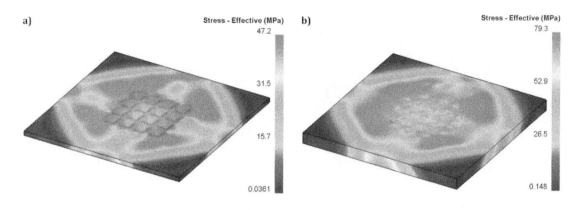

Figure 7.6. Effective stress distribution at 1.0-second ultrasonic welding in: (a) top coupon; (b) bottom coupon.

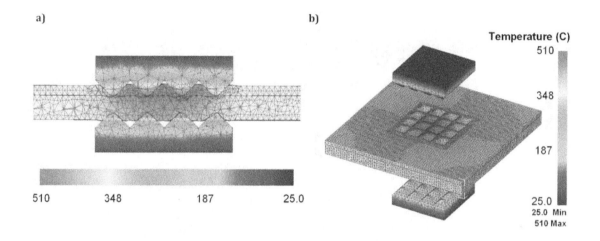

Figure 7.7. Temperature distribution of 1.0-second ultrasonic welding simulation: (a) at 1.0-second; (b) during cooling.

cooling step with the knurling tools disengaged from the coupons. Figure 7.8 compares the simulated temperatures with the experimental measurements undertaken by a welding time duration of 0.4 second [12]. Thermocouples could not be directly applied within the weld zone but were attached to the top Cu coupon at about 1.5 mm away from the weld zone, denoted as P1 and P2 as can be seen in Fig. 7.8. The temperature histories at these thermocouple locations were tracked from the simulation result. Under the friction heat flux of 18.15 W/mm², the simulated temperature histories agreed well with the experimental measurements for both thermocouple locations. This validated the accuracy of temperature prediction in this analysis.

Figure 7.9 shows the simulated microstructural variables in terms of volume fraction of DRX, grain size, and microhardness after 1-second welding and subsequent cooling, which were calculated using the post-processing user routine. As shown in Fig. 7.9a, DRX completed in most area of the top coupon within the weld zone due to the more plastic deformation, while DRX only occurred near the anvil indents in the bottom coupon due to less deformation. Grain size was determined from the temperature history, which was predicted about 34.7 μm in the weld zone and smaller in the surrounding area. Accordingly, the

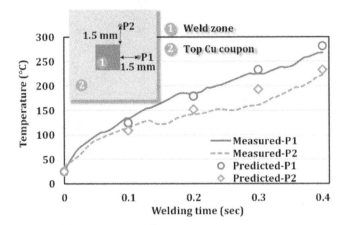

Figure 7.8. Simulated temperature histories at two locations on the Cu coupon during a 0.4-second welding experiment.

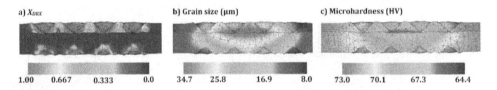

Figure 7.9. Microstructure prediction for 1.0-second welding. (a) X_{DRX}; (b) grain size (μm); (c) microhardness (HV).

microhardness followed the reversed trend of the grain size. A low hardness was predicted in the welding zone because of the coarse grains and became higher in the surrounding area.

The simulation results of process temperature under different welding conditions are shown in Fig. 7.10. Figure 7.10a shows the predicted process temperature, i.e., average temperature along the joint interface, for welding time durations of 0.6 and 1.0 second. The process temperature increased very fast during the welding step, and then dropped quickly within the first 10 seconds of the cooling step. In Fig. 7.10, microstructural evolution regimes are color highlighted by different temperature ranges. For instance, for 1.0 second

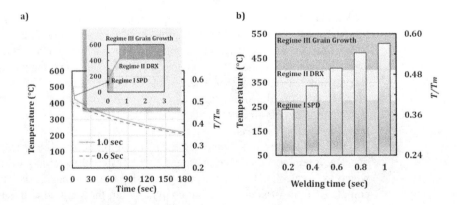

Figure 7.10. Simulated temperature histories and peak temperatures: (a) Temperature histories in both welding and cooling step; (b) welding time effect on the simulated process temperatures.

welding time duration, the material microstructure underwent different stages of evolution following the loading history, i.e., first, regime I SPD, then regime II DRX, and finally regime III grain growth. Because of the intensive heat generation under 1.0 second welding duration, the process temperature was predicted to be above 406°C for 16 seconds, during which grain growth occurred. Although the temperature increase was only increased to about 400°C under the welding time duration of 0.6 second, grain growth did not occur under that condition. Figure 7.10b summarizes the predicted process temperatures and microstructural evolution regimes under different welding time durations. For the short welding time duration of 0.2 second, the process temperature did not reach the DRX starting temperature (40% of the melting point T_m, or about 270°C for Cu), microstructural evolution was governed by SPD. For welding time of 0.4 to 0.6 second, the process temperatures were in the range of the DRX (0.4 to 0.5 T_m, or 270°C to 406°C for Cu), which dominated the microstructural evolution. For welding time of 0.8 and 1.0 second, the process temperature exceeded the starting temperature of grain growth (0.5 T_m, or 406 C for Cu), and the final grain size was determined by the grain growth mechanism. These findings agreed well with the experimental observations on microstructural evolution in Section 7.2 and validated the hypotheses in microstructural evolution.

Figure 7.11 shows the predicted weld joint geometry under various welding time durations. The model predictions show more compacted joint with welding time increasing. Larger knurling indents were predicted in the top sheets than the bottom sheet. These modeling results matched well with the experimental results. Figure 7.12 further examines the weld thickness from the simulations, which was defined as the thinnest distance from the top to bottom surface of the weld as shown in Fig. 7.11. The model accurately predicted the weld thickness under different welding time duration, which reduced from 1.4 mm achieved at 0.2-second welding duration to about 0.6 mm after a 1.0-second welding.

As a final note, the bonding between two coupons is not captured in this model. As a result, the simulated stress and strain field is not continuous across the weld interface, especially when the uniform microstructure is formed after a longer welding time. The current model is unable to capture this bonding physics. The future goal of this study is to integrate this model into a multi-scale model to capture the local change of weld interface, e.g., interlock formation between the layers, and material diffusion across the weld interface. In that case, the grain structure evolution due to DRX and the subsequent grain growth would be more accurate. Again, the application of ultrasonic softening effect needs to be improved in the future model as well. A flow stress user subroutine is required to apply the acoustic softening in the weld zone, not the bulk material of the coupon.

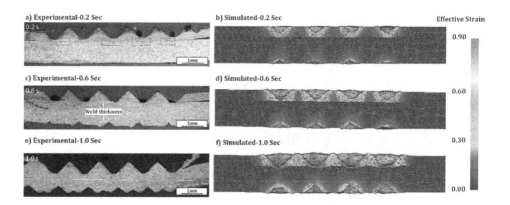

Figure 7.11. Comparison of the deformed geometry under different welding durations.

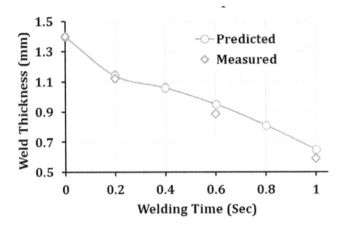

Figure 7.12. Weld thickness comparison for different welding durations.

7.5 SUMMARY AND CONCLUSIONS

The microstructural evolution mechanisms for ultrasonic spot welding were for the first time hypothesized as three regimes of SPD, DRX, and grain growth according to the material thermomechanical loading conditions. A novel metallo-thermo-mechanically coupled 3D FE model was successfully developed for ultrasonic spot welding to model both weld formation and microstructural evolution. A combined isotropic/kinematic hardening flow stress model with an acoustic softening term was implemented to predict the material response under the high frequency ultrasonic vibration. Using a post-processing user routine, a kinetics model was implemented to predict the material microstructural evolution under DRX and grain growth.

The simulated weld zone geometry agreed well with the experiments. The simulations demonstrated that the process temperature during ultrasonic welding was highly dependent on the welding time duration. For welding time duration longer than 0.8 second, weld material underwent three different stages of SPD, DRX, and grain growth. The final distributions of grain size and consequential microhardness were predicted based on the thermomechanical solution fields and agreed well with the experimental measurements. The simulation results validated the hypotheses proposed in microstructural evolution during ultrasonic welding. In future work, this numerical framework will be applied for ultrasonic spot welding of dissimilar materials, e.g., Al/Cu tabs, to simulate the weld formation and complicated microstructural evolution.

Acknowledgment

The authors gratefully acknowledge the financial support by the National Science Foundation under Grant Number EPS-1101284 and State Key Laboratory of Mechanical System and Vibration, Shanghai Jiao Tong University, China under grant MSV201514.

Nomenclature

a_i	material constants in the microstructure modeling, $i = 1, 2, …, 9$
b	the rate at which the size of the yield surface changes with changing plastic strains

C	the kinetic shift of yield surface
d	grain size
d_{DRX}	dynamically recrystallized grain size
$\boldsymbol{D}_{el}$	elasticity tensor
d_g	final grain size due to grain growth
d_o	initial grain size
d_u	ultrasonic softening parameter
d_λ	plastic multiplier
e	material constant related to ultrasonic softening
E_u	ultrasonic energy density
F	Yield function (criterion)
H	microhardness
H_o	material constant related to microhardness model
k	material constant related to microhardness model
k_d	material constant related to X_{DRX}
m	material constant related to thermal softening
m_i	material constants in the microstructure modeling, $i = 1, 2, ..., 9$
n_i	material constants in the microstructure modeling, $i = 1, 2, ..., 9$
Q	the maximum change in the size of the yield surface
Q_i	modified activation energy in the microstructure modeling, $i = 1, 2, ..., 9$
R	isotropic hardening
T	temperature
T_m	melting point
T_r	reference temperature
t	time
X_{DRX}	volume fraction of DRX
α	the back stress tensor due to kinematic hardening
α_1	the back stress at the start of the stabilized cycle
β_d	material constant related to X_{DRX}
γ	the rate at which saturation value of kinematic hardening decreases with increasing plastic strain
ε	total strain
$\varepsilon_{0.5}$	the strain at 50% recrystallization
ε_c	critical strain for the onsite of DRX
ε_{dot}	strain rate
ε^{el}	elastic strain
ε_p	peak stress strain
ε^{pl}	plastic strain
μ	temperature dependent friction coefficient at elevated temperature
μ_o	friction coefficient at room temperature
σ	flow stress
σ_1	flow stress at the start of the stabilized cycle
σ_n	flow stress at the start and end of the stabilized cycle
σ_0	initial yield stress
σ_s	yield stress at stabilized cycle

REFERENCES

[1] Lee, S. S., Kim, T.-H., Hu, S. J., Cai, W. W., Abell, J. A., and Li, J., 2013, "Characterization of Joint Quality in Ultrasonic Welding of Battery Tabs," *ASME Journal of Manufacturing Science and Engineering*, **135**(2), p. 021004.

[2] Xu, L., Wang, L., Chen, Y.-C., Robson, J. D., and Prangnell, P. B., 2016, "Effect of Interfacial Reaction on the Mechanical Performance of Steel to Aluminum Dissimilar Ultrasonic Spot Welds," *Metallurgical and Materials Transactions A*, **47**(1), pp. 334–346.

[3] Shen, N., Samanta, A., Ding, H., and Cai, W. W., 2016, "Simulating microstructure evolution of battery tabs during ultrasonic welding," *SME Journal of Manufacturing Processes*, **23**, pp. 306–314.

[4] Lee, S. S., Kim, T.-H., Hu, S. J., Cai, W. W., and Abell, J. A., 2015, "Analysis of Weld Formation in Multilayer Ultrasonic Metal Welding Using High-Speed Images," *ASME Journal of Manufacturing Science and Engineering*, **137**(3), p. 031016.

[5] Wu, X., Liu, T., and Cai, W., 2015, "Microstructure, welding mechanism, and failure of Al/Cu ultrasonic welds," *SME Journal of Manufacturing Processes*, **20**, pp. 321–331.

[6] Lee, S. S., Shao, C., Kim, T.-H., Hu, S. J., Kannatey-Asibu, E., Cai, W. W., Spicer, J. P., and Abell, J. A., 2014, "Characterization of Ultrasonic Metal Welding by Correlating Online Sensor Signals With Weld Attributes," *ASME Journal of Manufacturing Science and Engineering*, **136**(5), p. 051019.

[7] Zhao, N., Li, W., Cai, W. W., and Abell, J. A., 2014, "A Fatigue Life Study of Ultrasonically Welded Lithium-Ion Battery Tab Joints Based on Electrical Resistance," *ASME Journal of Manufacturing Science and Engineering*, **136**(5), p. 051003.

[8] Kang, B., Cai, W., and Tan, C.-A., 2014, "Vibrational energy loss analysis in battery tab ultrasonic welding," *SME Journal of Manufacturing Processes*, **16**(2), pp. 218–232.

[9] Kang, B., Cai, W., and Tan, C.-A., 2014, "Dynamic Stress Analysis of Battery Tabs Under Ultrasonic Welding," *ASME Journal of Manufacturing Science and Engineering*, **136**(4), p. 041011.

[10] Chen, J., Zhang, W., Feng, Z., and Cai, W., 2014, "Determination of thermal contact conductance between thin metal sheets of battery tabs," *International Journal of Heat and Mass Transfer*, **69**, pp. 473–480.

[11] Zhao, J., Li, H., Choi, H., Cai, W., Abell, J. A., and Li, X., 2013, "Insertable thin film thermocouples for in situ transient temperature monitoring in ultrasonic metal welding of battery tabs," *SME Journal of Manufacturing Processes*, **15**(1), pp. 136–140.

[12] Li, H., Choi, H., Ma, C., Zhao, J., Jiang, H., Cai, W., Abell, J. A., and Li, X., 2013, "Transient Temperature and Heat Flux Measurement in Ultrasonic Joining of Battery Tabs Using Thin-Film Microsensors," *ASME Journal of Manufacturing Science and Engineering*, **135**(5), p. 051015.

[13] Langenecker, B., 1966, "Effects of Ultrasound on Deformation Characteristics of Metals," *IEEE Transactions on Sonics and Ultrasonics*, **13**(1), pp. 1–8.

[14] Langenecker, B., 1961, "Work-softening of metal crystals by alternating the rate of glide strain," *Acta Metallurgica*, **9**(10), pp. 937–940.

[15] Elangovan, S., Semeer, S., and Prakasan, K., 2009, "Temperature and stress distribution in ultrasonic metal welding—An FEA-based study," *Journal of Materials Processing Technology*, **209**(3), pp. 1143–1150.

[16] De Vries, E., 2004, "Mechanics and Mechanisms of Ultrasonic Metal Welding," The Ohio State University.

[17] Lee, D., Kannatey-Asibu, E., and Cai, W., 2013, "Ultrasonic Welding Simulations for Multiple Layers of Lithium-Ion Battery Tabs," *ASME Journal of Manufacturing Science and Engineering*, **135**(6), p. 061011.

[18] Siddiq, A., and Ghassemieh, E., 2008, "Thermomechanical analyses of ultrasonic welding process using thermal and acoustic softening effects," *Mechanics of Materials*, **40**(12), pp. 982–1000.

[19] Siddiq, A., and Ghassemieh, E., 2009, "Theoretical and FE Analysis of Ultrasonic Welding of Aluminum Alloy 3003," *ASME Journal of Manufacturing Science and Engineering*, **131**(4), p. 041007.

[20] Siddiq, A., and El Sayed, T., 2011, "Acoustic softening in metals during ultrasonic assisted deformation via CP-FEM," *Materials Letters*, **65**(2), pp. 356–359.

[21] Siddiq, A., and Sayed, T. El, 2012, "A thermomechanical crystal plasticity constitutive model for ultrasonic consolidation," *Computational Materials Science*, **51**(1), pp. 241–251.

[22] Bakavos, D., and Prangnell, P. B., 2010, "Mechanisms of joint and microstructure formation in high power ultrasonic spot welding 6111 aluminium automotive sheet," *Materials Science and Engineering: A*, **527**(23), pp. 6320–6334.

[23] Ding, H., Shen, N., and Shin, Y. C., 2012, "Predictive modeling of grain refinement during multi-pass cold rolling," *Journal of Materials Processing Technology*, **212**(5), pp. 1003–1013.

[24] Ding, H., and Shin, Y. C., 2014, "Dislocation Density-Based Grain Refinement Modeling of Orthogonal Cutting of Titanium," *ASME Journal of Manufacturing Science and Engineering*, **136**(4), p. 041003.

[25] Sellars, C. M., and Whiteman, J. A., 1979, "Recrystallization and grain growth in hot rolling," *Metal Science*, **13**(3–4), pp. 187–194.

[26] Krishna, S., 2009, "Unified Constitutive Modeling for Proportional and Nonproportional Cyclic Plasticity Responses," North Carolina State University.

[27] Johnson, G., and Cook, W., 1983, "A constitutive model and data for metals subjected to large strains, high strain rates and high temperatures," *Proceedings of the 7th International Symposium on Ballistics*, p. 541.

[28] Bower, A. F., 1989, "Cyclic hardening properties of hard-drawn copper and rail steel," *Journal of the Mechanics and Physics of Solids*, **37**(4), pp. 455–470.

[29] Ding, H., Shen, N., and Shin, Y. C., 2011, "Modeling of grain refinement in aluminum and copper subjected to cutting," *Computational Materials Science*, **50**(10), pp. 3016–3025.

[30] Shen, N., Ding, H., Bowers, R., Yu, Y., Pence, C. N., Ozbolat, I. T., and Stanford, C. M., 2015, "Surface Micropatterning of Pure Titanium for Biomedical Applications Via High Energy Pulse Laser Peening," *ASME Journal of Micro and Nano-Manufacturing*, **3**(1), p. 011005.

[31] Shen, N., Ding, H., and Gao, J., 2015, "Cryogenic Cutting of AZ31B-O Mg Alloy for Improved Surface Integrity—Part II: Physics-based Process Modeling of Surface Microstructural Alteration," *Proceedings of ASME 2015 International Manufacturing Science and Engineering Conference, MSEC2015-9324*, Charlotte, North Carolina, USA.

[32] García, V. G., Cabrera, J. M., and Prado, J. M., 2007, "A Model for Multi Peak Dynamic Recrystallization in Copper," *Materials Science Forum*, **550**(November), pp. 565–570.

[33] Brown, A. A., and Bammann, D. J., 2012, "Validation of a model for static and dynamic recrystallization in metals," *International Journal of Plasticity*, **32–33**, pp. 17–35.

[34] Behnagh, R. A., Shen, N., Ansari, M. A., Narvan, M., Besharati Givi, M. K., and Ding, H., 2015, "Experimental Analysis and Microstructure Modeling of Friction Stir Extrusion of Magnesium Chips," *ASME Journal of Manufacturing Science and Engineering*, **138**(4), p. 041008.

[35] Yanagimoto, J., Karhausen, K., Brand, A. J., and Kopp, R., 1998, "Incremental Formulation for the Prediction of Flow Stress and Microstructural Change in Hot Forming," *ASME Journal of Manufacturing Science and Engineering*, **120**(2), p. 316.

[36] DEFORM V11.0 (PC) Documentation, 2014, Scientific Forming Technologies Corporation, Columbus, OH.

[37] Callister, W. D., and Rethwisch, D. G., 2012, "Fundamentals of materials science and engineering: An integrated approach," 4th Edition, John Wiley & Sons, Hoboken, New Jersey, USA.

[38] Erickson, S. C., 1990, "Properties of Pure Metals," Properties and Selection: Nonferrous Alloys and Special-Purpose Materials, Vol 2, ASM Handbook, ASM International, Materials Park, Ohio, USA, pp. 1099–1201.

[39] Zhang, C., Zhu, X., and Li, L., 2006, "A study of friction behavior in ultrasonic welding (consolidation) of aluminum," *Proceedings of the AWS Conference, Session 7: Friction & Resistance Welding/ Materials Bonding Processes*, pp. 151–156.

[40] Rabinowicz, E., 1951, "The Nature of the Static and Kinetic Coefficients of Friction," *Journal of Applied Physics*, **22**(11), p. 1373.

Chapter 8

PROCESS MONITORING USING ONLINE SENSOR SIGNALS[1]

S. Shawn Lee[1], Chenhui Shao[3], Tae Hyung Kim[2], S. Jack Hu[2], Elijah Kannatey-Asibu[2],
Wayne Cai[4], J. Patrick Spicer[4], and Jeffrey A. Abell[4]
[1]Intellectual Property Prosecution, McDermott Will & Emery LLP
[2]Department of Mechanical Engineering, The University of Michigan
[3]Department of Mechanical Science & Engineering, University of Illinois at Urbana-Champaign
[4]Manufacturing Systems Research Lab, General Motors Global R&D Center

ABSTRACT

Online process monitoring in ultrasonic welding of automotive lithium-ion batteries is essential for robust and reliable battery pack assembly. Effective quality monitoring algorithms have been developed to identify out of control parts by applying purely statistical classification methods. However, such methods do not provide the deep physical understanding of the manufacturing process that is necessary to provide diagnostic capability when the process is out of control. The purpose of this study is to determine the physical correlation between ultrasonic welding signal features and the ultrasonic welding process conditions and ultimately joint performance. A deep understanding in these relationships will enable a significant reduction in production launch time and cost, improve process design for ultrasonic welding, and reduce operational downtime through advanced diagnostic methods. In this study, the fundamental physics behind the ultrasonic welding process is investigated using two process signals, weld power and horn displacement. Several online features are identified by examining those signals and their variations under abnormal process conditions. The joint quality is predicted by correlating such online features to weld attributes such as bond density and post-weld thickness that directly impact the weld performance. This study provides a guideline for feature selection and advanced diagnostics to achieve a reliable online quality monitoring system in ultrasonic metal welding.

Keywords: horn displacement, online features, online process monitoring, weld attributes, weld power

8.1 INTRODUCTION

Ultrasonic metal welding is one of the processes used to join automotive lithium-ion batteries [1–3]. In ultrasonic metal welding, a high-frequency shear oscillation generated by a piezoelectric system, as described in Fig. 8.1, removes surface oxides or contamination by friction [4–6]. The continuous sliding action under pressure yields an increase in metal contact area, resulting in metallurgical adhesion [7–9] or diffusion [10, 11] at the metal contact interfaces. These solid-state bonding characteristics are advantageous for joining

---

[1] The content presented in this chapter has previously appeared in Ref. [12].

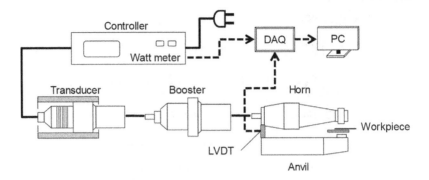

Figure 8.1. Ultrasonic metal welding system and sensor signal acquisition.

dissimilar metals, such as copper, aluminum, and nickel, commonly used materials for battery tabs. In addition, the temperature of this process does not exceed the melting point of the metal workpiece, avoiding undesirable intermetallic compounds and metallurgical defects that can result from most fusion welding processes [13]. Therefore, the ultrasonic welding process is well suited for battery tab joining.

In a typical battery pack for hybrid and electric vehicles, several hundred battery cells are joined together through tabs and bus bars to meet the desired power and energy capacity requirements. The battery joints should possess reliable electrical connections as well as robust mechanical strength because failure of a single weld can result in degradation in performance, even failure, of the entire battery pack. Therefore, quality monitoring is essential to ensure quality on every battery joint. As a quality assurance method, online process monitoring is widely used in manufacturing to ensure joint quality and process stability [14, 15]. Although monitoring algorithms can be developed by systematic feature selection from various online signals utilizing appropriate statistical methods without expert fundamental knowledge of the process [16], the selected features may not perform well when new abnormal process conditions are encountered. Thus, in order to develop a robust and reliable monitoring system, a fundamental understanding of sensor signals and their relationship to the welding process and eventually to weld quality should be established.

A significant amount of research has been done on the relationship between sensor signals and weld quality for various welding technologies. For example, Ling et al. [17] predicted the quality of resistance spot welds by analyzing input voltage and current signals during the welding process. Li et al. [18] estimated resistance spot weld quality by correlating online signal features such as dynamic resistance with nugget size. Tseng and Chuang [19] showed the influence of maximum electrode displacement on the nugget diameter and thickness in predicting spot weld quality. Park and Kim [20] indicated that the plasma light intensity obtained by optical sensors could express the plasma/keyhole behavior, which directly impacts laser weld quality. A comprehensive review was performed by Sun et al. [21] on the usage of multiple sensors in real-time monitoring of laser weld quality and incorporation of sensor fusion with a neural network approach. In gas metal arc welding, the welding voltage and current signals were correlated to the weld quality using a statistical process control method by Wu et al. [22]. Nevertheless, only limited research has been carried out on the sensor signals and their relationship to weld quality in ultrasonic metal welding. Or et al. [23] utilized a piezoelectric sensor to evaluate the weld quality during the ultrasonic wire-bonding process, which was different from ultrasonic welding for sheet metals. They monitored the changes in resonant frequency or vibration amplitude caused by mechanical impedance change in the bonding zone. Zhao et al. [24] developed a measurement system for monitoring transient temperature during the ultrasonic welding process using thin-film thermocouples fabricated on silicon substrates and inserted in a pre-machined slot in the weld tool. Their study showed that the heat flux and its rate change during the welding process provides good physical understanding of ultrasonic bonding at the weld interface [25]. The methodology provided in their study showed some feasibility for process monitoring and control. However, no further examination was conducted on how the temperature would vary when abnormal situations occurred during the process. As a potential nondestructive testing for ultrasonic welding, an experimental study on identifying effective welded area using a new shearography system has been carried out by Jia et al. [26].

In a previous study on ultrasonic welding of battery tabs [3], several weld attributes, such as bond density and post-weld thickness, were identified from optical micrographs and correlated to weld quality. According to this study, the performance of an ultrasonic metal weld, such as mechanical strength, can be indirectly linked to process parameters through such attributes. However, there are limitations of using weld attributes for process monitoring because they are only available through off-line post weld measurement. Therefore, this chapter attempts to investigate the fundamental physics behind the weld formation in ultrasonic welding using sensor signals and relating them to weld attributes, which in turn determine the weld quality.

The remainder of the chapter is organized as follows. We start by summarizing the weld formation mechanism in ultrasonic metal welding. Then, the experimental procedure and sensor signals are described and the signal variation under abnormal process conditions is analyzed. After that, the relationship between signal features and weld attributes is identified, which provides direct information of weld quality. Finally, conclusions are presented.

8.2 WELD FORMATION MECHANISM IN ULTRASONIC METAL WELDING

Ultrasonic metal welding is a solid-state welding process. The frictional work between the workpiece materials generated from high-frequency vibration in combination with the normal force breaks and disperses surface films (oxides, contaminants, etc.), and increases the actual contact area at the weld interface. This leads to localized intimate contact between exposed metal surfaces to form metallurgical bonds, which are atomic bonds between the metal lattices [27]. These locally created bonds (i.e., micro-welds) increase in density over the region affected by the weld tip as a result of the rise in temperature caused by extensive plastic deformation. In addition to metallurgical adhesion, the continuous vibration and static force from the horn result in bonding lines that curl around the micro-welds, and they play a role in mechanical interlocking. Thus, a weld in ultrasonic metal welding of similar materials, nickel-plated copper in this chapter, is formed mainly by metallurgical adhesion with partial aid of mechanical interlocking. Ultrasonic metal welding does not create any fusion zone where the temperature of the mating metals reaches the melting point.

Figure 8.2 shows the microstructure of weld sample cross-sections of 1.0 mm nickel plated copper and 0.4 mm copper (C11000). After the nickel layer (less than 2 μm) is broken by the oscillating shear force, a unified grain structure between the two bare copper sheets is formed as shown in Fig. 8.2(a). The nickel layer is broken into pieces and it curls along the weld line producing interfacial hooks, as shown in Fig. 8.2(b). The interfacial hooks provide additional mechanical strength.

In this chapter, two key weld attributes which have a direct impact on the final weld performance, bond density and post-weld thickness, are measured and correlated with signal features. Bond density is the proportion of bonded region to the entire weld width while post-weld thickness is the proportion of the indented thickness of the upper sheet to the original thickness. These non-dimensional parameters were defined in a previous study of joint quality characterization in ultrasonic metal welding by Lee et al. [3]. Figure 8.3 shows the effect of a key process variable, weld time, on joint performance, bond density and post-weld thickness.

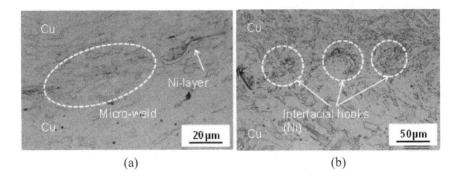

(a)   (b)

Figure 8.2. Optical micrographs with two main bonding mechanisms for ultrasonic metal welds: (a) metallurgical bonding; and (b) mechanical interlocking [3].

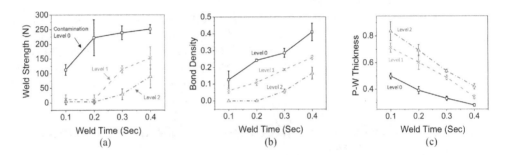

Figure 8.3. Influence of weld time on (a) weld strength obtained from U-tensile test; (b) bond density; and (c) post-weld thickness under different levels of contamination (level 0: cleaned with isopropyl alcohol, level 1: one drop of vanishing oil, level 2: two drops of vanishing oil).

As shown in Fig. 8.3(a), the weld strength increases dramatically in a short welding time. Then, it shows a slow increase as welding time keeps increasing despite a steady increase of bond density as described in Fig. 8.3(b). This is caused by the decrease of post-weld thickness over time as shown in Fig. 8.3(c), which may lead to excessive thinning of the material. Based on these results, the performance of an ultrasonic metal weld is in positive correlation with bond density while in negative correlation with post-weld thickness.

The welding process variation with contaminated surface in Fig. 8.3 is detailed as follows. An abnormal process condition was simulated by applying oil-based stamping fluid (Daphne vanishing oil) at the interface between the workpieces as surface contaminant. This has been reported in the assembly line of battery packs as a possible source of contamination. The level of contamination was controlled by a transfer pipette providing 0.05 mL per drop. Three different levels of contamination were applied in this experiment: level 0 (cleaned with isopropyl alcohol), level 1 (one drop of vanishing oil), and level 2 (two drops of vanishing oil). After the drops were applied and smeared over the surface evenly, the welding took place immediately to minimize the effect of oil evaporation on the result.

8.3 SENSOR SIGNALS FROM ULTRASONIC WELDING PROCESS

In this section, the signals collected on an AmTech Ultraweld® L-20 high-power welder are analyzed to describe the mechanism of weld formation during the ultrasonic welding process. The experimental procedure is described first. Then two sensor signals, power and displacement, are introduced, and their variations under surface contamination are examined.

8.3.1 Experiment

Prepared coupons of nickel plated copper sheets of dimensions 20 by 50 mm were welded for different welding times using the AmTech ultrasonic welder. The pressure and the vibration amplitude were fixed at 35 psi (241 kPa) and 40 μm, respectively. The lap joint of two copper sheets of different thicknesses, 0.2 mm and 1.0 mm, was designed for simulating joints between battery tabs and bus bars. Table 8.1 summarizes the factors, levels, and corresponding replication for this experiment. During the welding experiment, the power and displacement signals from the sensors built into the welder, as illustrated in Fig. 8.1, were collected and processed to analyze the relation between signal features and product or process quality. Three weld samples produced were then subjected to a U-tensile test for obtaining their mechanical properties. Another three weld samples were cross-sectioned, mounted, and polished using 0.03 μm colloidal silica suspension followed by etching [3] in order to conduct further microscopy and weld attribute measurement. More replicates for a 0.4-second weld time (12 for tensile test; three for cross-sectioning) were made in order to have enough data to analyze the trend of sensor signals with fixed weld time.

8.3.2 Sensor Signals

Two sensor signals are analyzed: (1) the electric power required for maintaining the mechanical vibration of the weld tool (i.e., horn) and (2) the linear displacement of the horn in the clamping direction.

Power

The ultrasonic vibration is provided by a piezoelectric system and transmitted to a booster/horn stack assembly with designated amplitude. To maintain this mechanical vibration at a constant level of amplitude, the amount of electrical power is controlled throughout the welding process depending on the mechanical loading conditions on the weld joint, which may vary during the process. The power can be defined as:

$$Power = F \frac{dS(t)}{dt} = \mu F_N \frac{dS(t)}{dt} \tag{8.1}$$

where F is the force exerted on the weld tip as a function of friction coefficient (μ) and clamping force (F_N), and $dS(t)/dt$ is the velocity profile of the weld tip function. Because the clamping force and the weld tip velocity are controlled at a constant value during the

TABLE 8.1. Factors and levels for experimental design.

Welding time (sec)	Surface contamination	Replicates	
		U-tensile test	Post-weld measurement
0.1	Level 0	3	3
0.1	Level 1	3	3
0.1	Level 2	3	3
0.2	Level 0	3	3
0.2	Level 1	3	3
0.2	Level 2	3	3
0.3	Level 0	3	3
0.3	Level 1	3	3
0.3	Level 2	3	3
0.4	Level 0	12	3
0.4	Level 1	12	3
0.4	Level 2	12	3

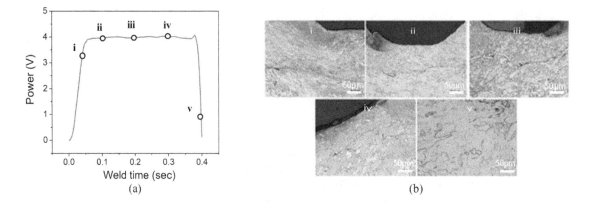

Figure 8.4. Power signal variation over time: (a) power profile for a single welding cycle; and (b) continuous cross-section images at the weld interface during welding cycle.

welding process, the power is only a function of friction coefficient. Therefore, the surface condition of the mating metal sheets directly impacts the power signal.

Figure 8.4 shows (a) the power required to initiate and maintain the vibration motion of the horn during the weld cycle and (b) the cross-section images of the weld interface over welding time. As shown in Fig. 8.4(a), the power rapidly ramps up for the initial 0.1 second of welding time and stays at a constant level to maintain the vibration. As ultrasonic energy is transmitted to the weld interface, the shear force generated from the high-frequency lateral movement results in yielding of the material. Extensive plastic deformation or cold work is observed in the elongated grains along the bonding line as seen in the initial stage of weld process (Fig. 8.4(b)). As welding proceeds, severely deformed grains and the migration of high angle grain boundaries lead to the formation of a new grain structure (i.e., recrystallization) [28–30], and a continuous welding action with increased temperature results in growth of the recrystallized grains [3]. Those recrystallized grain structures are seen in most normal quality welds, which have already been described in many previous studies [3, 28–30]. This is mainly due to the temperature rise at the weld interface with the aid of severe cold working of the material, which is caused from the dissipation of mechanical energy (i.e., vibration) by friction [31].

Displacement

A linear variable differential transformer (LVDT) was used to measure the horn displacement in the clamping direction. This signal data provides information on mechanical deformation, or material compaction, made by the knurl of the horn.

The displacement profile as shown in Fig. 8.5(a) shows the trend typically seen in normal quality welds. In the initial stage of the welding process (< 0.05 second), the material compaction of the material occurs at relatively high speed, but at a lower speed after that (> 0.05 second). Figure 8.5(b) describes a series of cross-section images that impose a material filling phenomenon into the space between knurl peaks. Based on the findings from the previous study [3], the material compacts faster in this initial stage because material is being moved into the knurl through plastic displacement. Once the material fills the space, the compaction rate becomes slower. The fast initial compaction usually leads to a good quality weld because the full engagement of the tool and the material provides good sliding motions at the weld interface. The quality of ultrasonic welds has a close relationship with the amount of material compaction. Thus, the linear displacement profile of the horn can be utilized as valuable data for process monitoring.

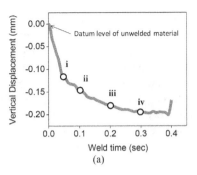
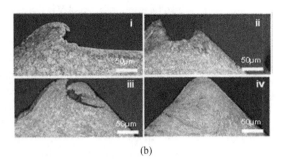

(a)   (b)

Figure 8.5. LVDT signal: (a) horn displacement; (b) cross-section images at the top of metal surface illustrating material filling behavior that corresponds to the displacements shown in (a).

8.3.3 Signal Variation under Process Disturbance

As discussed in Section 8.3.1, process disturbances during the ultrasonic welding process for battery tab joining was simulated by contaminating the workpiece surface with stamping fluid. The weld samples produced with three different levels of contamination—level 0, level 1, and level 2—are examined by microscopy.

Figure 8.6(a) illustrates the typical trend of power signals for the three contamination levels during the welding process. Fifteen replicated signals were collected from the welding experiment, and all showed similar patterns. The power for welding of materials with clean surface shows a fast increase up to about 2300 W, followed by a steady power level until welding is over, whereas the power for both contaminated cases does not reach the same power requirement as the clean surface case but only 70% to 75% of that (stage I in Fig. 8.6). Instead, the power decreases over a period of time (stage II) and gradually increases again (stage III) before settling as the end of the weld cycle is reached (stage IV). The lack of power ramp-up in stage I followed by a continuous reduction in stage II for contaminated surfaces mainly come from the low frictional resistance to the relative motion of metal sheets. So the welder does not require such high power to maintain the vibration with the designated amplitude. However, once the contaminants of the surface have been dispersed or removed, the welder regains its power in stage III as the friction resistance recovers back to the normal condition. The time duration for stage II depends on the amount of contamination at the interface as shown in Fig. 8.6(a).

Figure 8.6(b) shows the variation of the horn's absolute position during welding of copper sheets of different contamination levels. The same stage division as the power signal

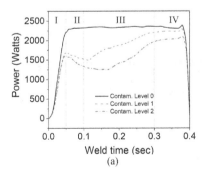
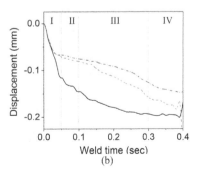

(a)   (b)

Figure 8.6. Variation of (a) power signal and (b) displacement signal for different levels of surface contamination.

can be applied to this LVDT signal. At stage I, the horn abruptly decreases its position as the weld tool penetrates the metal surface even though the amount of material compaction with contaminated surface differs from one with clean surface. For surface contamination cases, the low power level in stage I causes less heat generation, which results in less softening of the material [3] and, therefore, less amount of material compaction. This penetration helps the weld tool fully engaged in the metal surface. After the initial material compaction, the horn slows down its descent in stage II while very little descent is made for the contaminated surface case due to the decrease in power. Then, as the welder increases power again in stage III, the speed at which the horn is descending is regained whereas the horn slows down for clean surface case.

Figure 8.7 is a series of microscopic images focused at the weld interface of a weld sample with clean surface. It shows that, as power increases and the horn lowers its altitude, the nickel layer is dispersed or broken apart by a shear force exerted on the interface. Microwelds are developed along the weld line, which becomes curled as welding proceeds. The micrographs shown in Fig. 8.8 indicate that the contaminants are trapped in the weld inter-

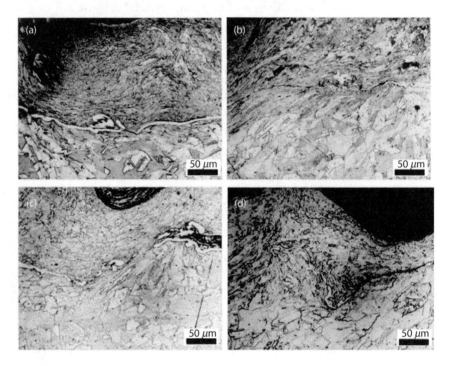

Figure 8.7. Optical micrographs showing weld line formation with welding time of (a) 0.1 sec, (b) 0.2 sec, (c) 0.3 sec, and (d) 0.4 sec.

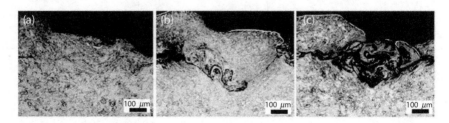

Figure 8.8. Optical micrographs at the weld interface for three levels of surface contamination: (a) level 0 (clean); (b) level 1; and (c) level 2.

face and formed as a swirl, which makes the joint weaker. This is because the remaining oil layer in the early stages of the welding process hinders the adhesion of two metal surfaces and delays the weld development.

8.4 RELATIONSHIP BETWEEN WELD ATTRIBUTES AND SIGNAL FEATURES

In this section, signal features are correlated to weld attributes to identify the relationship between sensor signals and product quality. First, several features in power and displacement profiles are introduced. Then we present the feature variations during the welding process. Finally, the relationship between those features and weld attributes is presented.

8.4.1 Features from Online Signals

Based on our understanding of the physics behind the signal variation under process disturbance as discussed in Section 8.3, the early stages of the welding process is crucial for sensing some abnormal process conditions. For example, the power required in this period changes depending on the level of surface contamination due to different friction conditions. These different power levels lead to different amounts of material deformation, resulting in changes in horn displacement. Thus, the energy used and the amount of material compaction in this early stages are two important features in both power and displacement signals. For the simplicity of calculation, the energy is obtained from the beginning to the mid-point of the welding process. In the same manner, the amount of material compaction of the mid-point of the welding process is chosen as one feature of the displacement signal. Those two features are named E_{mid} and D_{mid}, respectively.

As discussed previously, an ultrasonic metal weld is formed through continuous rubbing action that yields an increase of bonded areas between clean metal surfaces. The curved weld line is found in typical weld samples with normal weld quality. The welding experiments performed in this chapter show that the weld samples produced in 0.4s welding time have the strongest joint performance owing to high bond density and reasonable amount of material compaction, as described in Fig. 8.3. Therefore, the normal quality weld requires a certain level of welding time or energy input. In that sense, total energy used and total amount of material compaction during the entire welding process are also important features in the power and displacement curves. They are named E_{total} and D_{total}, respectively. Figure 8.9 illustrates the main features measured in the power and displacement signals.

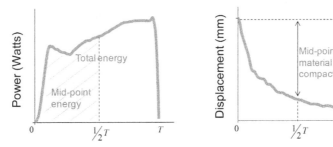

Figure 8.9. Features in power and displacement signals.

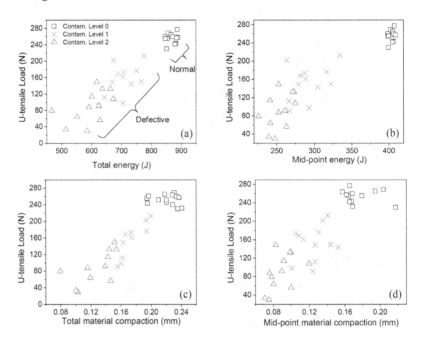

Figure 8.10. Relationship between weld performance and signal features: (a) Total energy (E_{total}); (b) Mid-point energy (E_{mid}); (c) Total material compaction (D_{total}); and (d) Mid-point material compaction (D_{mid}).

Figure 8.10 shows the relationship between weld strength and each signal feature. As shown in Figs. 8.10(a) and 8.10(b), E_{total} and E_{mid} of the power signal for normal weld samples is clearly distinguished from those for problematic welds caused by surface contamination. D_{mid}, as a displacement signal feature, also shows the capability of separating normal and defective weld groups as described in Fig. 8.10(d) while D_{total} in Fig. 8.10(c) shows some capability to distinguish two weld groups but not as much as D_{mid} does. All these four features show a linear relationship with joint performance, indicating that the welds with higher strength possess higher E_{total}, E_{mid}, D_{total}, or D_{mid}. As indicated in all four plots, the amount of contaminants on the metal surface also affects the level of weld energy or the amount of material compaction.

8.4.2 Effect of Welding Parameters on Signal Features

For the signal features that have been identified, their relationships to a key process variable, welding time, are established in this subsection. E_{total} and D_{total} are plotted against welding time, as illustrated in Fig. 8.11, which shows that E_{total} and D_{total} increase linearly over time regardless of the level of surface contamination. As welding time increases, more ultrasonic energy is consumed for frictional heating, plastic deformation and bond formation at the interface. Consequently, more heat generated by increased weld energy yields softening of the material, resulting in larger amount of material compaction by the weld tool. However, only a fraction of the energy is used for welding a surface contaminated workpiece. In the very early stages of the process (0.1 second), approximately 160 J is consumed for welding clean metals whereas only 60% of this energy is used for both contamination levels 1 and 2, as indicated in Fig. 8.11(a). As welding proceeds, the energy consumption for contamination level 1 and level 2 increases at different rates. At the very end of the welding process (0.4 second), approximately 82% energy of the clean surface

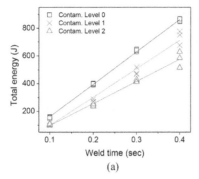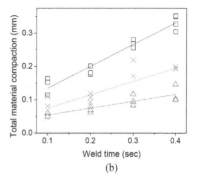

Figure 8.11. Effect of welding time on: (a) Total energy (E_{total}); and (b) Total material compaction (D_{total}).

case is used for level 1 contamination, and only 65% for level 2. This is because the larger amount of contaminants the workpiece possesses, the longer time is taken for removing the remaining contaminants by oscillating shears. D_{total} has a similar increasing trend with increasing weld time as E_{total}, as shown in Fig. 8.11(b), but the increasing rate depends on the level of contamination. For example, the difference in post material compaction from 0.1 to 0.4 second for level 0 is 0.19 mm, whereas that for level 1 and level 2 is only 30% and 50% of level 0, respectively. In a similar manner to that for weld energy, material compaction for contaminated surface cases is slower than that for clean surface.

8.4.3 Relationship between Weld Attributes and Signal Features

Weld attributes such as bond density and post-weld thickness were defined as the physical criteria for weld quality in the previous study [3]. Correlating these attributes with signal features ensures good understanding of the weld formation during the welding process so that the weld quality can be predicted by sensor signals.

Figure 8.12 illustrates the relationship between weld attributes and the signal feature extracted from the power signal. As seen in Fig. 8.12(a), bond density and E_{total} are in a positive linear relation for both clean and surface contaminated case while a negative linear relation exists between post-weld thickness and E_{total} as described in Fig. 8.12(b). Given the fact that normal quality welds that provide the highest joint performance in the preliminary U-tensile test (Fig. 8.3) have bond density around 40% and post-weld thickness around 28%, the minimum required value for E_{total} can be set to around 800 J. Figures 8.12(c) and 8.12(d) describe the scatter plots of bond density and post-weld thickness against another signal feature extracted from the power signal, E_{mid}. As seen in the figure, E_{mid} of clean surface case is clearly distinguished from that of contaminated surface case. This ability of separating normal and problematic weld quality makes E_{mid} a valuable feature for contamination detection. The required energy level at the mid-point of welding process can be set to around 400 J in order to achieve 40% bond density and 28% post-weld thickness.

In addition to E_{total} and E_{mid}, D_{total} and D_{mid} also show strong relationships to bond density or post-weld thickness as illustrated in Fig. 8.13. Of those two features, D_{mid}, as shown in Figs. 8.13(c) and 8.13(d) has ability in discriminating between normal and defective weld groups that result from surface contamination. Process variation due to such abnormal condition mostly occurs during the early welding stages. It should be noted that both E_{mid} and D_{mid} are the extracted features from the first half of the process. D_{total} of 0.3 mm or D_{mid} of 0.2 mm can be set as desired values for required post-weld thickness of normal quality welds, as indicated in Figs. 8.13(a) and 8.13(b).

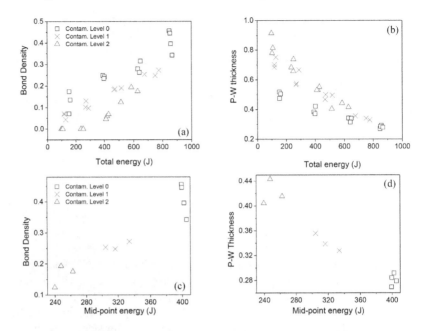

Figure 8.12. Relationship between weld attributes and power signal features: (a) bond density versus total energy (E_{total}); (b) post-weld thickness versus total energy (E_{total}); (c) bond density versus mid-point energy (E_{mid}); and (c) post-weld thickness versus mid-point energy (E_{mid}).

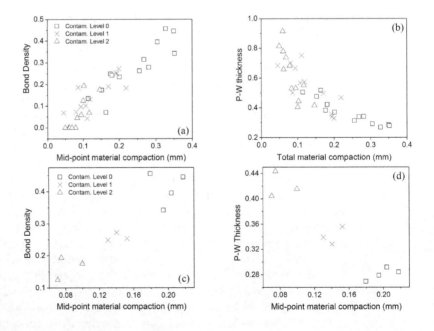

Figure 8.13. Relationship between weld attributes and displacement signal features: (a) bond density versus total material compaction (D_{total}); (b) post-weld thickness versus total material compaction (D_{total}); (c) bond density versus mid-point material compaction (D_{mid}); and (c) post-weld thickness versus mid-point material compaction (D_{mid}).

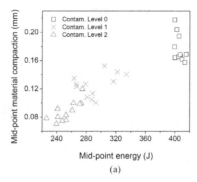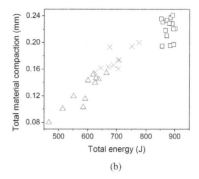

Figure 8.14. Relationship between signal features: (a) mid-point material compaction (D_{mid}) versus mid-point energy (E_{mid}); (b) total material compaction (D_{total}) versus Total energy (E_{total}).

By correlating online features to weld attributes, the physics behind the signal feature's change under process variation are understood: for example, one can learn how the feature variations are related to the change in geometric and mechanical attributes of an ultrasonic weld. Figure 8.13 shows the scatter plots of four online features, which enable the feasibility for online process monitoring to be ascertained.

Figure 8.14(a) shows the direct relationship between two signal features, E_{mid} and D_{mid}, halfway through the welding process, while Fig. 8.14(b) shows the relationship between two features, E_{total} and D_{total}, collected after the process is over. Both E_{mid} and E_{total} clearly distinguish problematic weld group (contamination levels 1 and 2) from normal quality group (level 0). D_{mid} and D_{total} also show this discriminative capability, but not as clearly as E_{mid} and E_{total} in terms of the distance generated between two data groups (normal vs. defective). E_{mid} and D_{mid}, can be used as in-line monitoring signatures because they capture the process variations in the early welding stages. A proper control action can then be taken, based on the characteristics shown in those signatures. On the other hand, E_{total} and D_{total} can be used as post-weld monitoring signatures so that the product quality after welding can be determined.

8.5 CONCLUSIONS

In this study, two online signals, weld power and horn displacement, are thoroughly examined to understand the physics behind the ultrasonic welding process. Several signal features are identified, based on the physical understanding of signal variations under abnormal process conditions, such as surface contamination. These signal features are then correlated to weld attributes measured from micrographs of cross-sectioned weld samples. By determining the relationship between those signal features and weld attributes, the joint quality can be predicted. This study will also provide a guideline for feature extraction/ selection and setting criteria on selected features in process monitoring of ultrasonic metal welding. More specifically:

1. The power signal provides useful information on the change of mechanical resistance at the weld interface during the ultrasonic welding process whereas the displacement signal relates to the pattern of material deformation.
2. The power signal for the first half of the welding process provides critical information on the mechanical loading on the weld tool. A low level of weld power is experienced in the early welding stages under process disturbances such as low friction between

surfaces due to residual stamping oil. Similarly, the amount of material compaction at the mid-point of the process as measured by an LVDT also can be used to distinguish between normal and abnormal process conditions.

3. The energy used and the total amount of material compaction for the whole welding process indicate whether the weld formation at the interface is completed.

The relationships between weld attributes and several signal features such as total energy (E_{total}), mid-point energy (E_{mid}), total material compaction (D_{total}), and mid-point material compaction (D_{mid}) provide additional physical understanding of the impact of process conditions on the weld quality. They can be used to establish criteria for weld quality monitoring.

Acknowledgment

This study was partially sponsored by U.S. Government under an Agreement/Project DE-EE0002217, Department of Energy Recovery and Reinvestment Act of 2009, Battery Pack Manufacturing.

REFERENCES

[1]   Kim, T. H., Yum, J., Hu, S. J., Spicer, J. P., and Abell, J. A., 2011, "Process Robustness of Single Lap Ultrasonic Welding of Thin, Dissimilar Materials," *CIRP Annals—Manufacturing Technology*, **60**(1), pp. 17–20.

[2]   Lee, S. S., Kim, T. H., Hu, S. J., Cai, W., and Abell, J. A., 2010, "Joining Technologies for Automotive Lithium-Ion Battery Manufacturing: A Review," *ASME Conference Proceedings*, 2010(49460), pp. 541–549.

[3]   Lee, S. S., Kim, T. H., Hu, S. J., Cai, W., Abell, J. A., and Li, J., 2013, "Characterization of Joint Quality in Ultrasonic Welding of Battery Tabs," *ASME Journal of Manufacturing Science and Engineering*, **135**(2), pp. 021004.

[4]   Zhang, C., and Li, L., 2009, "A Coupled Thermal-Mechanical Analysis of Ultrasonic Bonding Mechanism," *Metallurgical and Materials Transactions B*, **40**(2), pp. 196–207.

[5]   Kang, B., Cai, W., and Tan, C. A., 2013, "Dynamic Response of Battery Tabs under Ultrasonic Welding," *ASME Journal of Manufacturing Science and Engineering*, **135**(5), pp. 051013–051013.

[6]   Lee, D., Kannatey-Asibu, E., and Cai, W., 2013, "Ultrasonic Welding Simulations for Multiple Layers of Lithium-Ion Battery Tabs," *ASME Journal of Manufacturing Science and Engineering*, **135**(6), p. 061011.

[7]   Kong, C., Soar, R., and Dickens, P., 2003, "Characterisation of Aluminium Alloy 6061 for the Ultrasonic Consolidation Process," *Materials Science and Engineering A*, **363**(1–2), pp. 99–106.

[8]   Kong, C., Soar, R., and Dickens, P. M., 2005, "A Model for Weld Strength in Ultrasonically Consolidated Components," *Proceedings of the Institution of Mechanical Engineers, Part C: Journal of Mechanical Engineering Science*, **219**(1), pp. 83–91.

[9]   Siddiq, A., and Ghassemieh, E., 2009, "Theoretical and Fe Analysis of Ultrasonic Welding of Aluminum Alloy 3003," *ASME Journal of Manufacturing Science and Engineering*, **131**(4), p. 041007.

[10] Gunduz, I. E., Ando, T., Shattuck, E., Wong, P. Y., and Doumanidis, C. C., 2005, "Enhanced Diffusion and Phase Transformations During Ultrasonic Welding of Zinc and Aluminum," *Scripta Materialia*, **52**(9), pp. 939–943.

[11] Li, J., Han, L., and Zhong, J., 2008, "Short Circuit Diffusion of Ultrasonic Bonding Interfaces in Microelectronic Packaging," *Surface and Interface Analysis*, **40**(5), pp. 953–957.

[12] Lee, S. S., Kim, T. H., Hu, S. J., Kannatey-Asibu Jr, E., Cai, W., Spicer, P., and Abell, J. A., 2014, "Characterization of Ultrasonic Metal Welding by Correlating Online Sensor Signals with Weld Attributes," *ASME Journal of Manufacturing Science and Engineering*, **136**(5), p. 051019.

[13] Annoni, M., and Carboni, M., 2011, "Ultrasonic Metal Welding of Aa 6022-T4 Lap Joints: Part I-Technological Characterisation and Static Mechanical Behaviour," *Science and Technology of Welding & Joining*, **16**(2), pp. 107–115.

[14] Chu, Y., Hu, S., Hou, W., Wang, P., and Marin, S., 2004, "Signature Analysis for Quality Monitoring in Short-Circuit Gmaw," *Welding Journal*, **83**(12), pp. 336S–343S.

[15] Hu, S., Hou, W., Du, H., Wang, P.-C., and Menassa, R. J., 2011, "Method for Controlling the Consistency of an Arc Welding Process by Monitoring Welding Voltage to Determine Weld Droplet Detachment," Google Patents, US20090188903 A1.

[16] Shao, C., Paynabar, K., Kim, T. H., Jin, J., Hu, S. J., Spicer, J. P., Wang, H., and Abell, J. A., 2013, "Feature Selection for Manufacturing Process Monitoring Using Cross-Validation," *Journal of Manufacturing Systems*, **32**(4), pp. 550–555.

[17] Ling, S.-F., Wan, L.-X., Wong, Y.-R., and Li, D.-N., 2010, "Input Electrical Impedance as Quality Monitoring Signature for Characterizing Resistance Spot Welding," *NDT & E International*, **43**(3), pp. 200–205.

[18] Li, W., Hu, S. J., and Ni, J., 2000, "On-Line Quality Estimation in Resistance Spot Welding," *ASME Journal of Manufacturing Science and Engineering*, **122**(3), pp. 511–512.

[19] Tseng, K. H., and Chuang, K. J., 2012, "Monitoring Nugget Size of Micro Resistance Spot Welding (Micro Rsw) Using Electrode Displacement-Time Curve," *Advanced Materials Research*, **463**, pp. 107–111.

[20] Park, Y. W., and Kim, D., 2012, "Optimization of Laser Welding Parameters in Aluminum Alloy Welding and Development of Quality Monitoring System for Light Weight Vehicle," *Materials Science Forum*, 706–709, pp. 2998–3003.

[21] Sun, A., Kannatey-Asibu, E., and Gartner, M., 1999, "Sensor Systems for Real-Time Monitoring of Laser Weld Quality," *Journal of Laser Applications*, **11**(4), pp. 153–168.

[22] Wu, C., Gao, J., and Hu, J., 2007, "Real-Time Sensing and Monitoring in Robotic Gas Metal Arc Welding," *Measurement Science and Technology*, **18**(1), p. 303.

[23] Or, S., Chan, H., Lo, V., and Yuen, C., 1998, "Ultrasonic Wire-Bond Quality Monitoring Using Piezoelectric Sensor," *Sensors and Actuators A: Physical*, **65**(1), pp. 69–75.

[24] Zhao, J., Li, H., Choi, H., Cai, W., Abell, J. A., and Li, X., 2013, "Insertable Thin Film Thermocouples for in Situ Transient Temperature Monitoring in Ultrasonic Metal Welding of Battery Tabs," *SME Journal of Manufacturing Processes*, **15**(1), pp. 136–140.

[25] Li, H., Choi, H., Ma, C., Zhao, J., Jiang, H., Cai, W., Abell, J. A., and Li, X., 2013, "Transient Temperature and Heat Flux Measurement in Ultrasonic Joining of Battery Tabs Using Thin-Film Microsensors," *ASME Journal of Manufacturing Science and Engineering*, **135**(5), p. 051015.

[26] Jia, S., Hong, E., Katz, R., Lev, L. C., Smyth, S., and Abell, J., 2012, "Nondestructive Testing of Ultrasonic Welding Joints Using Shearography Technique," *ASME Journal of Manufacturing Science and Engineering*, **134**(3), p. 034502.

[27] Gao, Y., and Doumanidis, C., 2002, "Mechanical Analysis of Ultrasonic Bonding for Rapid Prototyping," *ASME Journal of Manufacturing Science and Engineering*, **124**(2), pp. 426–434.

[28] Bakavos, D., and Prangnell, P. B., 2010, "Mechanisms of Joint and Microstructure Formation in High Power Ultrasonic Spot Welding 6111 Aluminium Automotive Sheet," *Materials Science and Engineering: A*, **527**(23), pp. 6320–6334.

[29] Patel, V. K., Bhole, S. D., and Chen, D. L., 2011, "Influence of Ultrasonic Spot Welding on Microstructure in a Magnesium Alloy," *Scripta Materialia*, **65**(10), pp. 911–914.

[30] Prangnell, P., Haddadi, F., and Chen, Y., 2011, "Ultrasonic Spot Welding of Aluminium to Steel for Automotive Applications: Microstructure and Optimisation," *Materials Science and Technology*, **27**(3), pp. 617–624.

[31] Lee, S. S., Kim, T. H., Cai, W. W., and Abell, J. A., 2014, "Parasitic Vibration Attenuation in Ultrasonic Welding of Battery Tabs," *The International Journal of Advanced Manufacturing Technology*, **71**(1–4), pp. 181–195.

Chapter 9

TOOL WEAR MONITORING FOR ULTRASONIC METAL WELDING OF LITHIUM-ION BATTERIES[1]

Chenhui Shao[1], Tae Hyung Kim[2], S. Jack Hu[2], Jionghua (Judy) Jin[3],
Jeffrey A. Abell[4], and J. Patrick Spicer[4]
[1]Department of Mechanical Science & Engineering, University of Illinois at Urbana-Champaign
[2]Department of Mechanical Engineering, University of Michigan
[3]Department of Industrial and Operations Engineering, University of Michigan
[4]Manufacturing Systems Research Lab, General Motors Global R&D Center

ABSTRACT

This chapter presents a tool wear monitoring framework for ultrasonic metal welding which has been used for lithium-ion battery manufacturing. Tool wear has a significant impact on joining quality. In addition, tool replacement, including horns and anvils, constitutes an important part of production costs. Therefore, a tool condition monitoring (TCM) system is highly desirable for ultrasonic metal welding. However, it is very challenging to develop a TCM system due to the complexity of tool surface geometry and a lack of thorough understanding on the wear mechanism. Here, we first characterize tool wear progression by comparing surface measurements obtained at different stages of tool wear, and then develop a monitoring algorithm using a quadratic classifier and features that are extracted from space and frequency domains of cross-sectional profiles on tool surfaces. The developed algorithm is validated using tool measurement data from a battery plant.

9.1 INTRODUCTION

In manufacturing lithium-ion batteries for electrical vehicles such as the Chevy Volt, it is critical to create reliable interconnections among battery cells, from module to module, and from module to control unit. Ultrasonic metal welding is advantageous in joining multi-layer dissimilar, thin and conductive materials [1, 2]. It is a solid-state joining process which uses ultrasonic vibration to generate oscillating shears between metal sheets clamped under pressure [3, 4]. A typical ultrasonic metal welding system is shown in Fig. 9.1. The surfaces of the weld tools, i.e., horn and anvil, consist of a large number of pyramid-shape knurls as displayed by Fig. 9.2. The horn and anvil wear out quickly in production and are expensive to replace. As a result, monitoring of the horn and anvil wear is critically needed to ensure battery joining quality and reduce production cost.

The ultrasonic metal welding process is illustrated by Fig. 9.3. Workpieces are placed between the horn and anvil, and a clamping force is applied to hold the workpieces tightly. During welding, the horn vibrates at a frequency of around 20 kHz, whereas the anvil is stationary. It is reported in Ref. [5] that relative movements exist between the top metal sheet and the horn, as well as between the bottom sheet and the anvil, and these relative movements are believed to be a major cause of tool wear.

---

[1] The content presented in this chapter has previously appeared in Ref. [6].

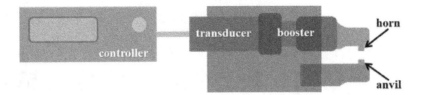

Figure 9.1. A typical ultrasonic metal welding system [2].

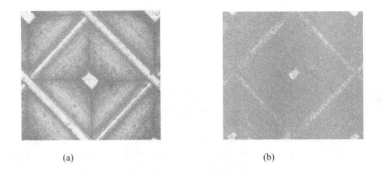

(a)   (b)

Figure 9.2. Pyramid-shape knurls on the (a) horn and (b) anvil.

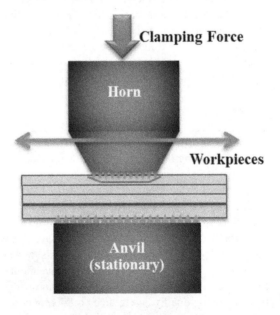

Figure 9.3. Ultrasonic welding mechanism.

In automotive lithium-ion battery manufacturing, horn and anvil are reported to be a major production cost. Specifically, production costs as a result of tool wear can be divided into two major categories [5]: (1) costs due to machine down-time as caused by tool wear induced quality problems or time needed for tool replacement; and (2) costs for fabricating, reworking, or refurbishing the replaced tools. Vehicle battery manufacturing has a strict quality requirement for battery tab joining because any low-quality joints may result in the failure of an entire battery pack, causing high production loss [2]. Consequently, when a TCM system is not available, a conservative tool replacement strategy is generally utilized to ensure satisfactory quality. For example, some battery plant uses the number of welds as a measure of tool wear, and replaces tools once the number of welds reaches a certain limit. Although this empirical strategy is straightforward to implement, it may sacrifice some useful tool lives and increases production costs.

TCM has been a popular and important research topic in manufacturing and has received tremendous attention over the past several decades. The majority of the TCM literature has been focused on machining processes [7–18] and forming processes [19–22]. Tool wear mechanism in cutting processes has been investigated in Refs. [8, 9] using physical or empirical models. Tool wear monitoring techniques have been developed in Refs. [10–17]. In general, tool wear monitoring techniques can be categorized into direct and indirect methods [18]. Direct methods determine tool conditions by measuring tool wear using visual inspection or computer vision. However, direct methods are not attractive economically or technically mainly due to the environmental restrictions on the plant floor [7]. Hence, indirect methods using on-line signals are often more desirable, and some exemplary scenarios can be found in Refs. [7, 9–14]. A typical method for developing an indirect monitoring system includes the following key steps [10]: (i) sensor selection, (ii) signal pre-processing, (iii) feature generation; (iv) feature selection/ extraction; (v) monitoring decision and faulty classification using artificial intelligence technique. A comprehensive review on indirect monitoring methods is presented in Ref. [10].

Tool wear in forming processes has also been investigated, especially in extrusion and forging processes [19–22]. Archard's wear model is widely applied in studies on extrusion processes [19, 20]. Statistical process control analysis of the tool wear progression in a metal extrusion process was conducted in Ref. [21]. On the TCM of forging processes, an on-line TCM system using artificial neural network was developed to integrate information from multiple sensors [22].

Despite extensive literature focusing on TCM development for machining and forming processes, limited studies have been conducted on TCM for ultrasonic metal welding. Developing a TCM system for ultrasonic welding is more challenging than machining or forming processes, mainly because: (1) the ultrasonic welding mechanism has not been thoroughly understood, and ultrasonic welding possesses the characteristics of high frequency (around 20 kHz) and short duration (each cycle lasts approximately 0.6 s), and (2) the geometry of welding tools is much more complicated [5].

To address the above challenges and develop an effective TCM system for ultrasonic welding, this chapter (1) characterizes tool wear progression by comparing tool surface measurements in different wear stages; (2) designs an efficient indirect method to efficiently obtain tool surface measurements in plant environment without taking the tools offline; and (3) develops a tool condition classification algorithm with application-dependent features which are generated from both space and frequency domains.

The remainder of this chapter is organized as follows. Section 9.2 characterizes tool wear progression using changes in the knurl geometry based on high-resolution 3-D measurements. An impression method is presented in Section 9.3 as an indirect tool geometry measurement strategy. Section 9.4 develops a tool condition classification algorithm. Section 9.5 concludes the chapter.

9.2 TOOL WEAR CHARACTERIZATION

This section characterizes the tool wear progression in ultrasonic metal welding based on the comparison of the optical images and height profiles at different wear stages. Representative samples of four different stages were collected from a battery plant and then measured using a 3D microscope. Specifically, Section 9.2.1 compares the optical images; Sections 9.2.2

and 9.2.3 depict the wear progression in the direction perpendicular to vibration and in the vibration direction, respectively. For brevity, we define the direction perpendicular to vibration as "horizontal direction" and the vibration direction as "vertical direction."

9.2.1 Monitoring Feature Generation

The optical images of the four stages are shown by Fig. 9.4, and the characteristics of each stage are summarized as follows [5].

Stage 1: Each knurl possesses regular a pyramid shape.
Stage 2: The peak remains at each knurl, but a small flat top forms, and the knurl shape becomes more complex geometrically than stage 1: more materials have been removed at the left and right sides than the upper and lower sides. In addition, the colors of peaks become shining.
Stage 3: The left and right sides of each knurl are almost flat, and only a small amount of materials remain in the upper side.
Stage 4: All peaks have been removed and the knurls take a frustum shape.

9.2.2 Tool Wear Progression in the Horizontal Direction

In each anvil, typical cross-sectional profiles are extracted in the horizontal direction, and the profiles are shown in Fig. 9.5. In Fig. 9.5(a), one can see that the cross sections of all knurls of a new tool have triangle shapes and similar peak height. In Fig. 9.5(b), three types of tool wear patterns can be observed: (1) flank wear, (2) side wear, and (3) breakage. The flank wear is at the upright direction, which occurs with the removal of peaks (height decreases); the side wear represents the wear around the peaks, where two shoulders form at the left and right sides; the breakage happens with a removal of the whole knurl peak and is indicated by a depressed shape. In Fig. 9.5(c), the height reduces significantly compared with Fig. 9.5(b), and some of the peaks are almost removed. Additionally, the width of shoulders increases. In Fig. 9.5(d), all peaks have disappeared, and the surface becomes completely flat.

Based on the findings revealed by Fig. 9.5, the characterization of each stage in the horizontal direction is summarized by Fig. 9.6 and described as follows [5]:

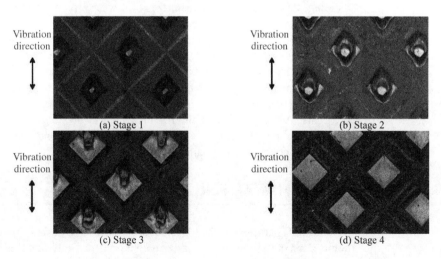

(a) Stage 1

(b) Stage 2

(c) Stage 3

(d) Stage 4

Figure 9.4. Optical images of different wear stages [5].

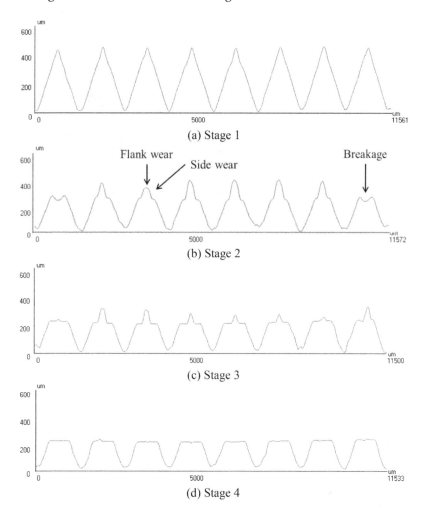

Figure 9.5. Cross-sectional profiles in the horizontal direction.

Stage 1: The knurl is new, and it possesses a triangle shape.
Stage 2: Material is removed in both downward and lateral directions, and shoulders appear on the left and right sides.
Stage 3: Height decreases significantly, and the width of shoulders increases.
Stage 4: Material is removed until the peak disappears, and a trapezoid shape forms.

9.2.3 Tool Wear Progression in the Vertical Direction

Similar to Section 9.2.2, the cross-sectional profiles in the vertical direction are also extracted and compared, and the results are shown in Fig. 9.7. As shown in Fig. 9.7(a), a new anvil has triangle shapes. In Fig. 9.7(b), an asymmetric pattern can be seen in two sides of the knurl in the vertical direction: more materials have been removed in the knurl's lower side, and a groove forms. A knurl in this stage has two peaks, i.e., a main peak and a side peak. In Fig. 9.7(c), one can see that after more material removal, the side peak in Fig. 9.7(b) disappears and only a main peak remains. Figure 9.7(d) shows the final wear stage in the vertical direction. The main peak in Fig. 9.7(c) has been completely removed, and a flat surface forms in the end.

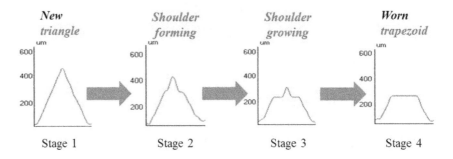

Figure 9.6. Anvil knurl wear progression in the horizontal direction [5].

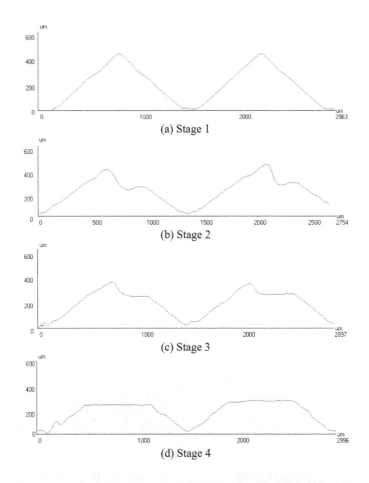

Figure 9.7. Cross-sectional profiles in the vertical direction [5].

According to the results shown in Fig. 9.7, the knurl-level wear progression in the vertical direction is illustrated in Fig. 9.8. The characteristics of the knurls in each stage are summarized as follows [5]:

Stage 1: The knurl is new, and it possesses a triangle shape.
Stage 2: Materials are mainly removed in the lower side, where a groove and a side peak form. The height of the main peak decreases compared with stage 1.

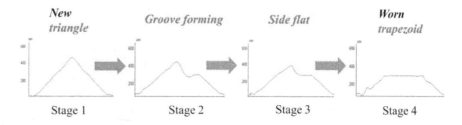

| *New triangle* | *Groove forming* | *Side flat* | *Worn trapezoid* |
| Stage 1 | Stage 2 | Stage 3 | Stage 4 |

Figure 9.8. Anvil knurl wear progression in the vertical direction [5].

Stage 3: More materials are removed until the side peak disappears. The height of the main peak continually decreases.

Stage 4: The main peak is completely removed, and a trapezoid forms.

9.3 IMPRESSION METHOD

In ultrasonic welding, tool surface geometry patterns provide essential tool condition information; hence, an efficient tool surface measurement method is necessary. Most 3D measurement systems require the tools to be removed from the welding machine and then placed on a flat and stable fixture. As a result, tool disassembly is necessary in order to directly measure the tool surfaces. However, tool disassembly and assembly for an ultrasonic welding machine are complicated and time-consuming, leading to a significant amount of machine down time, which is not desirable in production. As a result, an innovative measurement scheme is crucial in real productions.

To effectively obtain tool surface measurements without introducing significant interruption to production, an "impression method" is developed. Rather than measuring the tool, an "impression" is made on a weld coupon. The depth of deformation is measured under a microscope and then the inverse of the coupon image is created as a surrogate of the tool image. The process of obtaining the tool image from an "impression" is illustrated in Fig. 9.9. When a measurement is needed, one coupon will be generated using pre-determined weld parameters and materials, and then it will be measured using a 3D metrology system. Finally, data processing, i.e., horizontal flip and height inversion, will be applied, and the original tool surface profiles are finally reconstructed.

The weld parameters and the coupon materials need to be carefully selected in order to optimize the quality of the reconstructed tool surfaces. In practice, design of experiment [23] can be used to identify the optimal combination of the weld parameters and the coupon materials. In general, soft metals are recommended as they are more efficient in capturing tool surface profiles. In this study, four layers of pure aluminum are adopted, and the thickness of each layer is 0.2 mm.

To validate this method, several anvils and corresponding coupons are measured for comparison, and good agreement is achieved between the original tool surfaces and reconstructed ones. For illustrative purposes, only the results from one pair of anvil and coupon are presented as shown by Fig. 9.10.

Figures 9.10(a) and (b) display the images of anvil and coupon, respectively; (c) and (d) compare the cross-sectional profiles from the anvil and the coupon in the horizontal and vertical directions. The solid and dashed lines in (a) and (b) indicate the measurement paths for the cross-sectional profiles. In (c) and (d), the solid lines represent the measurement of the anvil, and the dashed lines correspond to the coupon measurement. It is indicated in Fig. 9.10 that the coupon impression is able to capture the knurl height profiles effectively. Additionally, the knurl shapes from the impression methods are also very similar to these

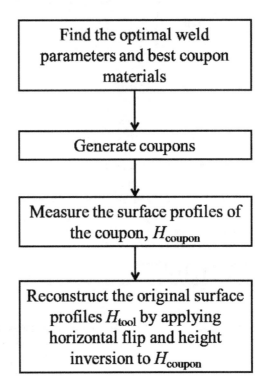

Figure 9.9. Flowchart for impression method.

from the direct measurement. Thus, the designed impression method is effective in constructing the tool surface geometry.

The correlation between the directly measured profiles and coupon profiles is shown by Table 9.1. The high correlation and low root mean squared error indicate that the coupon profiles are able to well capture the tool profiles.

9.4 TOOL CONDITION CLASSIFICATION

This section presents a tool condition classification algorithm to identify the state of wear. First, monitoring features are extracted from surface data to characterize tool conditions. Then Fisher's discriminant ratio is used to select features which are closely relevant to tool conditions. Finally, a linear classifier is developed to classify tool conditions.

9.4.1 Monitoring Feature Generation

In this section, several monitoring features are generated from surface data in both the space and frequency domains for tool condition classification.

As indicated by Figs. 9.6 and 9.8, cross-sectional profiles in the direction perpendicular to vibrations which cut cross through knurl centers can well capture the characteristics of different tool life stages. Accordingly, features are extracted from the cross-sectional profiles to quantify tool wear. The procedure of extracting features is illustrated by Fig. 9.11. First, tool surface is reconstructed by applying image processing algorithms, including noise elimination, image rotation, baseline adjustment, horizontal flip, and height inversion. Then representative cross-sectional profiles are obtained from tool surfaces.

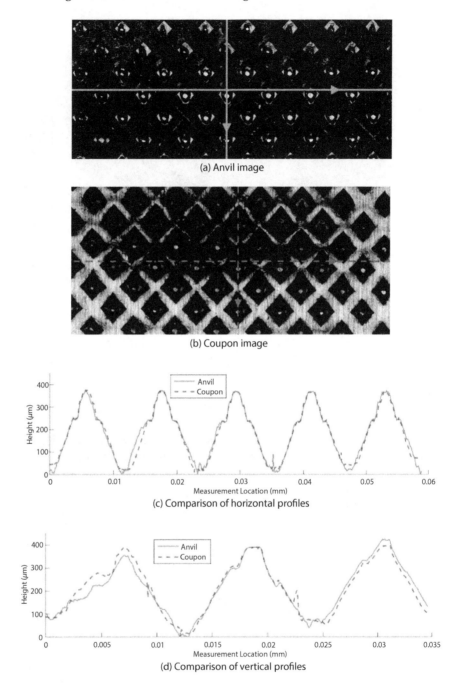

(a) Anvil image

(b) Coupon image

(c) Comparison of horizontal profiles

(d) Comparison of vertical profiles

Figure 9.10. Comparison between measurements of a tool and a coupon.

TABLE 9.1. Comparison results for impression method.

	Correlation coefficient	Root mean squared error
Horizontal	0.9864	18.7 μm
Vertical	0.9731	25.9 μm

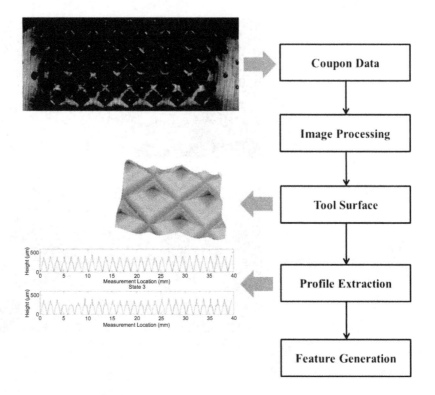

Figure 9.11. Process flowchart for feature extraction.

Assume the tool surface height is represented by a matrix **H**, the size of which is $n_r \times n_c$, where n_r and n_c are the numbers of rows and columns, respectively. The extraction of the horizontal profiles can be conducted based on the following algorithm.

Profile Extraction Algorithm

Step 1: Calculate the sum of each row for **H**. For the ith row, the sum is calculated using Eq. (9.1).

$$S_i = \sum_{j=1}^{n_c} \mathbf{H}_{ij} \tag{9.1}$$

where i is the row index, $i = 1, \ldots, n_r$, and j is the column index.

Step 2: Treat S_i as a profile, and identify the local maxima. We denote the indices of the local maxima as $m_1, \ldots, m_{n_p}$, where n_p is the number of knurls along the vertical direction.

Step 3: Obtain the horizontal profiles by extracting the row vectors with the indices from step 2. For the kth index, the corresponding profile is extracted using Eq. (9.2).

$$l_k = \mathbf{H}_{m_k} \tag{9.2}$$

where l_k is the kth profile, $k = 1, \ldots, n_p$.

Features are extracted from the obtained horizontal profiles in both space and frequency domains. In the space domain, two features are used to describe knurl geometry, i.e., average knurl height variance and average shoulder width. Knurl height variance is defined as the variance around knurl peaks. As tool wears out, materials are removed from knurl top, and a smaller height variance will present. Shoulder width is defined as the sum of the left and

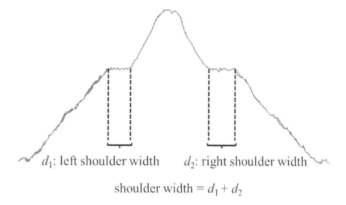

d_1: left shoulder width d_2: right shoulder width

shoulder width $= d_1 + d_2$

Figure 9.12. Shoulder width calculation.

right shoulders besides knurl peaks, as illustrated by Fig. 9.12. As the tool wear becomes more severe, the shoulder width will increase. After calculating knurl-level variance and shoulder width, tool level features are obtained by averaging them over all knurls.

Frequency-domain features are the amplitudes corresponding to the dominant frequencies after applying fast Fourier transform (FFT) to the cross-sectional profiles. These features are able to capture the overall periodic pattern which is closely related to the tool wear level. Figure 9.13 shows (a) original profiles in four wear stages and (b) FFT profiles. From (b), it is shown that the amplitude of the first dominant frequency, 0.7040, which is corresponding to the diameter of a knurl, 1.4 mm, has a decreasing trend as tool wear gets more severe; however, the amplitude of the second dominant frequency, 1.43, corresponding to half period, 0.7 mm, has an increasing trend. Thus, the amplitudes of first to fifth dominant frequencies are considered as candidate features.

A summary of candidate features is given by Table 9.2. Two features are extracted from the space-domain to depict the average knurl geometry, and five features are generated from the frequency-domain to acquire periodic patterns of cross-sectional profiles.

Figure 9.14 depicts the trend of the extracted features over the number of welds. In each subplot, the horizontal axis is the number of welds, and the vertical axis is the feature value. It is seen that features 1, 3, and 4 have decreasing trends; features 2, 5, and 6 have increasing trends, whereas feature 7 first increases and then decreases as the number of welds increases.

9.4.2 Feature Selection

In the development of monitoring algorithms, feature selection is an essential step for achieving best monitoring performance, because not all features have good separability between different classes [2]. Fisher's discriminant ratio is applied to perform feature screening in a computationally simple and fast manner. Fisher's discriminant ratio was first presented in Ref. [24], and it is a separability measure for feature selection [27]. A larger Fisher's ratio indicates more significant difference between two classes. Fisher's ratio is defined as

$$J = \frac{|\mu_1 - \mu_2|^2}{s_1^2 + s_2^2} \tag{9.3}$$

where μ_1 and μ_2 are the means of new and worn classes, s_1^2 and s_2^2 are respective variances.

56 coupons have been collected from a battery manufacturing plant, and expert knowledge is used to classify them as new (Class 1) and slightly worn (Class 2). Fisher's

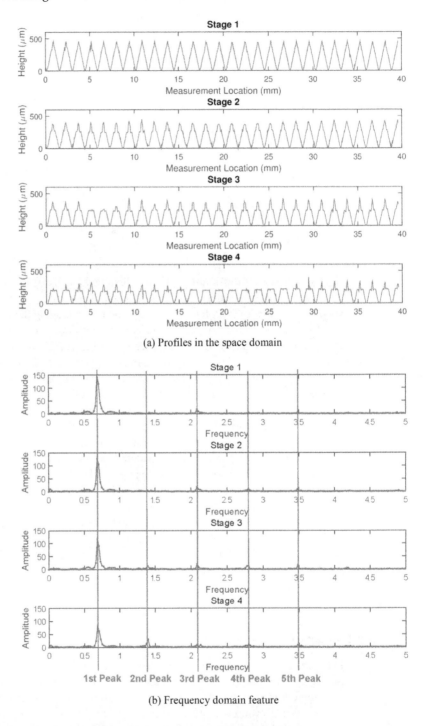

Figure 9.13. Frequency-domain features for different stages of wear.

ratio is calculated, and the result is given by Fig. 9.15. Features 2, 5, and 6 have higher ratios, indicating that they can provide better separability between new and slightly worn coupons. As a result, features 2, 5, and 6 (average shoulder width, third and fourth peak amplitudes in the frequency domain) are chosen for monitoring tool conditions. Scatter plots of these features are shown by Fig. 9.16, which indicates good class separability.

TABLE 9.2. Candidate feature list.

Feature no.	Feature name	Category
Feature 1	Average knurl-level variance	Space-domain
Feature 2	Average shoulder width	
Feature 3	First peak amplitude	
Feature 4	Second peak amplitude	
Feature 5	Third peak amplitude	Frequency-domain
Feature 6	Fourth peak amplitude	
Feature 7	Fifth peak amplitude	

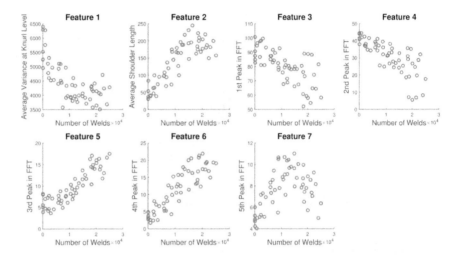

Figure 9.14. Feature trend versus the number of welds.

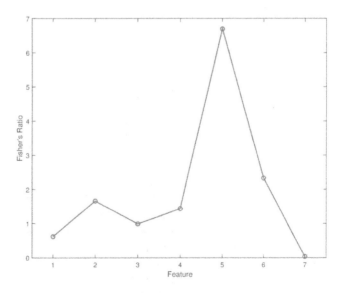

Figure 9.15. Fisher's ratio for all features.

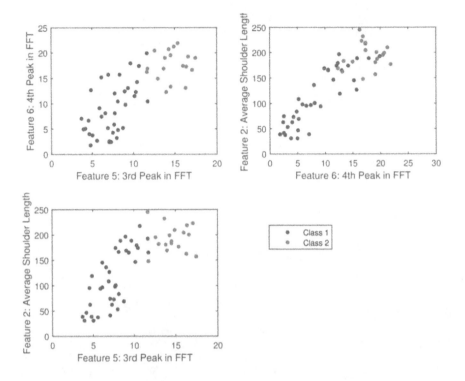

Figure 9.16. Scatter plots of selected features.

9.4.3 Classification

In this section, classifiers are designed for tool condition classification, and leave-one-out cross-validation (LOOCV) is applied to evaluate the performance. Candidate classifiers include linear classifier [24], quadratic classifier [25], and support vector machine (SVM) [26]. When the data sample size is limited, cross-validation is commonly used for evaluating and comparing learning algorithms [2]. LOOCV proposes to partition the data into two sets: one set only includes one observation and is used for model validation, and the remaining observations are used for model training. By repeating this partition for all observations, LOOCV is able to predict and compare the performance of different learning algorithms.

In order to ensure satisfactory welding quality, the battery plant applies a conservative tool replacement strategy and always replaces tools before they really get degraded. Therefore, it is very difficult to collect coupons that reflect truly worn tools' surface profiles from production. To obstacle this issue, eight coupon surfaces are simulated by truncating the knurl peaks from new or slightly worn surfaces, and examples of simulated profiles are shown by Fig. 9.17.

In this research, 64 coupons, including 38 new coupons (denoted as Class 1), 18 slightly worn coupons (denoted as Class 2), and eight simulated completely worn coupons (Class 3) are used for classifier training and LOOCV. The comparison of linear classifier, quadratic classifier, and SVM is shown by Tables 9.3 and 9.4.

From Tables 9.3 and 9.4, it is noticed that the quadratic classifier achieves the best performance, and the corresponding cross-validation misclassification rate is 3.13%. Additionally, all coupons in Class 3 are classified correctly, and no Class 1 or Class 2 coupons are misclassified as Class 3, indicating that the quadratic classifier is able to accurately distinguish Class 3 from the other two classes. On the other hand, the linear

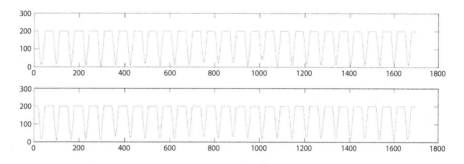

Figure 9.17. Simulated profiles for worn tools.

TABLE 9.3. Misclassification rates of different classifiers.

	Linear	Quadratic	SVM
Training error rate	7.81% (5/64)	1.56% (1/64)	7.81% (5/64)
Cross-validation error rate	10.94% (6/64)	3.13% (2/64)	15.63%(10/64)

TABLE 9.4. Confusion matrices for cross-validation.

(a) Linear classifier

Predicted Class

		Class 1	Class 2	Class 3
True class	Class 1	84.31% (34/38)	2.63% (1/38)	13.16% (5/38)
	Class 2	5.56% (1/18)	94.44% (17/18)	0
	Class 3	0	0	100% (8/8)

(b) Quadratic classifier

Predicted Class

		Class 1	Class 2	Class 3
True class	Class 1	97.37% (37/38)	2.63% (1/38)	0
	Class 2	5.56% (1/18)	94.44% (17/18)	0
	Class 3	0	0	100% (8/8)

(c) SVM

Predicted Class

		Class 1	Class 2	Class 3
True class	Class 1	86.84% (33/38)	7.89% (3/38)	13.16% (5/38)
	Class 2	0	100% (18/18)	0
	Class 3	25.00% (2/8)	0	75.00% (6/8)

classifier and the SVM have significantly larger misclassification rates, and neither of them is able to completely distinguish class 3 from the other two classes.

Note to Practitioners: When applying this tool wear monitoring framework on the plant floor, it is recommended to adopt a more efficient and cost-effective measurement system to measure the coupons. As shown by the previous results in this section, cross-sectional profiles along the horizontal direction contain rich information on the tool degradation level. Therefore, one potential measurement system may be a line scanner with sufficient resolutions, the measurement of which is generally completed within minutes. In this way, the tool condition monitoring can be conducted in a more timely manner.

9.5 CONCLUSIONS

Tool wear characterization and monitoring for ultrasonic welding of lithium-ion batteries have been investigated in this chapter. By comparing tool surface measurements at different tool life stages, tool wear is characterized by four stages using changes in the knurl geometry. A novel impression method is then developed to efficiently and accurately obtain tool surface profiles without introducing significant interruption to plant production. Finally, an effective monitoring algorithm is developed using a quadratic classifier and features that are extracted from space and frequency domains of cross-sectional profiles on tool surfaces. This study enhances our understanding of the tool wear mechanism in ultrasonic metal welding, and the algorithm can be utilized to accurately identify tool conditions, leading to decreased production costs while ensuring good joining quality in battery manufacturing.

Acknowledgment

This material is based on work supported by the Department of Energy under Award Number DE-EE0002217.

Disclaimer

This study was prepared as an account of work sponsored by an agency of the United States Government. Neither the United States Government nor any agency thereof, nor any of their employees, makes any warranty, express or implied, or assumes any legal liability or responsibility for the accuracy, completeness, or usefulness of any information, apparatus, product, or process disclosed, or represents that its use would not infringe privately owned rights. Reference herein to any specific commercial product, process, or service by trade name, trademark, manufacturer, or otherwise does not necessarily constitute or imply its endorsement, recommendation, or favoring by the United States Government or any agency thereof. The views and opinions of authors expressed herein do not necessarily state or reflect those of the United States Government or any agency thereof.

REFERENCES

[1] Kim, T. H., Yum, J., Hu, S. J., Spicer, J. P., and Abell, J. A., 2011, "Process Robustness of Single Lap Ultrasonic Welding of Thin, Dissimilar Materials," *CIRP Annals-Manufacturing Technology*, **60**(1), pp. 17–20.

[2] Shao, C., Paynabar, K., Kim, T. H., Jin, J. J., Hu, S. J., Spicer, J. P., and Abell, J. A., 2013, "Feature Selection for Manufacturing Process Monitoring Using Cross-Validation," *Journal of Manufacturing Systems*, **32**(4), pp. 550–555.

[3] Lee, S. S., Shao, C., Kim, T. H., Hu, S. J., Kannatey-Asibu, E., Cai, W. W., and Abell, J. A., 2014, "Characterization of Ultrasonic Metal Welding by Correlating Online Sensor Signals With Weld Attributes," *Journal of Manufacturing Science and Engineering*, **136**(5), p. 051019.

[4] Lee, S. S., Kim, T. H., Hu, S. J., Cai, W. W., Abell, J. A., and Li, J., 2013, "Characterization of Joint Quality in Ultrasonic Welding of Battery Tabs," *Journal of Manufacturing Science and Engineering*, **135**(2), p. 021004.

[5] Shao, C., Guo, W., Kim, T. H., Jin, J. J., Hu, S. J., Spicer, J. P., and Abell, J. A., 2014, "Characterization and Monitoring of Tool Wear in Ultrasonic Metal Welding," *Proceedings of the 9th International Workshop on Microfactories*, Honolulu, Hawai'i, October 5–8, 2014, pp. 161–169.

[6] Shao, C., Kim, T. H., Hu, S. J., Jin, J. J., Abell, J. A., and Spicer, J. P., 2016, "Tool Wear Monitoring for Ultrasonic Metal Welding of Lithium-Ion Batteries," *Journal of Manufacturing Science and Engineering*, **138**(5), p. 051005.

[7] Jantunen, E., 2002, "A Summary of Methods Applied to Tool Condition Monitoring in Drilling," *International Journal of Machine Tools and Manufacture*, **42**(9), pp. 997–1010.

[8] Cook, N. H., 1973, "Tool Wear and Tool Life," *Journal of Engineering for Industry*, **95**(4), pp. 931–938.

[9] Koren, Y., Ko, T.-R., Ulsoy, A. G., and Danai, K., 1991, "Flank Wear Estimation Under Varying Cutting Conditions," *Journal of Dynamic Systems, Measurement, and Control*, **113**(2), pp. 300–307.

[10] Abellan-Nebot, J. V., and Subirón, F. R., 2010, "A Review of Machining Monitoring Systems Based on Artificial Intelligence Process Models," *The International Journal of Advanced Manufacturing Technology*, **47**(1–4), pp. 237–257.

[11] Rehorn, A. G., Jiang, J., and Orban, P. E., 2005, "State-of-the-Art Methods and Results in Tool Condition Monitoring: A Review," *The International Journal of Advanced Manufacturing Technology*, **26**(7–8), pp. 693–710.

[12] Zhou, J. H., Pang, C. K., Zhong, Z. W., and Lewis, F. L., 2011, "Tool Wear Monitoring Using Acoustic Emissions by Dominant-Feature Identification," *IEEE Transactions on Instrumentation and Measurement*, **60**(2), pp. 547–559.

[13] Ertunc, H. M., Loparo, K. A., and Ocak, H., 2001, "Tool Wear Condition Monitoring in Drilling Operations Using Hidden Markov Models (HMMs)," *International Journal of Machine Tools and Manufacture*, **41**(9), pp. 1363–1384.

[14] Snr, D., and Dimla, E., 2000, "Sensor Signals for Tool-Wear Monitoring in Metal Cutting Operations— A Review of Methods," *International Journal of Machine Tools and Manufacture*, **40**(8), pp. 1073–1098.

[15] Kurada, S., and Bradley, C., 1997, "A Review of Machine Vision Sensors for Tool Condition Monitoring," *Computers in Industry*, **34**(1), pp. 55–72.

[16] Kurada, S., and Bradley, C., 1997, "A Machine Vision System for Tool Wear Assessment," *Tribology International*, **30**(4), pp. 295–304.

[17] Lanzetta, M., 2001, "A New Flexible High-Resolution Vision Sensor for Tool Condition Monitoring," *Journal of Materials Processing Technology*, **119**(1), pp. 73–82.

[18] Byrne, G., Dornfeld, D., Inasaki, I., Ketteler, G., König, W., and Teti, R., 1995, "Tool Condition Monitoring (TCM)—The Status of Research and Industrial Application," *CIRP Annals-Manufacturing Technology*, **44**(2), pp. 541–567.

[19] Kang, J. H., Park, I. W., Jae, J. S., and Kang, S. S., 1999, "A Study on a Die Wear Model Considering Thermal Softening: (I) Construction of the Wear Model," *Journal of Materials Processing Technology*, **96**(1), pp. 53–58.

[20] Kang, J. H., Park, I. W., Jae, J. S., and Kang, S. S., 1999, "A Study on Die Wear Model Considering Thermal Softening (II): Application of the Suggested Wear Model," *Journal of Materials Processing Technology*, **94**(2), pp. 183–188.

[21] Lepadatu, D., Hambli, R., Kobi, A., and Barreau, A., 2006, "Statistical Investigation of Die Wear in Metal Extrusion Processes," *The International Journal of Advanced Manufacturing Technology*, **28**(3–4), pp. 272–278.

[22] Kong, L. X., and Nahavandi, S., 2002, "On-Line Tool Condition Monitoring and Control System in Forging Processes," *Journal of Materials Processing Technology*, **125**, pp. 464–470.

[23] Wu, C. J., and Hamada, M. S., 2011, *Experiments: planning, analysis, and optimization.* Wiley, New York.

[24] Fisher, R. A., 1936, "The Use of Multiple Measurements in Taxonomic Problems," *Annals of Human Genetics*, **7**(2), pp. 179–188.

[25]   Zhang, M. Q., 1997, "Identification of Protein Coding Regions in the Human Genome by Quadratic Discriminant Analysis," *Proceedings of the National Academy of Sciences*, **94**(2), pp. 565–568.

[26]   Suykens, J. AK, and Vandewalle, J., 1999, "Least Squares Support Vector Machine Classifiers," *Neural Processing Letters*, **9**(3), pp. 293–300.

[27]   Duda, R. O., Hart, P. E., and Stork, D. G., 2001, *Pattern Classification*, 2nd ed. Wiley, New York.

Chapter 10

<hr style="border-top: 4px solid #000;" />

FUNDAMENTAL DYNAMICS OF ULTRASONIC WELDING

Bongsu Kang[1], Wayne Cai[2], and Chin-An Tan[3]
[1]Civil & Mechanical Engineering Department, Purdue University Fort Wayne
[2]Manufacturing Systems Research Lab, General Motors Global R&D Center
[3]Mechanical Engineering Department, Wayne State University

ABSTRACT

In ultrasonic metal welding of battery tabs, high-frequency ultrasonic energy is used to generate an oscillating shear force at the interface between metal sheets to produce solid-state bonds between the sheets clamped under a normal force. Experimental results show that the weld quality of battery tabs strongly depends on the vibrational properties of the weld parts and fixtures in addition to welding parameters such as weld frequency, amplitude, and clamping normal force. This chapter discusses the fundamental aspects of dynamics and vibrations involved in ultrasonic welding.

Using discrete mass-spring-damper models for ultrasonic welding, the basic concepts of vibration and the principle of work and energy are discussed to enable the readers to understand subsequent materials presented in Chapter 11. The underlying characteristics of energy dissipation by friction at weld interface and material damping are described along with the mechanical work by the harmonic force at sonotrode weld tip. It is shown that, in addition to the friction force at weld interface, the ratio between the welding frequency and natural frequencies of the weld parts plays a critical role in determining the amount of work (which is the energy used for weld formation) performed by the friction force at weld interface.

The longitudinal vibration of a bar with variable cross section and its resonance behavior are the basis of sonotrode design in power ultrasonics. An introductory discussion on the frequency response analysis by finite element method of a half wavelength sonotrode is presented.

Keywords: frictional energy loss, sonotrode dynamics, ultrasonic welding

10.1 INTRODUCTION

Battery packs for electric vehicles consist of hundreds of battery cells in order to meet the power and capacity requirements. These battery cells are connected together through robust mechanical joints before being assembled into a battery pack. Joining of battery cells and battery tabs (electrodes of battery cells) presents challenges because it requires to weld multiple, highly conductive, and dissimilar materials, with varying thickness combinations, while maintaining 100% reliability. The failure of one joint essentially results in a battery pack that is inoperative or cannot deliver the required power due to an open circuit caused by the failed joint. Moreover, this stringent joint quality standard is significant for battery pack manufacturers because automotive batteries are exposed to harsh driving environment such as vibration, severe temperature changes, and possibly crash, all of which can affect battery performance as well as vehicle safety. Characteristics of various joining technologies used for manufacturing battery packs, such as resistance welding, laser welding, ultrasonic welding, and other mechanical joining are well summarized by Lee et al. [1]. Among the above joining technologies, ultrasonic metal welding (USMW) is currently one of the most widely used joining techniques due to its ability to join multiple, thin, dissimilar, coated, and highly conductive metals at relatively low cost [1, 2]. For example, due to the high conductivity of aluminum, copper, and nickel, resistance welding cannot be applied effectively to joining such materials [3]. Anodized aluminum battery tabs and nickel-coated copper battery tabs are not laser weldable due to anodizing and coating on the metal surfaces. Moreover, in contrast to traditional fusion welding processes, USMW is a solid-state joining process [4, 5], and therefore does not require any filler material, gas, heat, or current, eliminating consumable materials costs and wastes, and post-assembly cleaning, and is thus environmentally-friendly.

In USMW processes, high-frequency (≥ 20 kHz) ultrasonic vibration is used to generate oscillating shears at the interface between a sonotrode (horn) and metal sheets to produce solid-state bonds between the sheets clamped under pressure between the sonotrode and anvil in a short period of time (less than a second). The amplitude of oscillation is normally in the range of 5 to 30 μm. Fundamental principles of USMW are discussed by Rozenberg and Mitkevitch [6]. Experimental studies of the USMW mechanisms and the resulting material microstructures can be found in the works of Devine [7], Flood [8], and Hetrick et al. [9]. Efforts to understand the USMW process through numerical studies using finite element models are presented by, for example, Viswanath et al. [10], Siddiq and Ghassemieh [11], Lee et al. [12], Elangovan et al. [13], and Gao and Doumanidis [14]. Among these studies, Lee et al. [12] presented the detailed discussion on finite element analysis procedures and simulation results for ultrasonic welding of a stack of three battery tabs to a bus bar. They suggested that the weld quality can be improved through workpiece preheating, weld tool insulation, or reduction of the bus bar thickness, based on their numerical simulation results and experimental validations. Transient temperature and heat flux measurements during ultrasonic welding by using thin-film thermocouples and thermopiles were presented by Lee et al. [12], Li et al. [15], and Zhao et al. [16]. Lee et al. [12] reported that the highest transient temperature at the weld spot area is around 600 C for Cu tabs and 260 C for Al tabs. However, at locations other than the weld spot area, the temperature drops significantly to about 200 C for Cu tabs and 70 C for Al tabs. The effects of transient temperatures on the dynamic behavior of the tab and weld quality warrants further analysis.

Shown in Fig. 10.1 is the schematic of a typical weld unit of a battery pack used in an electric vehicle and a tooling setup for ultrasonic welding [17]. Hundreds of weld units are connected through an interconnect board (ICB) conducting electricity in the battery pack. The weld unit consists of multiple lithium-ion battery cell pouches, each has two electrode extensions (battery tabs) sealed in the upper part of the pouch, and a bus-bar pre-mounted on the ICB. Thin copper or aluminum sheets are used for those battery tabs. The bus-bar is made of a copper plate which is several times thicker than the battery tab. Notice that the battery tabs are bent as shown in the schematic in order to connect multiple battery cell pouches to the bus-bar. Once the battery tabs and bus-bar are aligned and sandwiched under a clamping force between the sonotrode and anvil, electrical currents passing through the piezo-stacks cause the stacks to expand and contract (oscillate) at ultrasonic frequency. This oscillation is amplified through a booster to excite the sonotrode at a desired frequency. The amplitude of the sonotrode oscillation is generally controlled such that it maintains a constant amplitude during welding. Basic principles of power ultrasonics can be found in reference [18].

Ultrasonic welding of battery tabs is a multi-physics problem in which friction between weld parts and thermo-mechanical properties of weld parts play critical roles in determining the weld quality. During ultrasonic welding of sheet metals, ultrasonic oscillations of the sonotrode weld tip pressed onto the weld parts generate friction-induced shear stresses

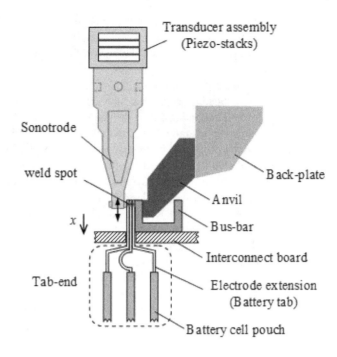

Figure 10.1. Schematic of the weld unit and ultrasonic welding setup.

at the interface of the weld parts. These stresses cause intense plastic deformation of the weld parts at the weld spot, forming a metal to metal bond. The quality of welds depends on a number of factors such as the metallurgical and mechanical properties of the weldment itself and welding parameters (i.e., welding conditions). In addition to these factors, the dynamics and vibration characteristics of weld parts, tools, and fixtures are also important factors in determining the weld quality. For example, a slight change in the weld spot location within the battery tab can cause a drastic change in the force required for the weld spot to oscillate or high stresses near the weld spot and this may result in a weld with unacceptable strength, perforation or cracks near weld spot, and sonotrode tip-sticking or extrusion. Another example of poor welding is due to the fluctuation of clamping pressure caused by subtle vibrations of weld tools and fixtures. Even few microns of anvil vibration in the direction normal to the weld surface could cause the battery tabs to buckle during welding. Figure 10.2 shows sketched sample data (the raw data information has been masked), drawn to the same scale, of the vibration of the anvil under normal operating condition and a fabricated condition in which the stiffness of the anvil was reduced. In Fig. 10.2,

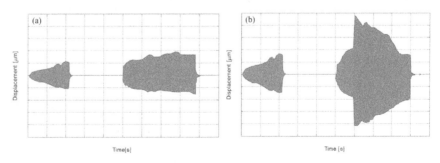

Figure 10.2. Comparison of anvil vibration displacement. (a) Baseline study and (b) system with softened anvil support.

the welding cycle was preceded by a short period when the tools and the product were engaged. Results show that the vibration amplitude of the anvil averaged few microns under the normal operating condition. However, the amplitude was amplified by 50% to 100% during welding in case (b). Moreover, tensile tests of the welds revealed that the strength of the welds in case (b) could be much lower than those of case (a). When the anvil stiffness was further reduced (meaning that its vibration amplitude could increase by few microns), the welds could debond and the tabs could also buckle. This demonstrates conclusively, at least for the cases examined, that increase in the vibration of the anvil due to changes in the subsystem stiffness or boundary conditions, even at *micron level*, can affect the weld quality significantly. Such intrinsic, fundamental relationships between micro-vibrations of structures and welding mechanics are not well understood, but can provide valuable insight and strategies to improve the USMW process stability and robustness, and weld quality. It should be noted that subsystem (fixture) stiffness may depend on the dynamics of robot assemblies in modern automated processes because welding systems are usually robotically-controlled for flexible manufacturing.

Understanding that vibration is the driving mechanism and also, at the same time, the cause of weld problems in USMW, the main objective of the present chapter is to introduce and discuss the fundamental aspects of dynamics and vibrations involved in ultrasonic welding of battery tabs. This presentation is motivated by numerous laboratory tests which shows a significant variation in weld quality of battery tabs caused by a slight change in geometry and structural properties of the weld part that alter the vibration characteristics of the system. Using a discrete mass-spring-damper model, the underlying principles of USMW, in particular the characteristics of energy dissipation due to friction, are discussed in Section 10.2. In Section 10.3, a brief discussion on the longitudinal vibration and frequency response analysis of a bar with variable cross section is presented as an introduction to sonotrode dynamics.

10.2 ENERGY DISSIPATION AT FRICTIONAL INTERFACE

10.2.1 Single Degree of Freedom System

Shown in Fig. 10.3 are the schematics of a typical single-layer (single weld) USMW setup and its single degree of freedom (1-DOF) mass-spring-damper model that represents the fundamental dynamics of USMW as follows:

1. m represents the mass of the weld spot element (weld part pressed by the sonotrode weld tip) which is excited by the sonotrode force f_s through the weld tip and subjected to the interface force over the weld zone from the other weld part. The weld spot element can be considered as a rigid body because no (or negligible) elastic wave motion within the

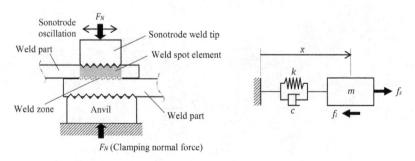

Figure 10.3. Schematics of a typical single-layer USMW setup and its single DOF discrete model.

element is likely to occur due to the clamping normal force F_N distributed over the weld spot element and constraint from the knurl-patterned sonotrode weld tip. Furthermore, note that the wavelength of the dominant elastic wave, which is longitudinal, in the weld part under ultrasonic excitation is mostly much larger than the longitudinal dimension of the weld part itself. For example, the wavelength of a 20 kHz longitudinal wave traveling along a thin copper bar is about 180 mm.

2. k represents the stiffness of the elastic constraint on the weld spot element, imposed by the weld part extended from the weld spot element. The shearing motion of the weld spot element during welding depends also on the kinetic interaction between the weld spot element and remaining weld part, in addition to the sonotrode force (f_s) and interface force (f_i) at the weld interface. For more accurate modeling of the weld spot element, note that it is necessary to include the dynamic coupling between the weld spot element and extended weld part by considering the elastic motion of the extended weld part itself during welding. By using a continuous vibration model for the weld part, a more detailed discussion on the effect of longitudinal vibration of the weld part is presented in Chapter 11.

3. c denotes the equivalent viscous damping coefficient of any energy dissipation mechanisms (such as material damping of the weld part, heat, or noise during welding) which inherently present during the weld process. Although well-designed USMW setups maximize the energy dissipation at the weld zone through friction and plastic deformation, unavoidable energy losses occur through unwanted vibrations of weld parts and tools, heat, and noise. The energy dissipation through friction and plastic deformation at the weld zone eventually results in weld formation. A more detailed treatment of the vibrational energy loss associated with unwanted vibration of weld parts is discussed in Chapter 11.

4. f_i represents the interface force between the weld parts at the weld zone. In the beginning of welding, f_i can be considered as a result of dry friction between the weld parts until the delamination of oxide films on the weld part surfaces and simultaneous plastic deformation occur. As the plastic deformation area increases at the weld zone, f_i is governed more by viscous friction associated with the plastic flow due to the continuous shearing action. Assuming that the entire weld zone is plastically yielded, which would render ideal welding in USMW (i.e., both weld parts are in metal-to-metal contact), the theoretical maximum value of f_i may be approximated as a force that shears the weld at an elevated temperature. More detailed discussion of the transient behavior of the interface force in USMW can be found in the studies by Gao and Doumanidis [14] and De Vries [19].

5. The sonotrode force, f_s, the driving force acting upon the weld part through the sonotrode weld tip, is sufficiently larger than the sum of the other forces acting on the weld spot element; otherwise extrusion or no welding may occur. It can be assumed that $f_s = F_s \sin \Omega t$ where F_s is the amplitude and Ω is the excitation frequency of the sonotrode.

Denoting x as the displacement of the weld spot element during welding, the governing equation of motion of the system in Fig. 10.3 is:

$$m\ddot{x} + c\dot{x} + kx + f_i = f_s \quad x(0) = \dot{x}(0) = 0 \tag{10.2.1}$$

From the definition of mechanical work $dW = f_s dx = f_s \dot{x} dt$, the work W performed by the sonotrode force on the weld spot element over the first n loading cycles can be found as

$$W = \int_0^{\frac{2n\pi}{\Omega}} f_s \dot{x}\, dt = \left(\frac{1}{2} m\dot{x}^2 + \frac{1}{2} kx^2 \right)_{t=\frac{2n\pi}{\Omega}} + c\int_0^{\frac{2n\pi}{\Omega}} \dot{x}^2\, dt + \int_0^{\frac{2n\pi}{\Omega}} f_i \dot{x}\, dt \tag{10.2.2}$$

Note that the first two terms in Eq. (10.2.2) are the kinetic energy (T) and elastic potential energy (V) at $t = 2n\pi/\Omega$, respectively, and the third term is the energy (W_d) dissipated by damping of the system. The last term is the work done by the interface force or the energy (W_w) used for weld formation. Therefore, it can be readily seen that $W_w = W - (T + V + W_d)$ and it is desirable in USMW to maximize W_w for efficient welding by minimizing the amount of energy directed to T, V, and W_d. In order to show that T and V can be neglected as they are small compared with W_d, let $f_i = 0$ and rewrite Eq. (10.2.1) as:

$$\ddot{x} + 2\zeta\omega_n\dot{x} + \omega_n^2 x = \delta\omega_n^2 \sin\Omega t \quad x(0) = \dot{x}(0) = 0 \tag{10.2.3}$$

where $\omega_n = \sqrt{k/m}$ denotes the natural frequency, $\zeta = c/2m\omega_n$ the damping ratio, and $\delta = F_s/k$ the static deformation of the system. Assuming that the system is underdamped (i.e., $\zeta < 1$), the response of the system to the given harmonic excitation is:

$$x(t) = X_h e^{-\zeta\omega_n t} \sin\left(\sqrt{1-\zeta^2}\,\omega_n t + \phi_h\right) + X \sin(\Omega t - \phi) \tag{10.2.4}$$

where X_h and ϕ_h are the coefficients of the transient response solution (first term) which are to be determined by applying the initial conditions and the amplitude X and phase angle ϕ of the steady state response solution (second term) are given by

$$X = \frac{\delta}{\sqrt{(1-r^2)^2 + (2\zeta r)^2}} \quad \phi = \tan^{-1}\left(\frac{2\zeta r}{1-r^2}\right) \quad r = \frac{\Omega}{\omega_n} \tag{10.2.5}$$

Note that the transient response vanishes after a sufficiently large number of loading cycle N, due to the presence of the exponential decay term $e^{-\zeta\omega_n t}$, and thus the forced response is mostly governed by the steady state response solution. For a underdamped system, the settling time $t_s = 4/\zeta\omega_n$ is known as an approximate response time after which the amplitude of the system response remains within 2% of the steady state response amplitude, hence one can approximate the amount of energy directed to T, V, W_d, and the work done by the sonotrode force W up to the response time $t = t_s$. Once the system response reaches to its steady state, the transient part of the response can be neglected. Integration of Eq. (10.2.3) over $0 \le t \le t_s$ yields

$$\left(\frac{1}{2}m\dot{x}^2 + \frac{1}{2}kx^2\right)_{t=t_s} + 2\zeta\omega_n \int_0^{t_s} \dot{x}^2 dt = \delta\omega_n^2 \int_0^{t_s} x\sin\Omega t\, dt \tag{10.2.6}$$

Applying x in Eq. (10.2.4) to Eq. (10.2.6) and normalizing the result against $F_s\delta$, one can determine the individual energy terms as a function of ζ and $r = \Omega/\omega_n$. Shown in Fig. 10.4 are the plots of normalized T, V, W_d, and W up to $t = t_s$ as a function of frequency ratio r for two different values of damping factor ζ. It can be seen that T and V are insignificantly small compared with W_d, especially when $r > 1$, indicating that most of work done by the sonotrode force is dissipated by damping. This indicates also that a relatively small amount of energy from the total work done by the sonotrode force is consumed to build up the kinetic or elastic potential energy of the system unless the system is excited at a frequency much lower than its natural frequency. Therefore one can neglect the transient response part in Eq. (10.2.4); i.e., $x(t) = X\sin(\Omega t - \phi)$ and find that the work (w) done per cycle by the sonotrode force and the energy dissipated (w_d) per cycle by damping are as follows:

$$w = \int_{-\frac{\phi}{\Omega}}^{\frac{(2\pi-\phi)}{\Omega}} f_s\dot{x}\,dt = \pi F_s X \sin\phi \tag{10.2.7}$$

$$w_d = \int_{-\frac{\phi}{\Omega}}^{\frac{(2\pi-\phi)}{\Omega}} c\dot{x}^2 dt = \pi c\Omega X^2 \tag{10.2.8}$$

It can be seen from the above expression that $w = 0$ when $\phi = 0$, implying simply that the work performed by a harmonic force in phase with a harmonic displacement is zero

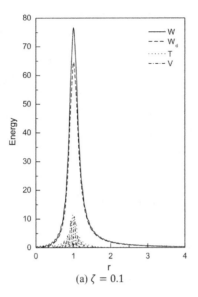
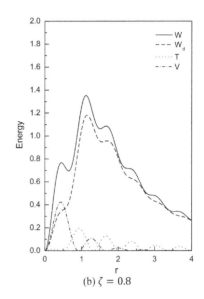

(a) $\zeta = 0.1$ (b) $\zeta = 0.8$

Figure 10.4. Work done (W) by the harmonic force up to $t = t_s$ and its distribution among the kinetic energy (T), elastic potential energy (V), and energy dissipated by damping (W_d). Note that these quantities are normalized against $F_s\delta$.

after a whole cycle as expected. In addition, note that w is maximum when $\phi = 90°$, and that this occurs only at resonance when the harmonic force and velocity are completely in phase. After some algebraic manipulations, it can be found that Eqs. (10.2.7) and (10.2.8) become

$$w = w_d = \frac{2\pi\zeta r}{(1-r^2)^2 + (2\zeta r)^2} F_s\delta \qquad (10.2.9)$$

The plots of w_d (normalized against $F_s\delta$) for different values of ζ are shown in Fig. 10.5. It can be clearly seen that a large amount of energy can be dissipated by damping at resonance even when the system is lightly damped. Note also that the amount of energy dissipated by damping decreases with increasing damping near resonance.

In what follows, assuming dry friction (Coulomb friction) to be the primary contact behavior at the weld interface, the work performed by the friction force is determined and approximated as the energy dissipated by friction at the weld interface or the energy used for weld formation. Coulomb damping is a damping effect caused by sliding friction and characterized by

$$f_i = \mu N \mathrm{sgn}(\dot{x}) \qquad (10.2.10)$$

where μ denotes the coefficient of kinetic friction, N the normal force (i.e., clamping force in USMW), and $\mathrm{sgn}(\alpha)$ the signum function defined to have the value 1 for $\alpha > 1$, -1 for $\alpha < 1$, and 0 for $\alpha = 0$ to signify that f_i is in the opposite direction of $\dot{x}$. It should be noted that the actual contact behavior at the weld interface during USMW is more complicated and may require a time- and temperature-dependent interface model for more accurate analysis. In particular, once the oxide films (and other contaminants) are removed at the asperities of the weld interface and subsequent metal-to-metal contact occurs there (i.e., bonding occurs), f_i is no longer governed by the Coulomb friction law, and it may need to be modified by including the plastic shear deformation at metal-to-metal contact areas which increase in number and size during welding. In an effort to develop a mechanics-based USMW model, De Vries [19] presented that the total interface force consists of two force components,

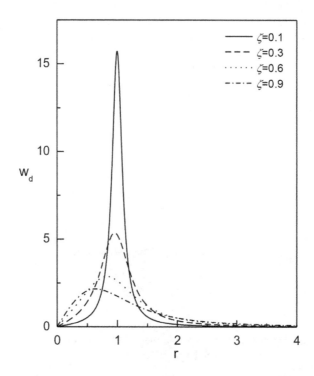

Figure 10.5. Energy dissipation (w_d) per cycle by damping, normalized against $F_s\delta$, for different values of damping factor ζ.

the shear force resulting from metal-to-metal contact which is responsible for the welding process and a net friction force which does not contribute to the actual bonding of the material. The net friction force is the sum of the friction force within the weld zone but on the surface contact areas separated by contaminants and the friction force outside the weld zone. In an attempt to develop a finite element model, based on the experimental results presented by Naidu and Raman [20] and Zhang et al. [21], Siddiq and Ghassemieh [11] proposed a kinematic friction model which is a function of contact pressure, slip, temperature, and number of loading cycles. Applying f_i defined in Eq. (10.2.10) and $x(t) = X \sin\Omega t$, it can be found that the work (W_w) done per cycle by the Coulomb friction force at the weld interface can be found as:

$$w_w = \int_0^{\frac{2\pi}{\Omega}} f_i \dot{x}\,dt = \mu NX \int_0^{2\pi} \text{sgn}(\cos\tau)\cos\tau\,d\tau = 4\mu NX \tag{10.2.11}$$

where $\tau = \Omega t$. This result suggests, for example, that 1,120 J of energy is dissipated (or consumed to form a weld) in 1 second at the weld interface for USMW with $\Omega = 20$ kHz, $\mu = 0.7$, $N = 2$ kN, and $X = 10$ microns. Because damping is often approximated as a linear dependence on velocity (i.e., viscous damping), let us devise a viscous damper of equivalent energy dissipation by equating the result in Eq. (10.2.11) to the energy dissipation due to viscous damping given in Eq. (10.2.8). Denoting c_{eq} as the equivalent viscous damping coefficient, it can be found that

$$c_{eq} = \frac{4\mu N}{\pi\Omega X} \quad \text{or} \quad \zeta_{eq} = \frac{c_{eq}}{2m\omega_n} \tag{10.2.12}$$

Now, replacing f_i in Eq. (10.2.1) with $c_{eq}\dot{x}$, one can find

$$\ddot{x} + 2(\zeta + \zeta_{eq})\omega_n\dot{x} + \omega_n^2 x = \delta\omega_n^2\sin\Omega t, \quad x(0) = \dot{x}(0) = 0 \tag{10.2.13}$$

and for which the steady state response amplitude X and the phase angle ϕ are:

$$X = \frac{\delta}{\sqrt{(1-r^2)^2 + \left(2(\zeta + \zeta_{eq})r\right)^2}} \qquad \phi = \tan^{-1}\left(\frac{2(\zeta + \zeta_{eq})r}{1-r^2}\right) \qquad (10.2.14)$$

Rewriting ζ_{eq} in Eq. (10.2.12) as

$$\zeta_{eq} = \frac{a}{2r}\left(\frac{\delta}{X}\right) \qquad a = \frac{4\mu N}{\pi F_s} \qquad (10.2.15)$$

and substituting for ζ_{eq} of X in Eq. (10.2.14) leads to

$$(1-r^2)^2\left(\frac{X}{\delta}\right)^2 + \left(2\zeta r\left(\frac{X}{\delta}\right)+a\right)^2 = 1 \qquad (10.2.16)$$

from which one can determine X. If ζ is small compared with ζ_{eq} and thus negligible, it can be found that

$$\frac{X}{\delta} = \frac{\sqrt{1-a^2}}{|1-r^2|} \qquad (10.2.17)$$

Unlike the case of viscous damping, it can be seen that X is unbounded at resonance (i.e., $r = 1$) under Coulomb damping alone. In addition, Eq. (10.2.17) indicates that the sonotrode force F_s must be larger in magnitude than $4\mu N/\pi$ (because α cannot be greater than 1) to maintain the steady state motion of the weld spot element. The primary effect of damping on oscillatory systems is that of limiting the amplitude of response at resonance; damping has little effect on the response in the frequency regions away from resonance. The amplitude of steady state response at resonance can be found from Eq. (10.2.16) as

$$\frac{x}{\delta} = \frac{1-a}{2\zeta} \qquad (10.2.18)$$

It can be seen from the results in Eqs. (10.2.11) and (10.2.18) that the mechanical work performed by the sonotrode is most efficiently converted into the energy for weld forma-tion when the sonotrode oscillates at the natural frequency of the weld spot element with the smallest non-zero damping. Recalling that ζ represents the equivalent viscous damping factor due to energy dissipation mechanisms other than friction and plastic deformation at the weld zone, let us consider material damping of the weld part as the main cause of the energy loss ΔE. In such a case, ΔE is known to be proportional to the square of the ampli-tude of vibration and stiffness; i.e.,

$$\Delta E = \pi \beta k X^2 \qquad (10.2.19)$$

where β is defined as the hysteric damping coefficient which can be experimentally deter-mined from the stress-strain hysteric loop plot of the weld part. Upon equating the expres-sions in Eqs. (10.2.8) and (10.2.19), one can find the equivalent viscous damping factor as

$$\zeta = \frac{\beta}{2r} \qquad (10.2.20)$$

In general material damping is considered negligible compared with structural damping—A result of mechanical energy dissipation by friction resulting from relative motion be-tween components—in a mechanical system or structure. However, as shown in Fig. 10.5, it should be noted that small material damping can dissipate a significant amount of energy near a resonant frequency.

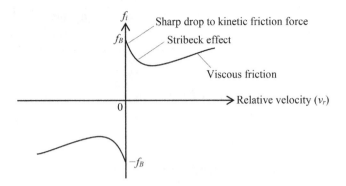

Figure 10.6. Friction force as a function of the relative velocity.

The interface force f_i defined in Eq. (10.2.10) is an ideal case where f_i is assumed to remain constant in each direction of relative motion. Although this simple Coulomb friction model allows for analytical approaches to the problem and provides the qualitative understanding of the dynamics involved in the USMW process, it is not expected to provide accurate analysis results as f_i depends on various factors, such as loading conditions, surface characteristics, material properties, and especially the magnitude of the relative velocity. A more complete friction model that agrees with the behavior of friction commonly observed in practice is depicted in Fig. 10.6. In this model, the friction force is a function of the relative velocity and assumed to be the combination of Coulomb, viscous, and Stribeck friction. f_B in Fig. 10.6 is the maximum friction force at impending motion, or the breakaway friction force, which drops instantaneously to the kinetic friction force as the motion begins. The Stribeck friction is the drop in friction with a negative slope at low velocities. A detailed discussion on friction modeling and compensation can be found in reference [22].

If the velocity dependent characteristics of the friction force are known, one may construct a mathematical model that simulates the frictional behavior; e.g., assuming the normal force N is constant,

$$f_i(v_r) = \mu(v_r)N = N \begin{cases} \left(\mu_C + (\mu_B - \mu_C)e^{-c_t|v_r|} \right)\text{sgn}(v_r) + c_v v_r \text{ for } |v_r| \geq v_C \\ (\mu_C + (\mu_B - \mu_C)e^{-c_t v_c})\dfrac{v_r}{v_c} + c_v v_r \text{ for } |v_r| < v_C \end{cases}$$

(10.2.21)

where μ_C is the coefficient of kinetic friction, μ_B the coefficient of static friction, c_t the coefficient that approximates the transition between μ_B and μ_C, v_c the critical velocity within which μ is assumed to be linearly proportional to the relative velocity v_r, and c_v the coefficient of viscous friction. Applying the interface force model assumed in Eq. (10.2.21), the equation of motion of the system in Fig. 10.3 can be written in the following non-dimensional form:

$$\bar{x}'' + 2\zeta\alpha\bar{x}' + \alpha^2\bar{x} + \mu(\bar{x}')\bar{N} = \bar{F}_s \sin \tau$$

(10.2.22)

where, $\bar{x} = x/a$, $\tau = \Omega t$, $(') = d/d\tau$, $\bar{N} = N/am\Omega^2$, $\bar{F}_s = F_s/am\Omega^2$, and $\alpha = \omega_n/\Omega$. The solution to the above equation requires numerical integrations due to the dependency of μ on $\bar{x}'$. Once the numerical solution to Eq. (10.2.22) is found, the energy ($\bar{E}_f$) dissipated by friction at the weld zone and the energy ($\bar{E}_d$) dissipated by damping up to $\tau = \tau_0$ can be determined by

$$\bar{E}_f = \int_0^{\tau_0} \mu(\bar{x}')\bar{N}\bar{x}'d\,\tau \qquad (10.2.23)$$

$$\bar{E}_d = 2\zeta\alpha\int_0^{\tau_0} (\bar{x}')^2 d\tau \qquad (10.2.24)$$

Note that the numerical examples presented in this study have assumed $\mu = \mu_0$ with $\mu_B = 1$, $\mu_C = 0.8$, $v_c = 10^{-4}$ m/s, $c_t = 10$ s/m, and $c_v = 0.5$ s/m for the velocity dependent friction model and $\zeta = 0.1$ for damping unless otherwise specified. Shown in Fig. 10.7(a) are the plots of $\bar{E}_f$ (solid curves) as a function of τ under different values of α. Shown also in the same graph are the plots of $\bar{E}_d$ (dashed curves) under the same conditions. When $\alpha = 2$, E_f has the time periods in which it remains almost unchanged, which indicates that stiction ($\bar{x} = 0$) occurs during these time periods. The period of stiction phase becomes longer as α further increases. Note that the higher the frequency ratio α, the stiffer the system. As α decreases further from 1, it can be seen E_f decreases. The overall slope of the E_f curve is the rate of energy dissipation which can be considered as the welding power if all the energy dissipated by friction is converted into welding energy at the weld zone. It can be seen that E_f for $\alpha = 1$ (i.e., at resonance) increases faster, at a rate of 0.4, than the ones with other values of frequency ratio α. The overall behavior of E_f and $\bar{E}_d$ as a function of frequency ratio α is shown in Fig. 10.7(b) which shows the energy dissipation rate by friction ($\bar{e}_f$, solid curves) and by damping ($\bar{e}_d$, dashed curves) for different values of ζ against frequency ratio α. As shown, $\bar{e}_f$ is at its peak when $\alpha = 1$, and as α deviates from 1, $\bar{e}_f$ decreases to a much lower value. In addition, it can be seen that a significant amount of energy provided by the sonotrode is dissipated by damping even with small damping.

As we recall from Eq. (10.2.17), if μ is constant, $\bar{F}_s$ must be larger than $4\mu\bar{N}/\pi$ in order to keep the weld spot element under steady state motion. When the velocity dependent behavior of friction is taken into account, it can be expected that too large of friction at the weld zone may cause long-period stiction when the weld spot element changes its direction of motion and this would cause $\bar{E}_f$ to decrease while too small of friction may require a long time for $\bar{E}_f$ to reach its critical value at which bonding starts to occur. Figure 10.8 shows $\bar{e}_f$ and $\bar{e}_d$ as a function of non-dimensional normal force $\bar{N}$ for three different values of sonotrode force $\bar{F}_s$. It can be seen that $\bar{N}_{max}$ corresponding to the maximum $\bar{e}_f$ depends on $\bar{F}_s$; i.e., $\bar{N}_{max}$ increases as $\bar{F}_s$ increases but at a much lower rate. It can be also seen that $\bar{e}_f$

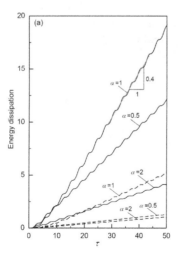
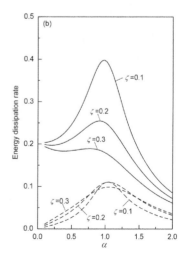

Figure 10.7. (a) $\bar{E}_f$ (solid curves) at the weld zone and $\bar{E}_d$ (dashed curves) against time τ and (b) $\bar{e}_f$ (solid curves) and $\bar{e}_d$ (dashed curves) against frequency ratio α for different values of ζ. $\bar{N} = 0.5$ and $\bar{F}_s = 1$.

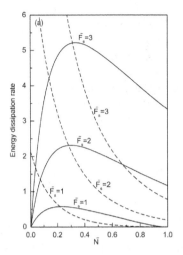
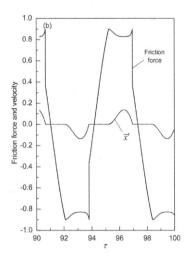

Figure 10.8. (a) $\bar{e}_f$ (solid curves) and $\bar{e}_d$ (dashed curves) as a function of normal force $\bar{N}$ for different values of sonotrode force $\bar{F}_s$ and (b) friction force at the weld zone and velocity ($\bar{x}'$). $\bar{N} = 0.9$, $\bar{F}_s = 1$, and $\alpha = 1$.

is significantly less than $\bar{e}_d$ when $\bar{N} < \bar{N}_{max}$. As $\bar{N}$ increases further from $\bar{N}_{max}$, both $\bar{e}_f$ and $\bar{e}_d$ decrease because the weld spot element is in the stiction phase for a longer period due to large static friction as shown in Fig. 10.8(b).

10.2.2 Multiple Degrees of Freedom System

In USMW, it is common to weld multiple layers of weld parts. For example, Fig. 10.9 shows the schematic of a typical inter-cell unit of a battery pack used in an electric vehicle for ultrasonic spot welding. Hundreds of inter-cell units are connected through an integrated circuit board conducting electricity in the battery pack. The inter-cell unit consists of multiple lithium-ion battery cell pouches with two tabs (battery cell terminals) sealed in the upper part of the pouch and a bus bar premounted on the integrated circuit board. Nickel-coated, thin copper or aluminum sheets are used for the tabs. The bus-bar is made of nickel coated copper plate which is several times thicker than the battery tab. Once the tabs and

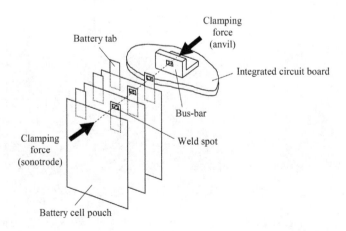

Figure 10.9. Schematic of a typical inter-cell unit of a battery pack used in an electric vehicle.

bus-bar are aligned and clamped between the sonotrode weld tip and anvil, the sonotrode oscillates to perform spot welding of the tabs to the bus-bar. The bus-bar is rigidly held by the anvil. When performing USMW on multiple metal sheets, it is important to ensure that bonding with acceptable strength occurs at all contact interfaces among the weld parts. Figure 10.10 shows the discrete model for multiple weld spot elements. The equations of motion for the weld spot elements are:

$$m_1\ddot{x}_1 + c_1\dot{x}_1 + k_1 x_1 + f_1(\dot{x}_1, \dot{x}_2) = F_s \sin\Omega t \qquad (10.2.25)$$

$$m_i\ddot{x}_i + c_i\dot{x}_i + k_i x_i + f_i(\dot{x}_i, \dot{x}_{i+1}) = f_{i-1}(\dot{x}_{i-1}, \dot{x}_i) \quad i = 2,3,\cdots,n \qquad (10.2.26)$$

where $f_i(\dot{x}_i, \dot{x}_{i+1})$ represents the friction force at interface i as a function of relative velocity $\dot{x}_i - \dot{x}_{i+1}$ between weld spot elements m_i and m_{i+1}. Assume $m_1 = m_i = m$ and normal N is constant. Applying the friction model in Eq. (10.2.21), the above equations of motion can be written in the following non-dimensional form to facilitate the numerical analysis:

$$\bar{x}_1'' + 2\zeta_1\alpha_1\bar{x}_1' + \alpha_1^2\bar{x}_1 + \mu_1(\bar{x}_1', \bar{x}_2')\bar{N} = \bar{F}_s \sin\tau \qquad (10.2.27)$$

$$\bar{x}_i'' + 2\zeta_i\alpha_i\bar{x}_i' + \alpha_i^2\bar{x}_i + \mu_i(\bar{x}_i', \bar{x}_{i+1}')\bar{N} = \mu_{i-1}(\bar{x}_{i-1}', \bar{x}_i')\bar{N} \quad i = 2,3,\cdots,n \qquad (10.2.28)$$

where $\zeta_i = c_i/2m\omega_i$, $\omega_i = \sqrt{k_i/m}$, $\alpha_i = \omega_i/\Omega$, and other parameters are previously defined in Eq. (10.2.22). Note that $\bar{x}_{n+1}' = 0$ as it refers to the velocity of the fixed weld part. The energy dissipated by friction at interface i can be determined by

$$\bar{E}_{fi} = \int_0^{\tau_0} \mu_i(\bar{x}_i', \bar{x}_{i+1}')\bar{N}(\bar{x}_i' - \bar{x}_{i+1}')d\tau \qquad (10.2.29)$$

The total energy ($\bar{E}_f$) dissipated by friction at interfaces 1 through n is

$$\bar{E}_{fi} = \sum_{i=1}^{n}\int_0^{\tau_0} \mu_i(\bar{x}_i', \bar{x}_{i+1}')\bar{N}(\bar{x}_i' - \bar{x}_{i+1}')d\tau \qquad (10.2.30)$$

If the velocity dependency of the coefficient of friction is neglected (i.e., μ_i is constant), Eq. (10.2.30) can be recast as

$$\bar{E}_f = \mu_1\bar{N}\int_0^{\tau_0} \bar{x}_1'd\tau + \sum_{i=2}^{n}(\mu_i - \mu_{i-1})\bar{N}\int_0^{\tau_0} \bar{x}_i'd\tau \qquad (10.2.31)$$

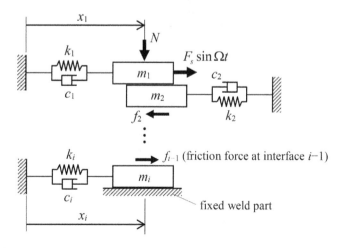

Figure 10.10. Discrete model for multiple weld spot elements.

It can be seen from the above equation, if the coefficients of friction at the interfaces are the same (i.e., $\mu_i = \mu_0$), the second term becomes zero and thus E_f is simply determined by the first term in the equation regardless of $\bar{x}'_i (i = 2,3,\cdots,n)$. However, when $\mu_i \neq \mu_{i-1}, \bar{E}_f$, E_f can be smaller or larger depending on the difference between μ_i and μ_{i-1} and $\bar{x}_1$.

Two numerical examples, two-mass ($n = 2$) and three-mass systems ($n = 3$), are considered for discussion. For the two-mass system, shown in Fig. 10.11 are the plots of energy dissipation rate by friction at interface 1 ($\bar{e}_{f1}$, solid curves) and interface 2 ($\bar{e}_{f2}$, dashed curves) against normal force $\bar{N}$ for different values of frequency ratio α_i. It can be seen that the energy dissipation rate at the frictional interface is greatly influenced by the frequency ratio. Notice that $\bar{N}_{max}$ corresponding to the maximum energy dissipation rate by friction depends also on the frequency ratio. Figure 10.12 shows the effect of frequency ratio α_i on energy dissipation rate $\bar{e}_{fi}$ for the two-mass system. It can be seen that $\bar{e}_{f1}$ is significantly larger than $\bar{e}_{f2}$, especially the difference is large when $\alpha_1 = 1$ regardless of α_2. However, when the friction force at interface 1 is larger than the one at interface 2 so that the relative velocity $(\bar{x}'_1 - \bar{x}'_2)$ at interface 1 is lower than the velocity (x'_2) at interface 2, $\bar{e}_{f2}$ can be larger than $\bar{e}_{f1}$ depending on the frequency ratio. For example, Fig. 10.13 shows the energy dissipation rates at interfaces 1 and 2 when $\mu_1 = \mu_0$ and $\mu_2 = 0.7\mu_0$. It can be seen that $\bar{e}_{f2}$ is larger than $\bar{e}_{f1}$ for certain values of α_1 and α_2. Notice that $\bar{e}_{f1}$ decreases when $\bar{e}_{f2}$ increases around $\alpha_1 = \alpha_2 = 1$. Shown in Fig. 10.14 are the ranges of frequency ratio α_1 and α_2 in which $\bar{e}_{f1} < \bar{e}_{f2}$ when $\mu_1 = \mu_0$ for three different values of μ_2. It can be seen that the

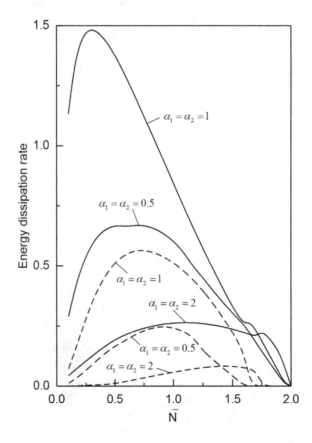

Figure 10.11. Energy dissipation rate by friction at interface 1 (solid curves) and interface 2 (dashed curves) for the two-mass system against normal force $\bar{N}$ for different values of $\alpha_1 (i = 1,2)$, where $\bar{F}_s = 2$.

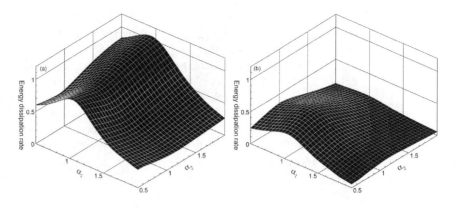

Figure 10.12. Energy dissipation rate by friction at (a) interface 1 ($\bar{e}_{f1}$) and (b) interface 2 ($\bar{e}_{f2}$) against frequency ratios $\alpha_i (i = 1,2)$ for the two-mass system when $\mu_i = \mu_0$, $\bar{F}_s = 2$, and $\bar{N} = 1$.

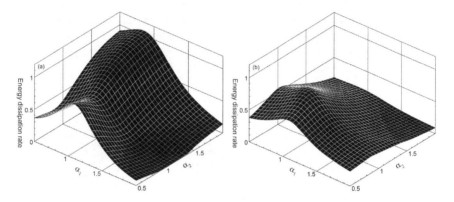

Figure 10.13. Energy dissipation rate by friction at (a) interface 1 ($\bar{e}_{f1}$) and (b) interface 2 ($\bar{e}_{f2}$) against frequency ratios $\alpha_i (i = 1,2)$ for the two-mass system when $\mu_i = \mu_0$, $\mu_2 = 0.7\mu_0$, $\bar{F}_s = 2$, and $\bar{N} = 1$.

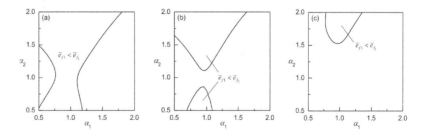

Figure 10.14. Parametric plane of α_1 and α_2 showing the area where the energy dissipation rate by friction at interface 2 is higher than the one at interface 1 when $\mu_i = \mu_0$, $\bar{F}_s = 2$, and $\bar{N} = 1$, with (a) $\mu_2 = 0.7\mu_0$, (b) $\mu_2 = 0.8\mu_0$, and (c) $\mu_2 = 0.9\mu_0$.

area where $\bar{e}_{f1} < \bar{e}_{f2}$ is quite large when $\mu_2 = 0.7\mu_0$, however this area diminishes rapidly as μ_2 increases. This example demonstrates that it is possible by altering the individual frequency ratios and coefficients of friction to control weld energy distribution among multiple weld interfaces for the reduction of weld time or uniform weld strength across the weld interfaces in USMW.

For the three-mass system, shown in Fig. 10.15 are the plots of energy dissipation rate by friction at interfaces 1 through 3 as a function of normal force $\bar{N}$, where $\mu_i = \mu_0 (i = 1,2,3)$ is assumed. It can be seen that the overall behavior is similar, showing $\bar{e}_{f1} > \bar{e}_{f2} > \bar{e}_{f3}$, to the case of the two-mass system. Note that $\bar{N}$ corresponding to the peak value of each $\bar{e}_{fi}$ is different; for example, $\bar{e}_{f1}$ is at its peak when $\bar{N} = 0.35$ while $\bar{e}_{f2}$ and $\bar{e}_{f3}$ are at their peaks when $\bar{N} = 0.95$ and $\bar{N} = 1.25$, respectively. Notice also that $\bar{e}_{f3} \approx 0$ when $\alpha_i = 2$ over the entire range of $\bar{N}$, indicating that $\bar{x}' \approx 0$ due to large friction.

Figure 10.16 shows the plots of energy dissipation rate by friction as a function of frequency ratios α_2 and α_3 for three different values of α_1 when $\mu_i = \mu_0$. It can be seen from Fig. 10.16(b) that all $\bar{e}_{f1}$ are the highest when $\alpha_1 = 1$ among the three cases considered. When $\alpha_2 = 1$, as shown in Fig. 10.16(c), all $\bar{e}_{fi}$ are very low compared with the other two cases. Notice also that the overall behavior of $\bar{e}_{f2}$ and $\bar{e}_{f3}$ against the change in frequency ratios α_2 and α_3 is similar to the behavior of $\bar{e}_{f1}$ and $\bar{e}_{f2}$ of the two-mass system, whereas $\bar{e}_{f1}$ decreases to its lowest value when $\alpha_2 = 1$.

Figure 10.17 shows the plots of energy dissipation rate by friction as a function of μ_3 for different values of μ_2 when $\mu_1 = 1$ and $\alpha_i = 1(i = 1,2,3)$. It can be seen that $\bar{e}_{f1} > \bar{e}_{f2} > \bar{e}_{f3}$ in overall over the ranges of μ_2 and μ_3 considered. As μ_2 increases both $\bar{e}_{f1}$ and $\bar{e}_{f3}$ increase while $\bar{e}_{f2}$ decreases. As μ_3 increases both $\bar{e}_{f1}$ and $\bar{e}_{f2}$ increases while $\bar{e}_{f3}$ decreases. When μ_2 is high and μ_3 is low, it can be seen $\bar{e}_{f2} < \bar{e}_{f3}$; for example, $\bar{e}_{f1} = 1.98$, $\bar{e}_{f2} = 0.66$, and $\bar{e}_{f3} = 0.76$ when $\mu_2 = 1$ and $\mu_3 = 0.7$.

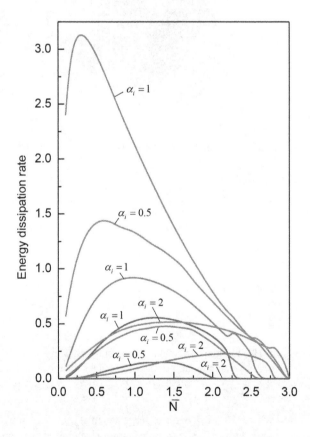

Figure 10.15. Energy dissipation rate by friction at interface 1 through 3 ($\bar{e}_{f1}$, red curve; $\bar{e}_{f2}$, green; $\bar{e}_{f3}$, blue) for the three-mass system as a function of normal force $\bar{N}$ for different values of $\alpha_i (i-1,2,3)$, where $\bar{F}_s = 3$ and $\mu_i = \mu_0$. Note that $\bar{e}_{f3} \approx 0$ for $\alpha_i = 2$.

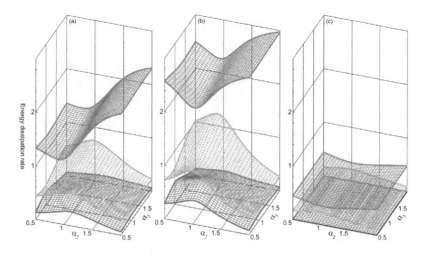

Figure 10.16. Energy dissipation rate by friction at interface 1 through 3 ($\bar{e}_{f1}$, red curve; $\bar{e}_{f2}$, green; $\bar{e}_{f3}$, blue) for the three-mass system as a function of frequency ratio $\alpha_i (i = 2,3)$ when (a) $\alpha_i = 0.5$, (b) $\alpha_i = 1$, and (c) $\alpha_i = 2$, where $\mu_i = \mu_0$, $\bar{F}_s = 3$, $\bar{N} = 1$.

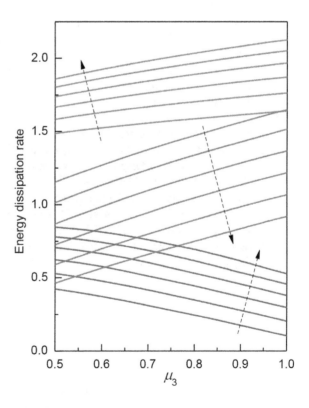

Figure 10.17. Energy dissipation rate by friction at interface 1 through 3 ($\bar{e}_{f1}$, red curve; $\bar{e}_{f2}$, green; $\bar{e}_{f3}$, blue) for the three-mass system against μ_3 for different values of μ_2 when $\mu_1 = 1$, $\alpha_i = 1 (i = 1,2,3)$, $\bar{F}_s = 3$, $\bar{N} = 1$. μ_2 changes from 0.5 to 1 by 0.1 and the direction of increase is indicated by the arrows.

10.2.3 Summary and Conclusions

Applying discrete mass-spring-damper models, the fundamental dynamics of the ultrasonic metal welding process is examined. It is shown that the vibration characteristics of weld spot element play an important role in determining weld performance inasmuch as the coefficient of friction, welding frequency, clamping normal force, and weld time. In particular, based on the calculated energy dissipation rate by friction at the weld interface (i.e., the welding power), it is confirmed that the ratio between the natural frequency of weld part and welding frequency has a great impact on the USMW process and its performance—the energy dissipation rate by friction is at its maximum when resonance occurs. For USMW applications with multiple weld interfaces, it is shown that the energy dissipation rate at the weld interface of the weld part directly excited by the sonotrode is significantly higher than the ones at other weld interfaces. It is also demonstrated with 2-DOF and 3-DOF systems that the energy dissipation rates at individual weld interfaces can be significantly altered by a small change in friction at one of the weld interfaces and/or a change in the natural frequency of one of the weld parts. In addition, it is shown that a substantial amount of energy can be dissipated through material damping of weld parts, especially at resonance.

10.3 DYNAMICS OF A SONOTRODE

The longitudinal vibration of a bar is the underlying mechanism of sonotrodes used in USMW. In typical ultrasonic welders, a stack of several piezoelectric disks (transducer) placed at one end of the sonotrode converts electrical energy to the longitudinal vibration of the sonotrode which has a weld tip placed at the other end as schematically shown in Fig. 10.18. When a driving voltage at the resonant frequency of the sonotrode is applied to the transducer, the sonotrode resonates and the weld tip oscillates generating shears at the weld interfaces. In order to produce displacement amplification at the weld tip, sonotrodes are engineered to have a variable cross-section as the vibration amplitude at the end with small cross-sectional area is greater than the one at the end with large cross-sectional area (i.e., $a > a_p$). Various types of sonotrodes and their vibration characteristics are discussed in reference [23]. Sonotrode design and optimization techniques with finite element method can be found in references [24 and 25].

In this section, a brief introduction to the longitudinal vibration of a bar and its application to the sonotrode design is presented. Consider a bar of two spans with different cross-sectional areas as shown in Fig. 10.19, where both ends of the bar is free. Neglecting the effects associated with lateral expansions and contractions during the motion, the equation governing the longitudinal vibration of each span can be written as:

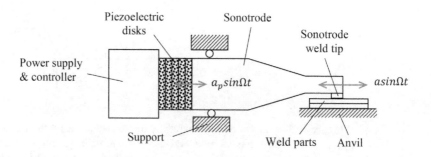

Figure 10.18. Schematic description of a typical ultrasonic welder.

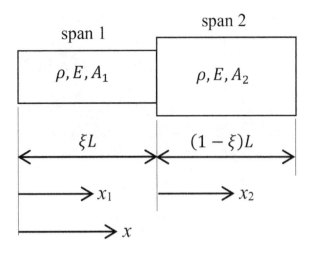

Figure 10.19. Bar of two spans with different cross-sectional areas.

$$\frac{\partial^2 u_n(x_n,t)}{\partial x_n^2} = \frac{1}{c_0^2}\frac{\partial^2 u_n(x_n,t)}{\partial t^2} \quad c_0 = \sqrt{E/\rho} \quad (n=1,2) \tag{10.3.1}$$

where u_n denotes the longitudinal displacement of span n and c_0 the bar velocity of the bar material, E the Young's modulus, and ρ the mass density of the bar.

10.3.1 Natural Frequencies and Modeshapes

The general harmonic solution to Eq. (10.3.1) is

$$u_n(x_n,t) = U_n(x_n)e^{i\omega t} = (C_n \cos\gamma x_n + D_n \sin\gamma x_n)^{i\omega t} \quad i=\sqrt{-1} \tag{10.3.2}$$

where, γ denotes the wavenumber and ω the longitudinal vibration frequency of the bar. Note that γ and ω are related to each other through $\gamma = \omega/c_0$. The unknown coefficients C_n and D_n are to be determined by imposing the boundary conditions of the bar. Because both left and right ends of the bar are free, the axial normal stress at those ends should vanish; i.e.,

$$E\frac{dU_1(0)}{dx_1} = 0 \quad \text{or} \quad D_1 = 0 \tag{10.3.3}$$

$$E\frac{dU_2((1-\xi)L)}{dx_2} = 0 \quad \text{or} \quad C_2 \sin\gamma(1-\xi)L - D_2 \cos\gamma(1-\xi)L = 0 \tag{10.3.4}$$

The axial displacement of the bar at the junction should be continuous and the axial force at the junction should be compatible, thus

$$U_1(\xi L) = U_2(0) \quad \text{or} \quad C_1 \cos\gamma\xi L + D_1 \sin\gamma\xi L = C_2 \tag{10.3.5}$$

$$EA_1\frac{dU_1(\xi L)}{dx_1} = EA_2\frac{dU_2(0)}{dx_2} \quad \text{or} \quad C_1 \sin\gamma\xi L - D_1 \cos\gamma\xi L = -rD_2 \quad r=\frac{A_2}{A_1} \tag{10.3.6}$$

The above algebraic equations can be recast in the following matrix form:

$$\begin{bmatrix} 0 & 1 & 0 & 0 \\ 0 & 0 & -\sin\gamma(1-\xi)L & \cos\gamma(1-\xi)L \\ \cos\gamma\xi L & \sin\gamma\xi L & -1 & 0 \\ \sin\gamma\xi L & -\cos\gamma\xi L & 0 & r \end{bmatrix} \begin{Bmatrix} C_1 \\ D_1 \\ C_2 \\ D_2 \end{Bmatrix} = 0 \qquad (10.3.7)$$

The determinant of the matrix in Eq. (10.3.7) must vanish in order for the homogeneous equation to have a non-trivial solution, which yields

$$r\cos\gamma\xi L \sin\gamma(1-\xi)L + \cos\gamma(1-\xi)L \sin\gamma\xi L = 0 \qquad (10.3.8)$$

Wavenumbers γ_k satisfying the above characteristic equation of the system are the natural wavenumbers at which the bar undergoes harmonic motion. The corresponding modeshapes for each span are:

$$U_{1k}(x_1) = C_1 \cos\gamma_k x_1 \quad 0 \le x_1 \le \xi L \qquad (10.3.9)$$

$$U_{2k}(x_2) = C_1\left(\cos\gamma_k\xi L \cos\gamma_k x_2 - \frac{1}{r}\sin\gamma_k\xi L \sin\gamma_k x_2 \right) \quad 0 \le x_2 \le (1-\xi)L \quad (10.3.10)$$

One would need to numerically solve Eq. (10.3.8) to determine γ_k ($k = 0,1,2...$) for given values of area ratio r and length ratio ξ to complete the free vibration analysis of the bar. For example, let $r = 2$ and $\xi = 1/3$. In this case, it can be found that the characteristic equation in Eq. (10.3.8) is satisfied when $\gamma_0 = 0$, $\gamma_1 = 3.451/L$, $\gamma_2 = 5.974/L$, ... Note that $\gamma_0 = 0$ corresponds to the rigid body motion of the bar as its both ends are not constrained. The natural frequencies can be found from $\omega_k = \gamma_k c_0$. Shown in Fig. 10.20 are the plots of modeshape of the bar for $\gamma_1 = 3.451/L$ and $\gamma_2 = 5.974/L$. It can be seen that the displacement at $x = 0$ of the bar is 1.63 times greater than the one at $x = L$ for both γ_1 and γ_2. Note that the modeshape for γ_1 has a single node at $x = 0.547L$. This particular vibration mode is often used as a basis for sonotrode design due to the amplitude gain at one end with a single node for support when excitation is given at the other end of the bar. Note that the support at the nodal point of the bar has almost no effect on altering the vibration characteristics, however it is required to prevent the rigid body motion of the bar. The modeshape for γ_2 has

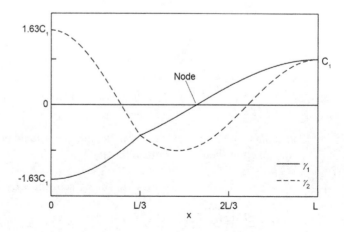

Figure 10.20. Modeshapes of the bar for $\gamma_1 = 3.451/L$ and $\gamma_1 = 5.974/L$ when $r = 2$ and $\xi = 1/3$.

the same amplification, however it has two nodes, which may be unnecessary for sonotrode applications.

10.3.2 Frequency Response Analysis

The frequency response of the sonotrode subjected to the harmonic force $F_0 e^{i\Omega t}$ at $x = L$ can be readily determined by assuming the solution for each span as

$$u_n(x_n,t) = U_n(x_n)e^{i\Omega t} = (C_n \cos \gamma x_n + D_n \sin \gamma x_n)e^{i\Omega t} \quad \gamma = \Omega/c_0 \quad (n=1,2) \quad (10.3.11)$$

The boundary condition at $x_2 = (1-\xi)L$ is

$$EA_2 \frac{dU_2((1-\xi)L)}{dx_2} = -F_0 \quad \text{or} \quad C_2 \sin \gamma(1-\xi)L - D_2 \cos \gamma(1-\xi)L = \frac{F_0}{EA_2\gamma} \quad (10.3.12)$$

Applying the boundary condition at $x_1 = 0$ and the continuity and compatibility conditions at the junction, which are given in the previous free vibration analysis, all four coefficients can be determined. Therefore, the frequency response solution for each span is found to be:

$$u_1(x_1,t) = \frac{F_0}{rEA_1\gamma H}\cos \gamma x_1 \, e^{i\Omega t} \quad 0 \le x_1 \le \xi L \quad (10.3.13)$$

$$u_2(x_2,t) = \frac{F_0}{rEA_1\gamma H}(r\cos \gamma\xi L \cos \gamma x_2 - \sin\gamma\xi L \sin \gamma x_2)e^{i\Omega t} \quad 0 \le x_2 \le (1-\xi)L \quad (10.3.14)$$

where

$$H = r \cos \gamma\xi L \sin \gamma(1-\xi)L + \cos \gamma(1-\xi)L \sin \gamma\xi L \quad \gamma = \Omega/c_0 \quad (10.3.15)$$

It can be seen that H in Eq. (10.3.15) approaches to zero, thus resonance occurs, as Ω becomes closer to one of the natural frequencies of the bar.

10.3.3 Frequency Response of a Bar with Variable Cross-Section

Sonotrodes used in USMW commonly use a variable cross section in order to achieve a desired amplification of displacement at the weld tip. Consider a bar of three spans with a varying cross-section subjected to a harmonic force $F(t)$ at $x = L$ as shown in Fig. 10.21. Because $A_2 = A_2(x)$, the equation governing the longitudinal vibration of span 2 becomes a non-wave equation of which exact solution involves Bessel's functions of the first and second kind. In this introductory discussion, instead of seeking an exact solution of the problem, the finite element analysis technique is used to approximate the natural frequencies, modeshapes, and damped frequency response solution. The discretized equation of motion for the three-span bar system in Fig. 10.21 can be written:

$$\mathbf{M\ddot{u} + C\dot{u} + Ku = F}(t) \quad (10.3.16)$$

where, $\mathbf{u}$ denotes the nodal displacement vector and $\mathbf{M}$ and $\mathbf{K}$ are the global mass and stiffness matrices, respectively, constructed by applying the following axial elemental mass ($\mathbf{m}_n$) and stiffness ($\mathbf{k}_n$) matrices

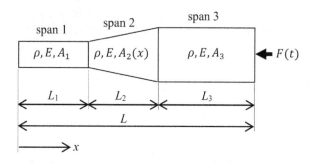

Figure 10.21. Three-span bar with a varying cross-section.

$$\mathbf{m}_n = \frac{\rho A_n l_n}{6} \begin{bmatrix} 2 & 1 \\ 1 & 2 \end{bmatrix} \quad \text{and} \quad \mathbf{k}_n = \frac{EA_n}{l_n} \begin{bmatrix} 1 & -1 \\ -1 & 1 \end{bmatrix} \quad (n = 1, 2, \cdots, N) \quad (10.3.17)$$

where l_n and A_n denote the elemental length and cross-sectional area, respectively. Note that $A_n = A_0$ for span 1 and $A_n = rA_0$ for span 3 while $A_n = A_0 f(x_n)$ for span 2 with $f(x_n)$ defines the rate of cross-sectional area change within the span. $\mathbf{C}$ is the Rayleigh damping matrix which is introduced to account for the effect of damping that keeps the modal displacements finite in the frequency response analysis of the bar. Note that $\mathbf{C}$ is proportional damping in the form

$$\mathbf{C} = \alpha \mathbf{M} = \beta \mathbf{K} \quad (10.3.18)$$

where α is the inertia damping coefficient representing the damping force on each discrete mass proportional to the momentum while β is the stiffness damping coefficient representing the damping force proportional to the local stress. $\mathbf{F}(t)$ denotes the nodal force vector $\{0\ 0\ \ldots\ F(t)\}$. The coupled equation of motion in Eq. (10.3.16) is to be decoupled by using the normal modes obtained from the associated eigenvalue problem, i.e., undamped free vibration problem: i.e.,

$$\mathbf{u}(t) = \mathbf{U}e^{i\omega t} \quad \text{and} \quad (-\omega^2 \mathbf{M} + \mathbf{K})\mathbf{U} = 0 \quad (10.3.19)$$

Now, let $\mathbf{P}$ the normalized modal matrix consisting of the normal modes, and by making the coordinate transformation $\mathbf{u} = \mathbf{Pq}$, the foregoing equation of motion becomes N decoupled equations in the form of

$$\ddot{q}_n + (\alpha + \beta \omega_n^2)\dot{q}_n + \omega_n^2 q_n = f_n(t) \quad (n = 1, 2, 3, \cdots, N) \quad (10.3.20)$$

where note that $\mathbf{P}^T \mathbf{M} \mathbf{P} = \mathbf{I}$, $\mathbf{P}^T \mathbf{K} \mathbf{P} = \omega_n^2$, and $f_n = \mathbf{P}^T \mathbf{F}(t)$ is the modal force vector. When $F(t) = F_0 \sin\Omega t$, $\alpha = 0$, and $\beta = 2\zeta_n/\omega_n$, the steady state response solution to Eq. (10.3.20) can be found as

$$q_n(t) = Q_n \sin(\Omega t - \phi_n) \quad (10.3.21)$$

$$Q_n = \frac{|f_n|}{\sqrt{(\omega_n^2 - \Omega^2)^2 + (2\zeta_n\omega_n\Omega)^2}} \quad \phi_n = \tan^{-1}\left(\frac{2\zeta_n\omega_n\Omega}{\omega_n^2 - \Omega^2}\right) \quad (10.3.22)$$

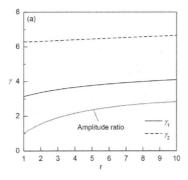 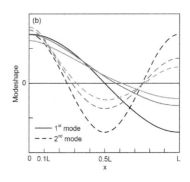

Figure 10.22. (a) First and second natural wavenumber loci against area ratio r and (b) modeshapes for $r = 1$ (black), $r = 4$ (blue), and $r = 9$ (red) of the bar. The red curve shown in (a) is the ratio of amplitude at $x = 0$ to the one at $x = L$ of the first mode.

Finally, the frequency response of the thee-span bar becomes

$$\mathbf{u}(t) = \mathbf{P}\mathbf{q}(t) \tag{10.3.23}$$

For example, consider a round bar with $L_1 = 0.1L$, $L_2 = 0.5L$, $L_3 = 0.4L$, $A_1 = A_0$, and $A_3 = rA_0$. The natural frequencies of the bar can be determined to be

$$\omega_n = \frac{\gamma_n}{L}\sqrt{\frac{E}{\rho}} \tag{10.3.24}$$

where γ is the natural wavenumber that depends on the area ratio r and the individual span lengths; for example it can be found that $\gamma_n = n\pi$ ($n = 0,1,2,\cdots$) when $r = 1$. Shown in Fig. 10.22(a) are the natural wavenumber loci of the first two vibration modes as a function of area ratio r, where note that the rigid body mode is excluded. It can be seen that both γ_1 and γ_2 increase with increasing r. The corresponding modeshapes are shown in Fig. 10.22(b) for $r = 1$, $r = 4$, and $r = 9$. It can be seen that the displacement at $x = 0$ is greater than the one at $x = L$ except for $r = 1$. The red curve in Fig. 10.22(a) shows how the amplitude ratio between the two ends of the bar (i.e., $U_1(0)/U_1(L)$) of the first vibration mode changes as r changes.

For the frequency response analysis of the bar system shown in Fig. 10.21, it is necessary to add a support at the node where the displacement is zero during longitudinal motion. The support is to suppress the unconstrained translational motion of the entire bar due to rigid body motion. One can determine the location of this node and corresponding nodal point by examining the modeshape. For example, $x_{node} = 0.57L$ when $r = 4$. Let k_s represent the longitudinal stiffness of the support at the node, then the local stiffness at the node can be increased to $EA_n/l_n + k_s$. Shown in Fig. 10.23 are the first 3 modeshapes with k_s added to the node, showing the effect of support at the node. The additional stiffness of k_s is measured in percentage relative to the local stiffness at the node. It can be seen that k_s has almost no effect on the first[1] mode (dashed curves) as expected, whereas the rigid body mode (solid curves) and the second mode (dotted curves) are altered by k_s. Figure 10.24 shows the non-dimensional displacement amplitudes of the bar when $F(t) = F_0 \sin\Omega t$ is applied at $x = L$ with $\Omega = \omega_1$, where $\beta = 1 \times 10^{-9}$ is assumed in order to introduce a modal damping factor of $\zeta_1 = 9.5 \times 10^{-5}$. It can be seen that the longitudinal vibration amplitudes of the bar remain almost the same.

---

[1] Note that the numbering of modes is based on the case when $k_s = 0$, where the rigid body mode is excluded.

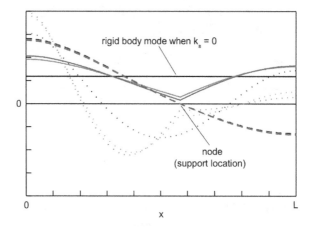

Figure 10.23. First 3 modeshapes when additional stiffness k_s due to support at the node is 0% (black), 5% (red), and 10% (blue) of the local stiffness. The solid, dashed, and dotted curves represent the rigid body, first, and second modes, respectively.

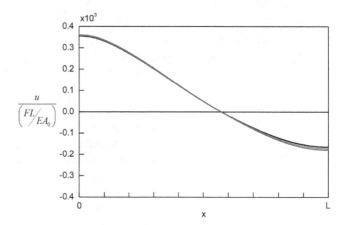

Figure 10.24. Non-dimensional displacement amplitudes when additional stiffness k_s due to support at the node is 0% (black), 5% (red), and 10% (blue) of the local stiffness.

The Matlab codes for the frequency response analysis of the three-span bar system are presented for the interested readers.

```
% === Finite element analysis for longitudinal vibration of
   three-span bar system === %
% === Performs free vibration and frequency response analy-
   sis===%
clear;
% === Specify the number of elements for each span === %
N1=25; % span 1
N2=150; % span 2
N3=100; % span 3

r=4; % cross-sectional area ratio of span 3 to span 1
s1=0.1; % length ratio of span 1 to total length L
```

```
s2=0.5; % length ratio of span 2 to total length L
s3=1-(s1+s2); % length ratio of span 3 to total length L

% === Discretize span 1 with constant cross-section === %
l1=s1/N1; % elemental length
m1=1/6*l1; % elemental mass
k1=1/l1; % elemental stiffness
M1=diag([2*m1  (2*m1+2*m1)*ones(1,N1-1)  2*m1])+diag(m1*ones
   (1,N1),-1)+diag(m1*ones(1,N1),1);
K1=diag([k1 2*k1*ones(1,N1-1)  k1])+diag(-k1*ones(1,N1),-1)+
   diag(-k1*ones(1,N1),1);

% === Discretize span 2 with varying cross-section === %
n2=1:N2; % nodal coordinate of span 2
l2=s2/N2; % elemental length
m2=1/6*((sqrt(r)-1)*n2/N2+1).^2*l2; % elemental mass
k2=((sqrt(r)-1)*n2/N2+1).^2/l2; % elemental stiffness
m2a=[m2(1)  m2(1:N2-1)  0];
m2b=[0  m2(2:N2)  m2(N2)];
M2=diag(2*m2a+2*m2b)+diag(m2,1)+diag(m2,-1);
k2a=[k2(1)  k2(1:N2-1)  0];
k2b=[0  k2(2:N2)  k2(N2)];
K2=diag(k2a+k2b)+diag(-k2,1)+diag(-k2,-1);

% === Discretize span 3 with constant cross-section === %
l3=s3/N3; % elemental length
m3=1/6*r*l3; % elemental mass
k3=r/l3; % elemental stiffness
M3=diag([2*m3  (2*m3+2*m3)*ones(1,N3-1)  2*m3])+diag(m3*ones
   (1,N3),-1)+diag(m3*ones(1,N3),1);
K3=diag([k3   2*k3*ones(1,N3-1)  k3])+diag(-k3*ones(1,N3),
   -1)+diag(-k3*ones(1,N3),1);
N=N1+N2+N3+1; % total number of nodes

% === Global mass matrix === %
M1x=zeros(N);M1x(1:N1+1,1:N1+1)=M1;
M2x=zeros(N);M2x(N1+1:N1+N2+1,N1+1:N1+N2+1)=M2;
M3x=zeros(N);M3x(N1+N2+1:N1+N2+N3+1,N1+N2+1:N1+N2+N3+1)=M3;
M=M1x+M2x+M3x;

% === Global stiffness matrix === %
K1x=zeros(N);K1x(1:N1+1,1:N1+1)=K1;
K2x=zeros(N);K2x(N1+1:N1+N2+1,N1+1:N1+N2+1)=K2;
K3x=zeros(N);K3x(N1+N2+1:N1+N2+N3+1,N1+N2+1:N1+N2+N3+1)=K3;
K=K1x+K2x+K3x;

% === Boundary conditions === %
%M(N,:)=[];M(:,N)=[]; % rem out for Free case
%K(N,:)=[];K(:,N)=[]; % rem out for Free case

% === Determine eigenvalues ev and modal matrix P === %
[P ev]=eig(K,M);
```

```
% === Add extra stiffness by support at node === %
% === Nodal coordinate corresponding to the node can be found
from the modeshape (2nd column of P) === %
% === ks is the additional stiffness by support === %
ks=0.1; % stiffness ratio of support to local stiffness
[c,nc]=min(abs(P(:,2))); % find the nodal coordinate of node
K(nc,nc)=K(nc,nc)*(1+ks); % modify the stiffness at the node

% === Recalculate eigenvalues and modal matrix === %
[P ev]=eig(K,M);

% === Determine frequencies and modeshapes === %
nwn=real(sqrt(diag(ev))); % natural wavenumber or non-dimensional
    natural frequency
r1=10e-3; % radius of span 1
A0=pi*r1^2; % cross-sectional area of span 1
L=0.1; % total span length [m]
rho=7850; % mass density of steel (7850 kg/m^3)
E=210e+9; % Young's modulus of steel (210e+9 N/m^2)
wi=nwn/L*sqrt(E/rho); % natural frequency [rad/s]
fi=wi/(2*pi)/1000; % natural frequency [kHz]
x=1000*L*[0 l1*(1:N1) l1*N1+l2*(1:N2) l1*N1+l2*N2+l3*(1:N3)];
  % x-coordinate [mm]
x=x';
figure(1);
plot(x,P(:,1:3));grid on; % plot first 3 modeshapes

% === Frequency response analysis === %
% === Displacement u is non-dimensional === %
% === Actual displacement in meters can be found by u*(F0*L)/
    (E*A0) === %
beta=1e-9; % beta damping constant [s]
F0=1; % magnitude of the excitation force [N]
om=nwn(2); % excitation wavenumber at resonance
zi=beta*wi/2; % modal damping factor
fi0=P'*[zeros(N-1,1);F0]; % modal force
Yi=fi0./sqrt((nwn.^2-om^2).^2+(2*om*zi.*nwn).^2);  %  modal
    displacement amplitude
u=P*Yi; % non-dimensional displacement amplitude
figure(2);
plot(x,u);grid on; % plot displacement amplitude
ri=om./nwn; % ratio of excitation wavenumber to natural wave-
    number
p_ang=atan2(2*zi.*ri,(1-ri.^2)); % phase angle
```

REFERENCES

[1] Lee, S. S., Kim, T. H., Hu, S. J., Cai, W. W., and Abell, J. A., 2010, "Joining Technologies for Automotive Lithium-Ion Battery Manufacturing—A Review," *Proceedings of the ASME 2010 International Manufacturing Science and Engineering Conference*, Erie, PA, Paper No. MSEC2010-34168, October 12–15.

[2]   Lee, S. S., Kim, T. H., Hu, S. J., Cai, W., Abell, J. A., and Li, J., 2013, "Characterization of Ultrasonic Metal Weld Quality for Lithium-Ion Battery Tab Joining," *ASME Journal of Manufacturing Science and Engineering*, **135**(2), p. 021004.

[3]   Kim, T. H., Yum, J., Hu, S. J., Spicer, J. P., and Abell, J. A., 2011, "Process Robustness of Single Lap Ultrasonic Welding of Thin, Dissimilar Materials," *CIRP Annals - Manufacturing Technology*, **60**, pp. 17–20.

[4]   Doumanidis, C., and Gao, Y., 2004, "Mechanical Modeling of Ultrasonic Welding," *Welding Journal*, **83**, pp. 140S-146S. Available at: http://www.aws.org/wj/supplement/04-2004-DOUMANDIS-s.pdf

[5]   Zhang, C., and Li, L., 2009, "A Coupled Thermal-Mechanical Analysis of Ultrasonic Bonding Mechanism," *Metallurgical and Materials Transactions B*, **40**(2), pp. 196–207.

[6]   Rozenberg, L., and Mitskevich, A., 1973, "Ultrasonic Welding of Metals", Physical Principles of Ultrasonic Technology, V.1, Part 2, Acoustic Institute Academy of Sciences of the USSR, Moscow, USSR, 1970, Plenum Press, New York.

[7]   Devine, J., 1984, "Joining Metals with Ultrasonic Welding," *Machine Design*, **56**(21), pp. 91–95.

[8]   Flood, G., 1997, "Ultrasonic Energy Welds Copper to Aluminum," *Welding Journal*, **76**(1), pp. 43–45.

[9]   Hetrick, E. T., Baer, J. R., Zhu, W., Reatherford, L. V., Grima, A. J., Scholl, D. J., Wilkosz, D. E., Fatima, S., and Ward, S. M., 2009, "Ultrasonic Metal Welding Process Robustness in Aluminum Automotive Body Construction Applications," *Welding Journal*, **88**, pp. 149–158.

[10]   Viswanath, A. G. K., Zhang, X., Ganesh, V. P., and Chun, L., 2007, "Numerical Study of Gold Wire Bonding Process on Cu/Low-K Structures," IEEE *Transactions on Advanced Packaging*, **30**(3), pp. 448–456.

[11]   Siddiq, A., and Ghassemieh, E., 2009, "Theoretical and FE Analysis of Ultrasonic Welding of Aluminum Alloy 3003," ASME *Journal of Manufacturing Science and Engineering*, **131**(4), pp. 1–11.

[12]   Lee, D, Kannatey-Asibu, Jr., E., and Cai, W., 2013, "Ultrasonic Welding Simulations for Multiple Layers of Lithium-Ion Battery Tabs, ASME *Journal of Manufacturing Science and Engineering*, **135**(6), p. 061011.

[13]   Elangovan, S., Semeer, S., and Prakasan, K., 2009, "Temperature and Stress Distribution in Ultrasonic Metal Welding—An FEA-Based Study," *Journal of Material Processing Technology*, **209**, pp. 1143–1150.

[14]   Gao, Y., and Doumanidis, C., 2002, "Mechanical Analysis of Ultrasonic Bonding for Rapid Prototyping," ASME *Journal of Manufacturing Science and Engineering*, **124**, pp. 426–434.

[15]   Li, H., Choi, H., Zhao, J., Li, X. C., Cai, W., and Abell, J. A., 2013, "Transient Temperature and Heat Flux Measurement in Ultrasonic Joining of Battery Tabs Using Thin-Film Micro Sensors," ASME *Journal of Manufacturing Science and Engineering*, **135**(5), p. 051015.

[16]   Zhao, J., Li, H., Choi, H., Cai, W., Abell, J. A., and Li, X., 2013, "Insertable Thin Film Thermocouples for in Situ Transient Temperature Monitoring in Ultrasonic Metal Welding of Battery Tabs," *Journal of Manufacturing Processes*, **15**(1), pp. 136–140.

[17]   Kang, B., Cai, W., and Tan, C. A., 2013, "Dynamic Response Of Battery Tabs Under Ultrasonic Welding," ASME *Journal of Manufacturing Science and Engineering*, **135**(5), p. 051013.

[18]   Graff, K. F., 1974, "Process Applications of Power Ultrasonics—A Review," *Proceedings of IEEE Ultrasonics Symposium*, pp. 628–641.

[19]   De Vries, E., 2004, "Mechanics and Mechanisms of Ultrasonic Metal Welding," Ph.D. Dissertation, The Ohio State University, Columbus, OH.

[20]   Naidu, N. K. R., and Raman, S. G. S., 2005, "Effect of Contact Pressure on Fretting Fatigue Behavior of Al-Mg-Si Alloy AA-6061," *International Journal of Fatigue*, **27**, pp. 283–291.

[21]   Zhang, C. B., Zhu, X. J., and Li, L. J., 2006, "A Study of Friction Behaviour in Ultrasonic Welding (Consolidation) of Aluminum," *Proceedings of the AWS Conference: Session 7: Friction and Resistance Welding/Materials Bonding Processes*.

[22]   Armstrong-Hélouvry, B., Dupont, P., and De Wit, C. C., 1994, A Survey of Models, Analysis Tools and Compensation Methods for the Control of Machines with Friction, *Automatica*, **30**, pp. 1083–1138.

[23]   Ensminger, D., and Bond, L. J., 2011, *Ultrasonics: Fundamentals, Technologies, and Applications*, 3rd Edition, CRC Press, Boca Raton, Florida.

[24]   Ming, Y., Fu, L. S., and Zheng, S., 2002, "A New Optimization Method for Horn Designs in Ultrasonic Welding Systems," *SIMTech Technical Report*, PT/02/006/JT, Singapore Institute of Manufacturing Technology.

[25]   Kim, S. A., Jang, H. S., Kim, E. M., and Park, D. S., 2010, "Vibration Analysis of Ultrasonic Metal Welding Horn for Optimal Design," *Proceedings of the 2010 International Conference on Mechanical, Industrial, and Manufacturing Technology (MIMT 2010)*, January 22–24, Sanya, China.

Chapter 11

DYNAMICS AND VIBRATIONS OF BATTERY TABS UNDER ULTRASONIC WELDING

Bongsu Kang[1], Wayne Cai[2], and Chin-An Tan[3]
[1]Civil & Mechanical Engineering Department, Purdue University Fort Wayne
[2]Manufacturing Systems Research Lab, General Motors Global R&D Center
[3]Mechanical Engineering Department, Wayne State University

ABSTRACT

The effect of structural vibration of the battery tab on the required sonotrode force during ultrasonic welding is studied by applying a longitudinal vibration model for the battery tab. It is found that the sonotrode force is greatly influenced by the kinetic properties, quantified by the equivalent mass, equivalent stiffness, and equivalent viscous damping, of the battery tab and cell pouch interface. This study provides a fundamental understanding of battery tab dynamics during ultrasonic welding and its effect on weld quality, and thus provides a guideline for design and welding of battery tabs.

The effects of longitudinal and flexural vibrations of the battery tab during ultrasonic welding on the development of axial normal stresses that occasionally cause cracks near the weld area are studied by applying a continuous vibration model. Analysis results show that fracture could occur near the weld area, due to low cycle fatigue as a result of large dynamic stresses induced by resonant flexural vibration of the battery tab during welding. The axial normal stresses due to longitudinal waves traveling along the battery tab are shown to be insignificant compared to those due to flexural waves as the longitudinal wavelength at a typical ultrasonic welding frequency (e.g., 20 kHz) is much larger than the battery tab length, whereas the flexural wavelength is much shorter.

It has been observed that sufficient energy is required to produce proper bonding of battery tabs, whereas excessive energy can cause quality issues such as weld fracture and perforation. Therefore, it is important to have a product/process design in ultrasonic welding to ensure efficient energy conversion from ultrasonics to welding energy, minimizing energy loss in the process. Vibrational energy loss due to material damping of the Cu coupon during ultrasonic welding is discussed, where the material damping is modeled as Kevin-Voigt damping and determined experimentally. It is shown that substantial energy loss can occur during welding due to the flexural vibration of the Cu coupon, especially when the overhang (the upper part of the Cu coupon extended from the anvil) of the Cu coupon resonates at or close to the welding frequency, degrading the weld quality of battery tabs.

Keywords: battery tabs, dynamics of battery tabs, ultrasonic welding, vibration of battery tabs, vibrational energy loss

11.1 INTRODUCTION

Ultrasonic metal welding for battery tabs must be performed with 100% reliability in battery pack manufacturing as the failure of one weld essentially results in a battery that is inoperative or cannot deliver the required power due to the electrical short caused by the failed weld. Moreover, this stringent weld quality control is of great concern for battery pack manufacturers as automotive batteries are exposed to harsh driving environment such as vibration, severe temperature, and possibly crash, all of which can affect battery performance and safety. Therefore, one of the main issues arising in ultrasonic welding of battery tabs is to ensure consistent weld quality that meets design specifications such as electrical conductivity and shear strength of the weld. The quality of ultrasonic metal welds depend on a number of factors such as weld configuration, mechanical and metallurgical properties of weld parts, and weld process parameters—weld power, time, frequency, amplitude, clamping pressure, welding temperature, etc. [1].

Understanding that vibration is the driving mechanism and also, at the same time, the cause of weld problems in USMW, the main objective of the present chapter is to introduce and discuss the fundamental aspects of dynamics and vibrations involved in ultrasonic welding of battery tabs. The present work is motivated by numerous laboratory tests which shows a significant variation in weld quality of battery tabs caused by a slight change in geometry and structural properties of the weld part that alter the vibration characteristics of the system.

This chapter presents three main topics. In Section 11.2, the dynamic response of the battery tab during ultrasonic welding and its effect on the sonotrode force required for welding are presented. Section 11.3 discusses the effects of geometry, dimensions, and boundary conditions of the battery tab on the development of dynamic stresses induced by the longitudinal and flexural vibrations of the battery tab during ultrasonic welding. In Section 11.4, vibrational energy loss associated with the longitudinal and flexural vibrations of the copper coupon during ultrasonic welding is studied.

11.2 DYNAMICS OF BATTERY TABS UNDER ULTRASONIC WELDING[1]

Combinations of these factors determine the *sonotrode force* which is required to cause the shearing motion at the weld interface for solid-state bonding. It should be noted that if the required sonotrode force for welding is larger than the gripping force of the sonotrode tip (welding tip), the sonotrode tip will slide against the weld part, resulting in extrusion or even no welding. Note that the gripping force of the sonotrode tip is traction at the interface between the sonotrode weld tip and weld part which solely depends on the size and knurl pattern of the sonotrode tip and the clamping pressure. Therefore it is a prerequisite for USMW that the required sonotrode force for welding should be as small as possible and must not exceed the gripping force of the sonotrode tip during the weld cycle [2].

The sonotrode force required for welding is a resultant force of the inertia force of the weld spot element (weld part pressed by the sonotrode tip) and the elastic/plastic friction force at the weld interface. The sonotrode force must be larger than this resultant force to induce a shearing motion at the weld interface for welding. For a weld part whose size is not significantly larger than the size of weld area, e.g., electrical contact pads or thin wires, the weld part may be considered as a rigid body because the entire weld part oscillates in phase with the sonotrode tip. However, when the dimensions of weld part is significantly larger

[1] The content presented in this section has previously appeared in reference [3].

than those of the weld area, e.g., spot welding of thin wall sections, the elastic vibrations of the weld part during welding should be taken into account for the determination of the upper limit of required sonotrode force. When the wavelength of ultrasonic excitation is comparable to the vibrational wavelengths of the weld part itself, the elastic vibrations of the weld part during welding may interact with the weld spot element causing the required sonotrode force to fluctuate beyond the maximum gripping force of the sonotrode tip. For the present ultrasonic welding of battery tabs, because the dimensions of the battery tab are much larger than the dimensions of the weld area, the structural vibrations of battery tabs are expected to play an important role in determining the weld quality by constantly changing the required sonotrode force during welding.

Although a significant amount of research work on USMW and its applications has been made, most efforts have been focused on the aspects of weld metallurgy and weldability of different materials, however, there is only a limited amount of work to understand the overall dynamics of the ultrasonic welding system, particularly including the structural vibrations of weld parts and supporting structures (tools and fixtures). Jagota and Dawson [4] presented experimental and finite element analyses showing that the bonding strength of thin-walled thermoplastic parts by ultrasonic welding is strongly influenced by the lateral vibration of the weld parts. The impact of waveform designs, by controlling the wavelength of the ultrasonic input, on vibration response reduction of weld parts for the battery welding system is studied by Lee et al. [5].

The main objective of the present study is to examine the dynamic response of the battery tab during ultrasonic welding and assess its effect on the sonotrode force required for welding. This study is motivated by preliminary laboratory tests which show a significant variation in weld strength of battery tabs resulted from a slight alteration in structural properties of the weld part, such as boundary conditions of the battery tab or anvil rigidity. A brief discussion on the free and forced longitudinal vibration of a thin bar is presented in Section 11.2.1 as the battery tab is modeled as a thin bar extended in the direction parallel to the excitation direction of the sonotrode. In Section 11.2.2, the tab-end force which is part of the required sonotrode force due to the elastic vibration of the battery tab is calculated for different end conditions of the battery tab. Experimental results on the kinetic properties of the tab-end are presented in Section 11.2.3. Summary and conclusions are presented in Section 11.2.4.

11.2.1 Theory and Modeling

In the present study, the battery tab is modeled as a thin bar extended parallel to the direction of ultrasonic excitation of the sonotrode, based on the fact that thickness of the battery tab is much smaller than other dimensions, particularly the longitudinal dimension, and on the assumption that the shear stresses developed in the weld spot element during welding result in a body force distributed over the weld spot. A brief introduction to the underlying theory applied to the longitudinal vibration analysis of the battery tab is presented in this section.

Longitudinal Vibration of a Thin Bar
Consider a thin, infinitely long, straight bar with a uniform cross-section subjected to an arbitrarily distributed axial body force $p(x,t)$ (measured as a force per unit length) as shown in Fig. 11.1. The equation governing the longitudinal vibration of the bar can be found as [5]:

$$EA \frac{\partial^2 u}{\partial x^2} + p(x,t) = \rho A \frac{\partial^2 u}{\partial t^2} \qquad (11.2.1)$$

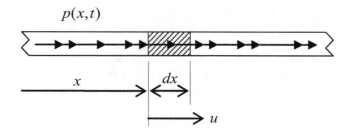

$p(x,t)$

Figure 11.1. Slender bar with coordinate x and displacement u.

TABLE 11.1. Phase velocity c_0 for the battery materials.

	Mass density ρ (kg/m³)	Young's modulus E (GPa)	Phase velocity c_0 (m/s)
Aluminum	2,700	70	5,092
Copper	8,940	110	3,508

where $u = u(x,t)$ denotes the axial displacement of a cross-section, x the spatial coordinate, t the time, E the Young's modulus, A the cross-sectional area, and ρ the mass density of the bar. In the absence of the body force, Eq. (11.2.1) reduces to the classical wave equation:

$$\frac{\partial^2 u}{\partial x^2} = \frac{1}{c_0^2}\frac{\partial^2 u}{\partial t^2} \quad c_0 = \sqrt{E/\rho} \tag{11.2.2}$$

where c_0 is the phase velocity (or *bar velocity*) at which longitudinal waves propagate. Typical phase velocities in most metals are quite high compared with the velocity of sound in air of 340 m/s. Table 11.1 shows the phase velocities for the battery tab materials.

Longitudinal Vibration of a Thin Bar with a Finite Length
The solution of Eq. (11.2.1) can be found by assuming that

$$u(x,t) = U(x)G(t) \tag{11.2.3}$$

where

$$U(x) = C_1 \cos\gamma x + C_2 \sin\gamma x \tag{11.2.4}$$

$$G(t) = D_1 \cos\omega t + D_2 \sin\omega t \tag{11.2.5}$$

where the radial frequency ω, longitudinal wavenumber γ, and longitudinal wavelength λ (the distance between two successive points of constant phase) are related by

$$\omega = c_0\gamma = 2\pi\frac{c_0}{\lambda} \tag{11.2.6}$$

The arbitrary constants in Eqs. (11.2.4) and (11.2.5) depend on the boundary and initial conditions. For example, consider a bar free at one end ($x = 0$) and fixed at the other end

($x = L$). The free boundary condition at $x = 0$ implies that the stress at the bar end must be zero, therefore,

$$E\frac{\partial u(0,t)}{\partial x} = E\frac{dU(0)}{dx}G(t) = E\gamma C_2 G(t) = 0 \tag{11.2.7}$$

Because $G(t) \neq 0$ and $\lambda \neq 0$, Eq. (11.2.7) dictates $C_2 = 0$. The fixed boundary at $x = L$ requires that

$$u(L,t) = U(L)G(t) = C_1 \cos \gamma L\, G(t) = 0 \tag{11.2.8}$$

Because $C_1 \neq 0$, Eq. (11.2.8) yields

$$\cos \gamma L = 0 \tag{11.2.9}$$

which is the frequency equation for the free-fixed bar. Eq. (11.2.9) is satisfied only when

$$\gamma_n = \frac{(2n-1)\pi}{2L} \quad n = 1,2,3,\dots \tag{11.2.10}$$

Thus, the longitudinal natural frequencies of the bar system can be found from

$$\omega_n = \frac{(2n-1)\pi}{2L}c_0 \tag{11.2.11}$$

where ω_n represents the discrete frequency at which the bar system undergoes harmonic motion. For a given value of n, the vibrational pattern (called the nth normal mode or modeshape function) of the bar is described by

$$U_n(x) = \cos \gamma_n x \tag{11.2.12}$$

Combining the time and spatial dependence for a given n, the assumed solution in Eq. (11.2.3) becomes

$$u_n(x,t) = (D_{1n}\cos \omega_n t + D_{2n}\sin \omega t)\cos \gamma_n x \tag{11.2.13}$$

The general solution to Eq. (11.2.2) is then obtained by superposing all normal mode solutions as

$$u(x,t) = \sum_{n=1}^{\infty} u_n(x,t) = \sum_{n=1}^{\infty} (D_{1n}\cos \omega_n t + D_{2n}\sin \omega t)\cos \gamma_n x \tag{11.2.14}$$

where the coefficients D_{1n} and D_{2n} are to be determined by applying the given initial conditions.

Frequency Response Analysis
As a simple example, consider the case of a bar, free at $x = 0$ and fixed at $x = L$, subjected to a harmonic end force $p(t) = p_0 \sin \Omega t$ at $x = 0$. Assuming the bar is initially at rest, the frequency response solution of the bar can be obtained by assuming a solution of the form

$$u(x,t) = U(x)\sin \Omega t \tag{11.2.15}$$

where $U(x)$ is given in Eq. (11.2.4). Applying the boundary conditions at $x = 0$ and $x = L$; i.e.,

$$EA\frac{dU(0)}{dx} = -p_0 \quad U(L) = 0 \qquad (11.2.16)$$

the coefficient C_1 and C_2 in $U(x)$ can be found as

$$C_1 = \frac{p_0}{EA\gamma}\tan\gamma L \quad C_2 = -\frac{p_0}{EA\gamma} \qquad (11.2.17)$$

The resulting forced longitudinal motion of the bar is

$$u(x,t) = \frac{p_0}{EA\gamma}(\tan\gamma L\cos\gamma x - \sin\gamma x)\sin\Omega t \qquad (11.2.18)$$

It can be seen that the response becomes unbounded at the frequencies corresponding to $\cos\gamma L = 0$, or

$$\Omega = \frac{(2n-1)\pi}{2L}c_0 \quad n = 1,2,3,\dots \qquad (11.2.19)$$

11.2.2 Dynamics of the Battery Tabs

Shown in Fig. 11.2 is the cross-sectional view of a single battery cell assembly, where the battery tabs and bus bar are clamped between the sonotrode tip and anvil. For the present study, noting that the thickness of the tab is much smaller than the other dimensions of the tab, the tab is modeled as a thin bar under longitudinal (x-direction) vibration subjected to boundary excitation due to the oscillatory motion of the weld spot element, based on the following observations and assumptions:

1. Only the top tab that is in contact with the sonotrode weld tip is considered in the present study. The coupling through friction and shearing motion at the weld interface between the top tab and the subsequent tab is represented by the interface force F_i (see Fig. 11.2). Note that F_i is the resulting effect of the dynamic behavior of other weld parts below the top tab during welding.
2. No (or negligible) elastic wave motion within the weld spot element beneath the sonotrode tip is possible because the weld spot element is pressed and constrained by the knurl-patterned sonotrode tip. This implies that the weld spot element can be considered as a rigid body oscillating in phase with the sonotrode tip, which is the source of longitudinal excitation to the extended part of the tab.

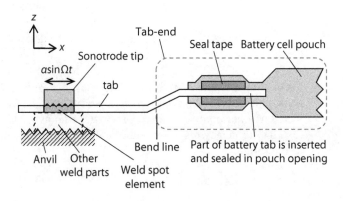

Figure 11.2. Schematic of the battery cell assembly (with the cell pouch partially shown).

3. The sonotrode force, the driving force acts upon the top tab ($F_s = a\sin\Omega t$ in Fig. 11.2), is sufficiently larger than the interface force F_i, otherwise extrusion or no welding occurs.
4. The sonotrode oscillates in the x-direction only, and its amplitude remains constant during welding; transverse (z-direction) vibration does not exist.
5. For the modeling purpose, a term *tab-end* is defined. As indicated in Fig. 11.2, the tab-end includes part of the tab extended from the bend line and *some* part of the battery cell pouch that surrounds the inserted tab.

   Note that the shearing motion of the weld spot element in the tab during welding depends on not only the sonotrode force and friction at the weld interface but also the elastic vibration of the tab. The vibration characteristics of the tab is governed by the boundary conditions of the tab as discussed in Section 11.2.1, then it can be seen from Fig. 11.2 that the tab-end constitutes a natural (kinetic) boundary condition for the tab. During ultrasonic welding, part of the vibration energy injected by the oscillating sonotrode tip travels along the tab, through the tab-end, and then eventually dissipates in the battery cell pouch which contains viscoelastic materials. Hence, the kinetic properties of the tab-end become an important factor determining the longitudinal vibration characteristics of the tab during welding. The kinetic properties of the tab-end are represented by the equivalent mass (m_{eq}), equivalent stiffness (k_{eq}), and equivalent viscous damping (k_{eq}) as shown in Fig. 11.3. Due to complex geometry and material properties of the tab-end which consists of both parts of the battery tab and battery cell pouch, the determination of the equivalent mass, stiffness, and damping of the tab-end by analytical or numerical methods seems limited. An experimental dynamic test to measure the equivalent mass is outlined in Section 11.2.3. Note that the equivalent stiffness of the tab-end can be readily measured through a simple tensile test of the battery tab and cell pouch assembly.

   Shown in Fig. 11.3 is the free body diagram for the weld spot element in a battery cell sketched in Fig. 11.2, subjected to three forces: sonotrode force F_s, interface force F_i from the neighboring tab, and *tab-end force* $F_e = F_{e1} + F_{e2}$ which is due to the elastic vibration of the extended part of the tab during welding. From the free body diagram for the weld spot element in Fig. 11.3, one can find that the minimum sonotrode force F_s required for welding, i.e.,

$$F_s = m\ddot{x} + F_i + F_e \qquad (11.2.20)$$

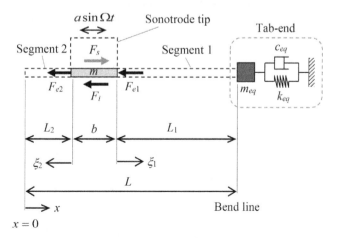

Figure 11.3. Free body diagram for the weld spot element and coordinate system.

The first term on the right side of Eq. (11.2.20) is the inertia force of the weld spot element due to the vibration of the sonotrode. Assuming that the sonotrode maintains its grip against the weld spot element during welding and that the sonotrode oscillates at the frequency f [Hz] with the amplitude of a, i.e., $a\sin\Omega t$, it can be found that

$$m\ddot{x} = -a\Omega^2 \sin\Omega t \quad \Omega = 2\pi f \tag{11.2.21}$$

It is not an easy task to quantify the interface force F_i. This force is expected to be significantly larger than the other forces in Eq. (11.2.20). Note that due to the transitional behavior of friction migrating from dry to viscous friction as welding progresses, F_i is not constant. Quantification of F_i is not a trivial task and may require rigorous theoretical, numerical, and experimental analyses, and thus, it is beyond the scope of the present study and left as future work. However, assuming that the entire weld interface is plastically yielded (i.e., ideal full metal-to-metal contact), one may theoretically approximate the maximum value of F_i as a force that shears the weld. By applying the Tresca maximum-shear yield criterion for the two dimensional stress state [2] and noting that $\sigma_Y \gg p$, the theoretical maximum of F_i can be found to be

$$\max F_i = \frac{A_p}{2}\sqrt{\sigma_Y^2 - p^2} \cong 0.5\sigma_Y A_p \tag{11.2.22}$$

where A_p is the area of plastic deformation zone (weld area) at the weld spot, p the clamping pressure, and σ_Y the yield strength of the tab material. More comprehensive discussion regarding the transitional behavior of the friction coefficient in USMW can be found in the study by Gao and Doumanidis [7].

The tab-end force F_e acting on the weld spot element during welding can be determined by the boundary value analysis of the tab under longitudinal vibration. It is shown in the present study that the tab-end force F_e can be significantly large and very sensitive to the effective mass m_{eq} of the tab-end due to high acceleration (over 16,000 G at 20 kHz with sonotrode amplitude of 10 μm) during welding. A detailed analysis of the tab-end force is as follows.

Natural Frequency Analysis of the Battery Tab

When the wavelength of ultrasonic excitation is comparable to the vibrational wavelengths of the weld part itself, the weld part may be induced to vibrate by the ultrasonic welding system, i.e., resonance can occur. This resonance could cause inconsistent weld quality or a structural failure of the weld part. In order to examine possible resonance of the tab during welding, the natural frequencies of the tab are determined and compared with the ultrasonic welding frequency. With reference to Fig. 11.3, the boundary conditions for the tab are

$$U'(0) = 0 \quad U'(L) = \frac{m_{eq}\omega^2 - k_{eq}}{EA}U(L) \tag{11.2.23}$$

where L is the tab length, i.e., $L = L_1 + L_2 + b$. Applying the above boundary conditions to Eq. (11.2.4), it can be found that the natural frequencies of the tab must satisfy the following frequency equation

$$\hat{m}_{eq}\beta_n^2 + \beta_n \tan\beta_n - \hat{k}_{eq} = 0 \quad \beta_n = \frac{L}{c_0}\omega_n \tag{11.2.24}$$

where β_n denotes the wavenumber (number of repeating waves) for the nth vibration mode and $\hat{m}_{eq}$ and $\hat{k}_{eq}$ are the nondimensional equivalent mass and stiffness of the tab-end, respectively, normalized by

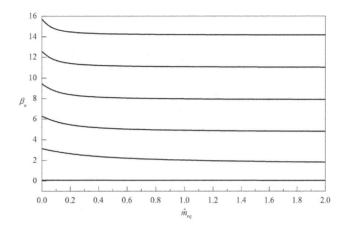

Figure 11.4. Wavenumber loci of the first 6 longitudinal vibration modes. $\hat{k}_{eq} = 5.23 \times 10^{-3}$.

$$\hat{m}_{eq} = \frac{m_{eq}}{\rho A L} \qquad \hat{k}_{eq} = \frac{k_{eq} L}{EA} \tag{11.2.25}$$

The frequency equation in Eq. (11.2.24) needs to be solved numerically, hence $k_{eq} = 150$ kN/m is assumed for both aluminum and copper tabs, which gives $\hat{k}_{eq} = 5.23 \times 10^{-3}$ for the aluminum tab and $\hat{k}_{eq} = 3.33 \times 10^{-3}$ for the copper tab. Assuming $L = 20$ mm, $0 \le \hat{m}_{eq} \le 2$ is considered for numerical simulations, which corresponds to $0 \le m_{eq} \le 0.89$ g for the aluminum tab and $0 \le m_{eq} \le 2.93$ g for the copper tab. Shown in Fig. 11.4 are the wavenumber loci as a function of $\hat{m}_{eq}$ for the first six longitudinal vibration modes of the tab. Notable findings are as follows.

- The wavenumber of the fundamental longitudinal vibration mode of the tab is very small. For example, $\beta_1 = 0.07$ for $\hat{m}_{eq} = 0$ and $\beta_1 = 0.04$ for $\hat{m}_{eq} = 2$, each corresponding to the wavelength of 1,795 and 3,142 mm. This suggests that the fundamental longitudinal vibration mode of the tab behaves almost like a rigid body mode.
- The effect of increasing $\hat{m}_{eq}$ on the longitudinal wavenumbers of the tab becomes quickly saturated for all vibration modes.
- Although not presented, under the presence of $\hat{m}_{eq}$, $\hat{k}_{eq}$ has an insignificant effect on altering the wavenumbers of the tab for all vibration modes unless it is very large. Note that the fundamental wavenumber is $\pi/2$ when $\hat{k}_{eq} = \infty$.

Shown in Fig. 11.5 are the natural frequency loci of the longitudinal vibration for each tab against the equivalent mass of the tab-end when $k_{eq} = 150$ kN/m. It can be noticed that the current ultrasonic welding frequency (20 kHz) is not close to any of the natural frequencies for both aluminum and copper tabs, regardless of m_{eq}, indicating little possibility for resonance of the tab during welding.

Dynamic Effects of the Tab-End

Ultrasonic weld quality of battery tabs depends on the mechanical properties of the battery tab itself including its geometry/dimensions in addition to weld parameters such as weld frequency, clamping pressure, pre-weld surface condition, and weld time. Although the thickness of the individual battery tabs is an important factor that determines the weldability of multiple battery tabs and bus bar, the weld quality (weld strength in general) depends on the size of the tab relative to the weld spot area, especially the dimension of the tab in

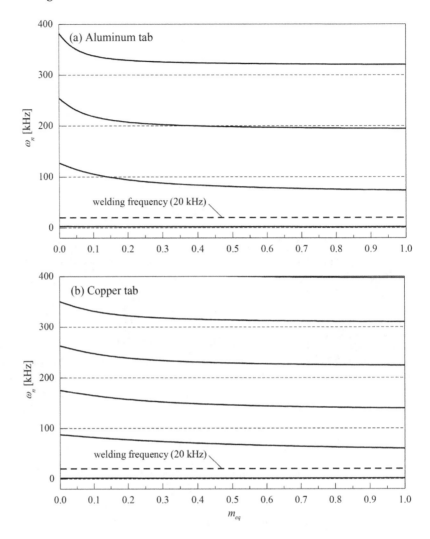

Figure 11.5. Longitudinal natural frequency loci up to 400 kHz against m_{eq} for $L = 20$ mm and $k_{eq} = 150$ kN/m. The dashed line represents the ultrasonic welding frequency Ω.

the direction of excitation. If this dimension is comparable with the ultrasonic wavelength, the elastic vibration of the tab in the direction of welding will significantly increase the sonotrode force required for welding, and could be detrimental to welding when resonance occurs. The elastic vibration of the battery tab and its resonant behavior are characterized by the length (L_1 in Fig. 11.3) between the weld spot and tab-end as well as the kinetic properties of that tab-end. Under the current welding practice of battery tabs, L_1 varies depending on the location of weld spot.

A typical ultrasonic metal weld cycle is less than 1 second. It should be noted that ultrasonic weld process is transient by its nature as the friction/shearing force at the weld interface is not steady, but usually increases as bonding areas at the weld interface increase. Nevertheless, the concept of steady state can be applied to the present tab-end force analysis for the following two reasons; (1) the sonotrode of ultrasonic welder is under feedback control to maintain its vibration amplitude constant during welding and (2) the sonotrode force (that grabs and excites the weld part) is larger than the sum of other resistant forces (inertia force of weld element, interface force, and tab-end force), otherwise the sonotrode tip loses its grip against the weld part and extrusion or no welding occurs.

Therefore, the weld spot element which is pressed and constrained by the sonotrode tip can be modeled as a rigid body oscillating in phase with the sonotrode tip. This rigid body motion of the weld spot element acts as sinusoidal boundary excitation to the extended part of the battery tab. Various experiments (not shown in the present study) show that the sonotrode weld tip reaches its steady state at the very beginning of the weld cycle with the weld frequency of 20 kHz.

In order to determine the tab-end forces F_{e1} and F_{e2} acting on the weld spot element, the tab is divided into two segments with respect to the weld spot element, i.e., S_1 segment ($0 \leq \xi_1 \leq L_1$) which is on the right side of the weld spot element and S_2 segment ($0 \leq \xi_2 \leq L_2$) on the left side of the weld spot element as shown in Fig. 11.3. To determine F_{e1}, consider S_1 segment of the tab. Because the weld spot element is rigid and oscillates with the sonotrode in the same phase, the velocity at $\xi_1 = 0$ of S_1 segment must be the same as the sonotrode tip velocity $a\Omega$. Moreover, at the other end ($\xi_1 = L_1$), S_1 segment interacts with the tab-end. Therefore, the boundary conditions for S_1 segment of the tab are:

$$U(0) = a \qquad \frac{dU(L_1)}{d\xi_1} = \frac{k_{eq}L - ic_{eq}\Omega - k_{eq}}{EA} U(L_1) \qquad (11.2.26)$$

Applying the above boundary conditions to Eq. (11.2.4), the steady-state longitudinal displacement of S_1 segment of the tab can be found as

$$u(\xi_1, t) = a \, |H(\xi_1, i\Omega)| \sin(\Omega t - \phi) \qquad 0 \leq \xi_1 \leq L_1 \qquad (11.2.27)$$

where $H(\xi_1, i\Omega)$ is the complex frequency response function, defined by

$$H(\xi_1, i\Omega) = \cos\left(\frac{\Omega}{c_0}\xi_1\right) + \alpha(i\Omega)\sin\left(\frac{\Omega}{c_0}\xi_1\right) \qquad (11.2.28)$$

$$a(i\Omega) = \frac{\dfrac{(m_{eq}\Omega^2 - ic_{eq}\Omega - k_{eq})}{EA}\cos\left(\dfrac{\Omega}{c_0}L_1\right) + \dfrac{\Omega}{c_0}\sin\left(\dfrac{\Omega}{c_0}L_1\right)}{\dfrac{\Omega}{c_0}\cos\left(\dfrac{\Omega}{c_0}L_1\right) - \dfrac{(m_{eq}\Omega^2 - ic_{eq}\Omega - k_{eq})}{EA}\sin\left(\dfrac{\Omega}{c_0}L_1\right)} \qquad (11.2.29)$$

and ϕ the phase angle, defined by $\phi = \angle H(\xi_1, i\Omega)$. If $c_{eq} = 0$, $a(i\Omega) = \tan((\Omega/c_0)L_1)$ when either $\Omega = \sqrt{k_{eq}/m_{eq}}$ or $m_{eq} = k_{eq} = 0$ and that $H(\xi_1, i\Omega)$ reduces to

$$H(\xi_1, i\Omega) = \cos\left(\frac{\Omega}{c_0}\xi_1\right) + \tan\left(\frac{\Omega}{c_0}L_1\right)\sin\left(\frac{\Omega}{c_0}\xi_1\right) \qquad (11.2.30)$$

This implies, when $c_{eq} = 0$ and $\Omega = \sqrt{k_{eq}/m_{eq}}$, the dynamic effect of the tab-end is identical to the one with the free boundary condition. For S_2 segment of the tab, because $m_{eq} = k_{eq} = c_{eq} = 0$, it can be readily found that

$$u(\xi_1, t) = a\left(\cos\left(\frac{\Omega}{c_0}\xi_2\right) + \tan\left(\frac{\Omega}{c_0}L_2\right)\sin\left(\frac{\Omega}{c_0}\xi_2\right)\right)\sin\Omega t \quad 0 \leq \xi_2 \leq L_2 \quad (11.2.31)$$

Axial Stress Distribution in the Tab

Because $\sigma_x = E\,\partial u/\partial x$, the axial stress distribution in each segment of the tab can be found from Eqs. (11.2.27) and (11.2.31). For S_1 segment,

$$\sigma_x(\xi_1, t) = Ea\left|\frac{\partial H(\xi_1, i\Omega)}{\partial \xi_1}\right| \sin(\Omega t - \phi) \qquad 0 \leq \xi_1 \leq L_1 \qquad (11.2.32)$$

and for S_2 segment

$$\sigma_x(\xi_2,t) = Ea\frac{\Omega}{c_0}\left(\tan\left(\frac{\Omega}{c_0}L_2\right)\cos\left(\frac{\Omega}{c_0}\xi_2\right) - \sin\left(\frac{\Omega}{c_0}\xi_2\right)\right)\sin\Omega t \qquad 0 \le \xi_2 \le L_2 \quad (11.2.33)$$

Figure 11.6 shows the axial stress distributions in S_1 segment of the tab for different values of m_{eq}, where $L_1 = 20$ mm and $k_{eq} = 150$ kN/m and $c_{eq} = 0$. The cases for free ($m_{eq} = k_{eq} = c_{eq} = 0$) and fixed ($k_{eq} = \infty$ and $m_{eq} = c_{eq} = 0$) boundary conditions are also shown as the limiting cases. Notable behavior is summarized as follows:

- Stress distributions in the tab are monotonic with a gradual decrease in slopes toward the tab-end, indicating that the stress wavelength is much larger than the tab length.
- Depending on the equivalent mass of the tab-end, the entire or part of the tab can be subjected to dynamic stresses exceeding the material's yield strength ($\sigma_Y = 55$ MPa for aluminum and $\sigma_Y = 172$ MPa for copper at 25°C). These high stresses could plasticize the tab material and make the tab prone to buckling during welding under certain conditions, for example the transverse vibration of the tab or material irregularity.
- Large stresses in the tab during welding may be indicative of the loss of welding energy. In other words, part of the welding energy gives rise to increase in the

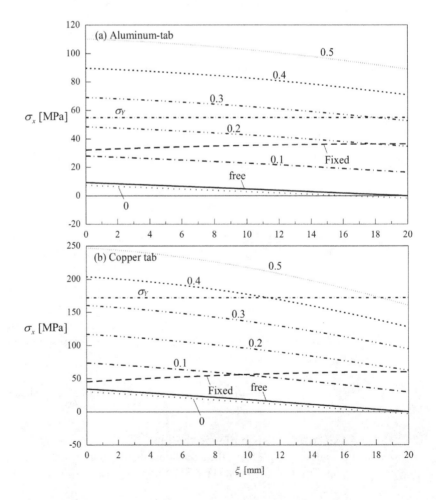

Figure 11.6. Axial stress distribution in the tab due to longitudinal vibration of the tab with $k_{eq} = 150$ kN/m, where $L_1 = 20$ mm and the numbers indicate m_{eq} in grams.

overall strain energy of the tab. It is necessary to employ a design to minimize the equivalent mass (or its effect) of the tab-end.

- As previously mentioned, when $\Omega = \sqrt{k_{eq}/m_{eq}}$ and $c_{eq} = 0$, the tab-end behaves as if it is free of constraints. This fact could be utilized for the design of tab-pouch interface to lower the stresses in the tab during welding.
- The effect of the equivalent stiffness of the tab-end is not as drastic as the equivalent mass. This can be inferred by comparing the stress distribution curves between the two extreme cases, free and fixed boundary conditions. It can be seen that the difference in stresses is relatively small, even between these two extreme cases, indicating that the dynamics of the tab during welding is more affected by the equivalent mass rather than the equivalent stiffness.

Effect of Weld Spot Location on the Tab-End Force
The weld spot location (L_2 in Fig. 11.3) is an important design parameter for battery tab welding as it has been observed in various experiments that a slight change (less than 1 mm) of the weld spot location causes excessive vibration of the tab during welding, resulting in unacceptable weld strength or extrusion due to increase of sonotrode force required for welding. From Eq. (11.2.32), the tab-end force $F_{e1} = A\sigma_x(0,t)$ exerting on the weld spot element due to the elastic vibration of S_1 segment of the tab can be found as

$$F_{e1} = EAa \left| \frac{\partial H(0, i\Omega)}{\partial \xi_1} \right| \sin(\Omega t - \phi) \tag{11.2.34}$$

In a similar manner, from Eq. (11.2.33), the tab-end force exerted by S_2 segment of the tab is

$$F_{e2} = EAa \frac{\Omega}{c_0} \tan\left(\frac{\Omega}{c_0} L_2\right) \sin \Omega t \tag{11.2.35}$$

The total amplitude of the tab-end force acting on the weld spot element becomes $F_e = F_{e1} + F_{e2}$. It can be seen from Eqs. (11.2.34) and (11.2.35) that the tab-end force acting on the weld spot element depends on the span length of each segment as well as the equivalent mass, stiffness, and damping of the tab-end. In other words, the location of the weld spot relative to the entire tab length also affects the sonotrode force required for welding. Figure 11.7 shows the total tab-end force F_e acting on the weld spot element for each of the aluminum and copper tabs as a function of the weld spot location measured from the free end (i.e., $x = 0$ in Fig. 11.3) of the tab, for slightly different values of the equivalent mass of the tab-end, demonstrating the effect of tab-end dynamics. Some notable behavior is summarized as follows:

- The weld spot location plays an important role in determining the tab-end force, and thus the sonotrode force required for welding. A slight change in the equivalent mass of the tab-end significantly changes the tab-end force.
- For the aluminum tab, the tab-end force is not a simple linear function of the equivalent mass. For example, when $L_2 = 0$, the smallest tab-end force is when $m_{eq} = 0.5$ g. A similar behavior can be found for the copper tab, however, in this case m_{eq} for the smallest tab-end force is much larger than the one for the aluminum tab.
- The tab-end force strongly depends on the elastic vibration of the tab. Because the elastic vibration of the tab depends on the mechanical properties (i.e., ρ and E), tab length, and boundary conditions at the tab-end, depending on the combinations these parameters, the tab-end force may increase or decrease as the weld spot location changes. In comparison of Figs. 11.7(a) and (b), if one shifts the curves in Fig. 11.7(b) toward the origin, it can be seen that the overall behavior of the tab-end force for both aluminum and copper tabs is similar. In other words, the inflection points of the individual curves for the copper tab are located at larger

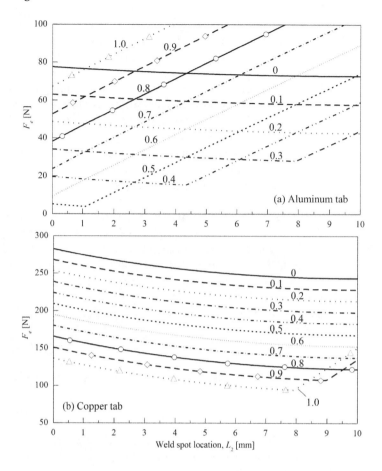

Figure 11.7. Tab-end force as a function of the weld spot location with $k_{eq} = 150$ kN/m, where the total length of the tab is $L = 20$ mm and the numbers indicate m_{eq} in grams.

values of L_2. This is due to the natural frequencies of the copper tab are lower than the ones of the aluminum tab. Note also that as L_2 increases, i.e., as the weld spot location moves closer to the tab-end, the elastic vibration of Segment 2 of the tab (see Fig. 11.3) results in increasing the tab-end force.

- Although not shown in the plots, it is found that the effect of the equivalent stiffness of the tab-end on the tab-end force is not as drastic as the equivalent mass.
- The relation between the weld spot location and tab-end force may serve as a guideline for battery tab design and welding. For example, when $m_{eq} = 0.5$ g for the aluminum tab, $L_2 = 1.1$ mm is the optimal *Z-height* for the minimum tab-end force.

Effect of Damping on the Tab-End Force and Energy Dissipation
Shown in Fig. 11.8 is the total tab-end force as a function of the weld spot location for several different values of the equivalent viscous damping coefficient, c_{eq}, at the tab-end. Note that the welding (excitation) frequency ($\Omega = 20$ kHz) is between the first and second natural frequencies, being closer to the first one, of both aluminum and copper tabs when $L_1 = 20$ mm. Note also that the critical modal damping coefficient for the first vibration mode is about 18 Ns/m for the aluminum tab with $k_{eq} = 105$ kN/m and $m_{eq} = 0.0063$ g, and 32 Ns/m for the copper tab with $k_{eq} = 147$ kN/m and $m_{eq} = 0.012$ g. It can be seen that the tab-end force increases with increasing c_{eq}. When damping is present, it is of more interest to know the amount of vibration energy dissipated by the damping during welding.

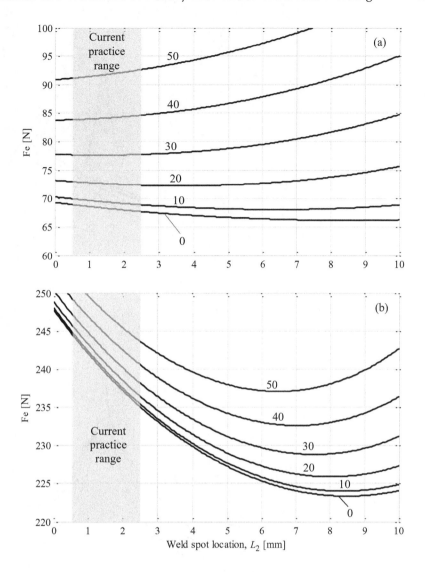

Figure 11.8. Tab-end force as a function of the weld spot location, where the total length of the tab is $L =$ 20 mm. The numbers indicate c_{eq} in [Ns/m]. (a) Aluminum tab, C-bend, $k_{eq} = 105$ kN/m, and $m_{eq} = 0.0063$ g and (b) copper tab, C-bend, $k_{eq} = 147$ kN/m, and $m_{eq} = 0.0102$ g.

Denoting ΔE_d as the energy dissipation per cycle by the equivalent viscous damper at the tab-end (i.e., $\xi_1 = L_1$), it can be found that

$$\Delta E_d = \int_{-\frac{\phi}{\Omega}}^{\frac{2\pi-\phi}{\Omega}} c_{eq}\dot{u}^2(L_1,t)dt = \pi c_{eq}\Omega a^2|H(L_1,i\Omega)|^2 \qquad (11.2.36)$$

Figure 11.9 shows the plots of ΔE_d as a function of the tab length L_1 for different values of c_{eq}. Note that the steady-state response amplitude of aluminum tab with $L_1 = 44$ mm, $k_{eq} = 105$ kN/m, and $m_{eq} = 0.0063$ g is largest as the excitation frequency Ω is close to the second damped natural frequency of the tab when $c_{eq} = 10$ Ns/m, and that the steady state response amplitude of copper tab with $L_1 = 44$ mm, $k_{eq} = 147$ kN/m, and $m_{eq} = 0.012$ g is largest for the values of c_{eq} considered in this numerical example. As expected it can be seen that the energy dissipation by damping peaks at resonance. For example, when $c_{eq} = 10$ Ns/m, about

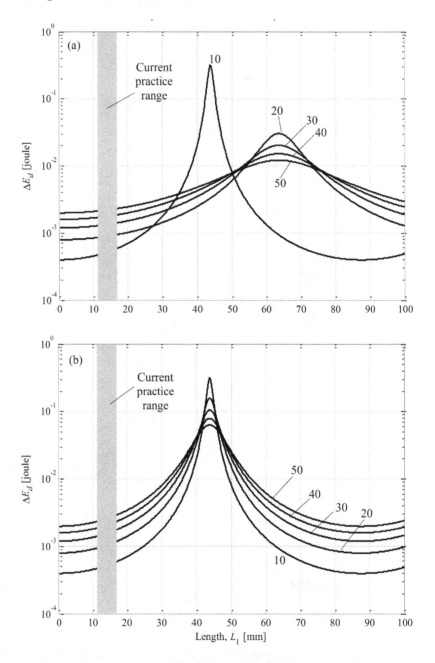

Figure 11.9. Energy dissipation per cycle by the equivalent viscous damper at the tab-end, as a function of tab length L_1. The numbers indicate c_{eq} in [Ns/m]. (a) Aluminum tab, C-bend,
$k_{eq} = 105$ kN/m, and $m_{eq} = 0.0063$ g and (b) copper tab, C-bend, $k_{eq} = 147$ kN/m, and
$m_{eq} = 0.012$ g.

0.3 J of energy is dissipated per each excitation cycle at resonance, which amounts to 3,000 J
of energy dissipation for 0.5 seconds steady-state welding time at $\Omega = 20$ kHz. Note that the
power of the ultrasonic welder used for the current welding of battery tabs is 3,000 watts.
However, a typical tab length (L_1) in the current practice of battery tabs welding is within 11
and 17 mm as indicated in the figure. In this range, the energy dissipated by the damping at
the tab-end is of the order of 10^{-3} J per cycle for the values of c_{eq} considered in this example.

Sonotrode Force Required for Welding

Recalling Eq. (11.2.20), the required sonotrode force F_s for welding is the sum of the three non-constant forces; inertia force $ma\Omega^2$ of the weld spot element, elastic/plastic friction force F_i at the weld interface, and tab-end force F_e due to the longitudinal vibration of the tab. It has been suggested by the present analysis that $F_i > F_e > ma\Omega^2$ in general. The interface force F_i rapidly increases as welding progresses to its maximum value, inducing plastic deformation at the weld interface [7]. Although F_i is at its maximum, it is possible that the sum of the other two forces $(ma\Omega^2 + F_e)$ causes the required sonotrode force to exceed its upper limit which is the gripping force (F_g) at the sonotrode-tab interface. Noted that F_g is a constant force which depends solely on the clamping pressure and knurl pattern of the sonotrode tip. When $F_s > F_g$, the sonotrode tip loses its grip on the tab, which would result in extrusion or unacceptable welding. For welding to occur, the peak value of the required sonotrode force must not exceed the gripping force during the weld cycle. As demonstrated in the present analysis results, the tab-end force is significantly influenced by the longitudinal vibration of the tab itself which in turn depends on the kinetic properties of the tab-end, i.e., equivalent mass and stiffness. Therefore a proper design of the battery tab and cell pouch interface can minimize the tab-end force, thus lowering the required sonotrode force during welding.

11.2.3 Experimental Results and Discussion

Experimental Measurement of the Equivalent Mass and Stiffness of Tab-End

The equivalent stiffness of the tab-end can be readily measured through a typical tensile test. Although the battery cell pouch and tab assembly is secured (by using a fixture) in the same manner as it is constrained in the battery module during welding, the tab is quasi-statically pulled by a tensile testing machine to generate a force-displacement curve, where note that grip on the tab must be right above the bend line. The maximum slope of the force-displacement curve is the measure of the equivalent stiffness of the tab-end. Figure 11.10(a) shows schematically the technique to measure the equivalent mass using an ultrasonic welder, a laser vibrometer with DAQ, and a *dummy mass* securely affixed to the battery tab. In addition, a fixture is required to clamp the battery cell pouch in the same manner as

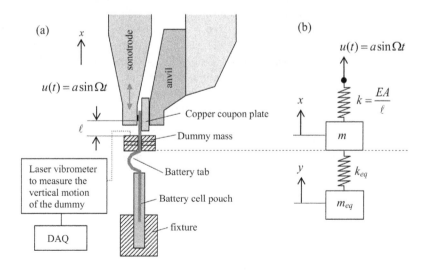

Figure 11.10. (a) Experimental setup for measurement of the equivalent mass of the tab-end and (b) equivalent 2-DOF system.

in actual welding. During welding, the dummy mass vibrates in response to the sonotrode excitation through the longitudinal motion of the tab.

Once the response amplitude of the dummy mass is measured with the laser vibrometer, the equivalent mass of the tab-end can be calculated from the sinusoidal transfer function of the equivalent 2-DOF mass-spring system shown in Fig. 11.10(b). The equations of motion of the equivalent system are

$$m\ddot{x} + (k + k_{eq})x = ku + k_{eq}y \tag{11.2.37}$$

$$m\ddot{y} + k_{eq}y = k_{eq}x \tag{11.2.38}$$

where m is the mass of the dummy mass and k is the longitudinal stiffness of the tab between the weld spot and dummy mass as shown in Fig. 11.10(a). From the above equations, the sinusoidal transfer function for the dummy mass can be found as

$$G(i\omega) = \frac{ka}{(k + k_{eq}) - m\Omega^2 - \dfrac{k_{eq}^2}{(k_{eq} - m_{eq}\Omega^2)}} \tag{11.2.39}$$

Hence, the steady-state response amplitude of the dummy mass is

$$x_{ss} = aG(i\omega) \tag{11.2.40}$$

where a is the sonotrode amplitude. Because k_{eq} and X_{ss} are known from the measurement, m_{eq} can be found by solving Eq. (11.2.40) for m_{eq}. According to the methodologies described above, the equivalent mass (m_{eq}) and stiffness (k_{eq}) of the tab-end have been experimentally determined. For the measurement of k_{eq}, a single battery cell-pouch, insulation form, and cooling plates are placed between two nylon frames clamped by a specially built fixture in order to replicate the same boundary conditions for the battery cell-pouch as it is secured in the battery module during welding. Instron tensile testing machine with DAQ is used to obtain the p-δ curve for each of the C-bend and S-bend tabs, from which k_{eq} of the tab-end is obtained and summarized in Table 11.2.

In order to determine m_{eq} of the tab-end, the velocity ($\dot{X}_{45°}$) of the dummy mass is measured at 45° (due to interference with the fixture and welder) by using the Polytec laser vibrometer, and from which the velocity ($\dot{X}$) in the weld direction can be found by $\dot{X} = \sqrt{2}\dot{X}_{45°}$. Figures 11.11 and 11.12 show the measured velocity ($\dot{X}_{45°}$) of the dummy mass. Applying $m = 4.7$ g, and k_{eq}, and the steady-state velocity amplitude for each tab to Eq. (11.2.40), m_{eq} of the tab-end is determined as summarized in Table 11.3. It can be seen that m_{eq} of the tab-end is found to be insignificantly small. It is believed that the tab-bend effectively weakens the dynamic coupling between the battery tab and cell-pouch.

Dynamic Effects of the Tab-End

By applying the measured values of the effective mass and stiffness of the tab-end, the axial stress distribution in the tab during welding and the resulting tab-end force are

TABLE 11.2. Equivalent stiffness (k_{eq}) of the tab-end.

Bend shape	Al-tab (kN/m)	Cu-tab (kN/m)
C-bend (⌐⌐)	94–115	114–180
S-bend (⌐)	21–42	33–53

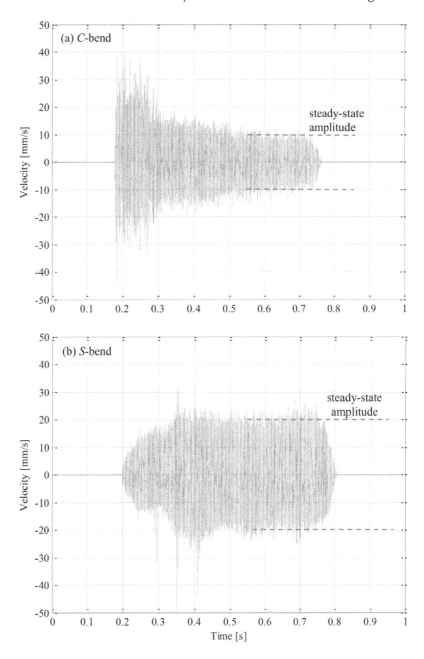

Figure 11.11. Velocity ($\dot{X}_{45°}$) of the dummy mass for aluminum tab.

computed. Shown in Fig. 11.13 is the axial stress distribution of the tab (Segment 1). It can be seen that axial stresses are well below the yield strength (55 MPa for Al-tab and 172 MPa for Cu tab at 25°C) and very little differences in stresses between C-bend and S-bend. Figure 11.14 shows the tab-end force as a function of the weld spot location. It can be seen that 1 mm change in the Z-*height* toward the battery cell-pouch lowers the tab-end force by about 1 N for Al-tab and 5 N for Cu-tab within a practical range of weld spot location. Note that the range of the weld spot location in the current practice is between 0 and 2 mm.

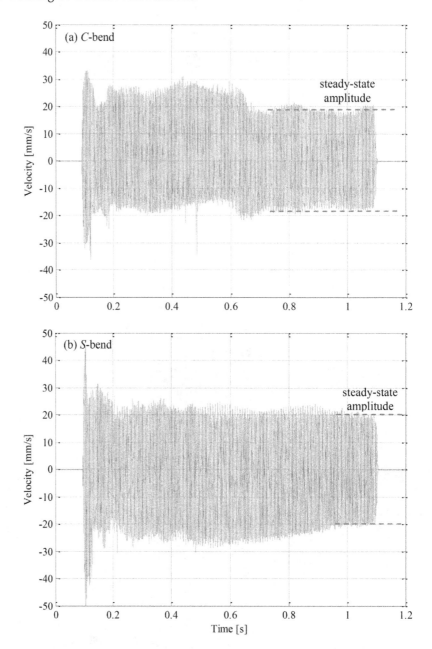

Figure 11.12. Velocity ($\dot{X}_{45°}$) of the dummy mass for copper tab.

TABLE 11.3. Equivalent stiffness (m_{eq}) of the tab-end.

Bend shape	Al-tab [g]	Cu-tab [g]
C-bend (⌒)	0.006–0.0066	0.0091–0.0114
S-bend (⌒)	0.0013–0.0027	0.0021–0.0034

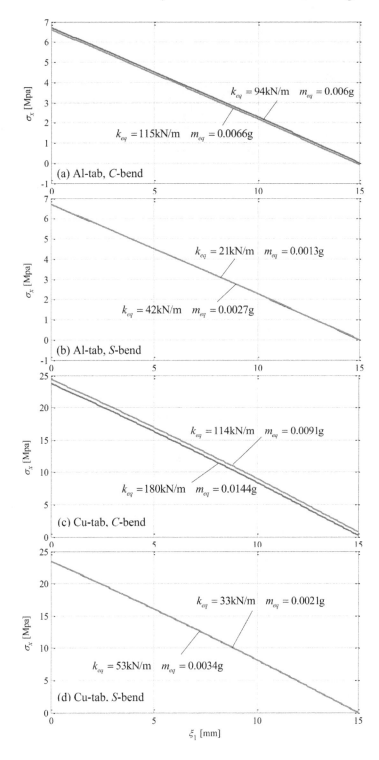

Figure 11.13. Axial stress distribution due to longitudinal vibration of the tab, where $L_1 = 20$ mm.

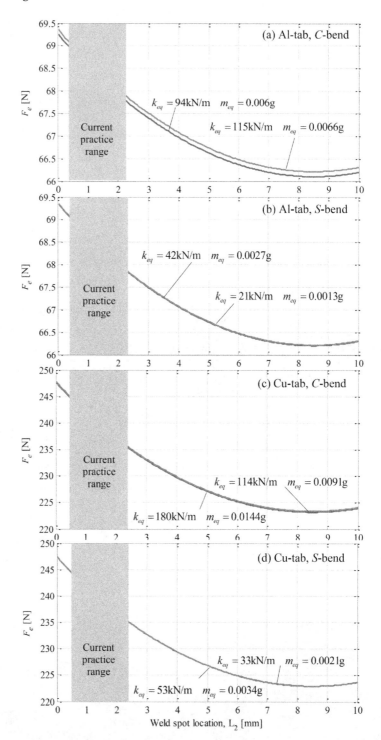

Figure 11.14. Tab-end force against weld spot location, where the total length of the tab is $L = 23$ mm.

11.2.4 Summary and Conclusions

The effect of dynamic response of a single battery tab on the sonotrode force required for welding is studied by applying a one-dimensional continuous vibration model for the battery tab. The battery tab is modeled as a thin bar vibrating longitudinally under ultrasonic excitation from the sonotrode. This study serves as the foundation for a scientific understanding of battery tab dynamics during ultrasonic welding and its effect on weld quality, and thus provides a guideline for design and welding of battery tabs. Notable findings are summarized as follows:

1. A slight change in the kinetic properties of the battery tab-end (interface between the tab and battery cell pouch), being amplified by the longitudinal vibration of the battery tab at high acceleration during ultrasonic welding, causes a significant change in the sonotrode force required for welding. Experimental quantification of the kinetic properties of the tab-end in terms of the equivalent mass, stiffness, and viscous damper as key design parameters is needed for the design of battery tabs to improve the weld quality.
2. Axial stresses of the battery tab during ultrasonic welding could exceed the material's yield strength when the equivalent mass of the tab-end is large, suggesting that the battery tab is prone to plastic deformation and buckling due to dynamic instability triggered by subtle transverse motions such as anvil or bus bar vibrations. Reduction of the equivalent mass of the battery tab-end can lower the required sonotrode force for welding.
3. The difference in sonotrode forces required for welding between the aluminum and copper tab is significantly large. That is, the sonotrode force required for welding of the aluminum tab is significantly lower than welding the copper tab. Studies on the effect of an excessive sonotrode force on weld quality are warranted.
4. The sonotrode force required for welding is substantially affected by the weld spot location. The optimal location of weld spot for the minimum sonotrode force also depends on the kinetic properties of the battery tab end.

Nomenclature

A	Cross-sectional area of battery tab (45×0.2 mm)
a	Sonotrode amplitude ($20\ \mu$m peak-to-peak)
A_p	Weld area (= sonotrode tip areas, $3 \times (3 \times 5$ mm$) = 45$ mm^2)
b	Longitudinal dimension of weld spot (3 mm is used for numerical examples)
c_0	Phase velocity (= $\sqrt{E/\rho}$)
c_{eq}	Equivalent viscous damping coefficient (see Fig. 11.3)
E	Young's modulus (70 GPa for aluminum and 110 GPa for copper)
F_s	Sonotrode force [N]
F_e	Tab-end force [N] ($F_e = F_{e1} + F_{e2}$, see Fig. 11.3)
F_i	Interface force at weld spot [N]
k_{eq}	Equivalent stiffness of the tab-end (see Fig. 11.3)
L	Tab length (see Fig. 11.3)
l	Distance between the top of dummy mass and the bottom of sonotrode tip (see Fig. 11.10)
L_1	Length of the tab between the weld spot and tab-end (see Fig. 11.3)
L_2	Length of the tab between the weld spot and free end (see Fig. 11.3)
m	Mass of the weld spot element [kg]
m_{eq}	Equivalent mass of the tab-end (see Fig. 11.3)
u	Longitudinal displacement of the tab [mm]
U_n	Normal mode function

x	Longitudinal coordinate
α	See Eq. (11.2.19)
β_n	Longitudinal wavenumber of the battery tab. See Eq. (11.2.24)
γ	Wavenumber of a thin bar under longitudinal vibration
λ	Wavelength ($\lambda = 2\pi/\gamma$)
ρ	Mass density (2700 kg/m^3 for aluminum and 8940 kg/m^3 for copper)
σx	Axial stress
σ_Y	Yield strength ($\sigma_Y = 55$ MPa for aluminum and $\sigma_Y = 172$ MPa for copper at 25°C)
Ω	Sonotrode frequency [rad/s] ($\Omega = 2\pi f$, $f =$ sonotrode frequency [Hz])
ω_n	Natural frequency [rad/s]

11.3 DYNAMIC STRESS ANALYSIS OF BATTERY TABS[2]

One of the main issues arising in ultrasonic welding of battery tabs is to ensure consistent weld quality that meets design specifications such as the electrical conductivity and shear strength of the weld [8]. The quality of ultrasonic metal welds depends on a number of factors such as the weld configuration, mechanical and metallurgical properties of the weld parts, and weld process parameters—amplitude, clamping pressure, and welding energy [9, 10]. It is also important to carefully design the weld parts and tools to avoid resonance of any of the weld parts and tools to prevent failure during welding and post-welding. Through experimental and finite element analyses, Jagota and Dawson [4] showed that the bonding strength of thin-walled thermoplastic parts by ultrasonic welding is strongly influenced by the lateral vibration of the weld parts. The impact of waveform designs, by controlling the wavelength of the ultrasonic input, on vibration response reduction of weld parts for the battery welding system was studied by Lee et al. [5]. The effects of dynamic responses of weld parts on the sonotrode force required for welding in USMW was studied by Kang et al. [3, 11]. They showed that the sonotrode force is substantially affected by the weld spot location and also that the axial stresses of the battery tab during welding could exceed the material's yield strength depending on the kinetic properties of the interface between the tab and battery cell pouch. However, in that study, the flexural vibration of the battery tab due to the transverse motion of the anvil during welding was not considered, which could cause large dynamic stresses near the weld spot under certain conditions. In our prior work [12], extensive experiments were conducted to gain understanding of the vibration characteristics of the ultrasonic welding process of battery tabs. Vibration response of the welder system including the anvil was measured using a high precision (resolution of 2 nm) single-point laser vibrometer at a sampling rate of 256 kHz. Experimental data consistently showed transverse (i.e., normal to the weld surface) vibrations of the anvil with amplitudes up to several microns. In particular, when the transfer stiffness of the anvil was deliberately reduced, the vibration amplitude of the anvil increased and some of the weld spots debonded or the tabs bulged near the weld spots. These experiments demonstrated that the transverse vibration of the anvil, even at the level of a few microns, could have a significant adverse effect on the weld quality of battery tabs.

Although a significant amount of research work on USMW and its applications has been made, most efforts have been focused on the aspects of weld metallurgy and weldability of different materials. There is, however, only a limited amount of work to understand the overall dynamics of the ultrasonic welding system, particularly including the structural vibrations of weld parts and supporting structures (tools and fixtures). De Vries [2] summarized a number of studies related to USMW and presented a mechanics-based model to

---

[2] The content presented in this section has previously appeared in reference [13].

estimate the tangential forces during ultrasonic welding that act on the weld parts and interface, and correlate them to weld quality. Jagota and Dawson [4] presented experimental and finite element analyses showing that the bonding strength of thin-walled thermoplastic parts by ultrasonic welding was strongly influenced by the lateral vibration of the weld parts.

The present study is motivated by the observation of the sensitivity of weld quality, particularly the tab surface cracks and perforations, to the geometry, dimensions, and boundary conditions of tabs and busbar. These cracks and perforations are suspected to be low-cycle[3] fatigue fractures [14, 15] induced by alternating axial stresses due to the vibration of the tab during welding. The objective of this study is to address the effects of geometry, dimensions, and boundary conditions of the battery tab (along with its material and mechanical properties) on the development of dynamic stresses induced by the longitudinal and flexural vibrations of the battery tab during ultrasonic welding. To this end, the battery tab is modeled as a continuous elastic beam extended in the direction parallel to the excitation direction of the sonotrode. In addition, the anvil vibration in the normal direction of the battery tab is considered as the excitation source to the flexural vibration of the tab during welding.

11.3.1 Longitudinal and Flexural Vibrations of a Beam

The thickness of the battery tab is much smaller than its other dimensions. Therefore, the battery tab can be modeled as a thin beam extended parallel to the excitation direction of the sonotrode, and under longitudinal and flexural vibrations. A brief discussion of vibration theory [6, 16] related to the axial normal stress induced by the longitudinal, and flexural vibrations of the battery tab are presented in this section.

Dynamic Stresses Due to Axial Boundary Excitation in a Thin Beam

Consider a thin beam, free at $x = L$, under harmonic displacement excitation $a_l \sin \Omega t$ at $x = 0$ in the axial direction as shown in Fig. 11.15, where u denotes the axial displacement.

The steady state longitudinal displacement of the beam due to the boundary excitation at $x = 0$ can be obtained by assuming a solution of the form

$$u(x,t) = (C_1 \cos \lambda x + C_2 \sin \lambda x)\sin \Omega t \qquad (11.3.1)$$

where λ is the longitudinal wavenumber which is

$$\lambda = \Omega/c_0 \qquad c_0 = \sqrt{E/\rho} \qquad (11.3.2)$$

It can be seen that the velocity of the left end (i.e., $x = 0$) of the beam must be the same as the excitation velocity at the steady state, thus

$$\frac{\partial u(0,t)}{\partial t} = a_l \Omega \cos \Omega t \qquad (11.3.3)$$

In addition, the right end (i.e., $x = L$) of the beam must be stress-free as no constraint is imposed at that point, thus

$$E\frac{\partial u(L,t)}{\partial t} = 0 \qquad (11.3.4)$$

---

[3] Low-cycle fatigue fracture is associated with fatigue that occurs at lower than about 10^4 to 10^5 cycles [14].

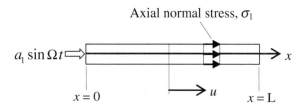

Figure 11.15. Thin beam with coordinate x and longitudinal displacement u.

Applying the above boundary conditions, the coefficients C_1 and C_2 can be determined, and therefore the steady state response of the beam due to the displacement excitation at $x = 0$ is found to be:

$$u(x,t) = a_l(\cos \lambda x + \tan \lambda L \sin \lambda x)\sin \Omega t \qquad (11.3.5)$$

Notice that the response becomes unbounded (i.e. resonance occurs) when $\cos \lambda L = 0$ which is the characteristic equation for the longitudinal vibration of a fixed-free thin beam. Thus, one can find the longitudinal excitation frequencies that resonate the beam, which are:

$$\Omega = \frac{(2n-1)\pi}{2L}c_0 \qquad n = 1,2,3,\cdots \qquad (11.3.6)$$

Once $u(x, t)$ is known, the axial normal stress distribution along the thin beam can be determined by

$$\sigma_l(x,t) = E\frac{\partial u(x,t)}{\partial x} = Ea_l\lambda(\tan \lambda L \cos \lambda x - \sin \lambda x)\sin \Omega t \qquad (11.3.7)$$

In a similar manner, one can find the steady state stress distribution for other boundary conditions; for example, the axial normal stress distribution along a thin beam fixed at $x = L$ is

$$\sigma_l(x,t) = -Ea_l\lambda(\sin \lambda x + \cot \lambda L \cos \lambda x)\sin(\Omega t + \phi_l) \qquad (11.3.8)$$

For this case, the response becomes unbounded when $\sin \lambda L = 0$, which is the frequency equation for the longitudinal vibration of a fixed-fixed thin beam. The resonant frequencies are:

$$\Omega = \frac{n\pi}{L}c_0 \qquad n = 1,2,3,\cdots \qquad (11.3.9)$$

Shown in Table 11.4 are the shortest beam length (i.e., $n = 1$) corresponding to resonance at $\Omega = 20$ kHz for two different materials, aluminum and copper. It can be seen that when the unconstrained tab is modeled as a thin beam, it will not resonate under either boundary conditions at $x = L$ as its longitudinal length is much smaller than the resonant lengths.

Dynamic Stresses Due to Transverse Boundary Excitation in a Thin Beam
Consider a thin beam, free at $x = L$, subjected to harmonic displacement excitation $a_f \sin \Omega t$ at $x = 0$ in the transverse direction as shown in Fig. 11.16, where w denotes the transverse displacement due to the flexural vibration of the beam.

TABLE 11.4. Shortest beam length corresponding to resonance at $\Omega = 20$ kHz.

Boundary conditions	Aluminum $\rho = 2700$ kg/m³ $E = 70$ Gpa	Copper $\rho = 8940$ kg/m³ $E = 110$ Gpa
Fixed-free	$L = 127$ mm	$L = 44$ mm
Fixed-fixed	$L = 254$ mm	$L = 88$ mm

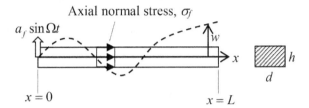

Figure 11.16. Thin beam with coordinate x and transverse displacement w.

The steady state transverse displacement of the beam can be obtained by assuming a solution of the form

$$w(x,t) = (C_1 \cos \gamma x + C_2 \cosh \gamma x + C_3 \sin \gamma x + C_4 \sinh \gamma x)\sin \Omega t \qquad (11.3.10)$$

where γ represents the flexural wavenumber which is defined as

$$\gamma^2 = \sqrt{A/I}\,\frac{\Omega}{c_0} \qquad c_0 = \sqrt{E/\rho} \qquad (11.3.11)$$

where $A = dh$ is the cross-sectional area and $I = dh^3/12$ the second area moment of inertia of the beam, respectively. The unknown coefficients C_1 through C_4 can be found by imposing the boundary conditions as follows. Due to the velocity continuity and zero slope at $x = 0$,

$$\frac{\partial w(0,t)}{\partial t} = a_f \Omega \cos \Omega t \qquad \frac{\partial w(0,t)}{\partial x} = 0 \qquad (11.3.12)$$

In addition, the bending moment M and shear force V due to bending must vanish at $x = L$, thus

$$M(L,t) = EI \frac{\partial^2 w(L,t)}{\partial x^2} \qquad V(L,t) = -EI \frac{\partial^3 w(L,t)}{\partial x^3} = 0 \qquad (11.3.13)$$

Upon application of the above boundary conditions, one can find that the steady state transverse response of the beam is to be

$$w(x,t) = a_f [\cosh \gamma x + C_A (\cos \gamma x - \cosh \gamma x) + C_B (\sin \gamma x - \sinh \gamma x)]\sin \Omega t \qquad (11.3.14)$$

where

$$C_A = \frac{1}{2}\left(1 - \frac{\sin \gamma L \sinh \gamma L}{1 + \cos \gamma L \cosh \gamma L}\right) \qquad C_B = \frac{1}{2}\left(\frac{\cosh \gamma L \sin \gamma L + \cos \gamma L \sinh \gamma L}{1 + \cos \gamma L \cosh \gamma L}\right) \qquad (11.3.15)$$

Notice that both C_A and C_B become unbounded, so does the transverse displacement w of the beam, when

$$1 + \cos \gamma L \cosh \gamma L = 0 \qquad (11.3.16)$$

which is the characteristic equation for a clamped-free thin beam under flexural vibration. The values of γL satisfying Eq. (11.3.16) are

$$\gamma_n L = \{1.875\ \ 4.694\ \ 7.855\ \ 10.996\ \ 14.137\} \text{ and } \gamma_n \cong (2n-1)\pi/2L \text{ for } n > 5 \quad (11.3.17)$$

Therefore, combining with Eq. (11.3.14), the transverse excitation frequencies that resonate the clamped-free beam can be found by

$$\Omega = \gamma_n^2 \sqrt{EI/\rho A} \qquad n = 1,2,3,\cdots \qquad (11.3.18)$$

Once $w(x,t)$ is determined, the axial normal stress distribution (on the surface of the beam) at steady state due to bending caused by the flexural vibration of the beam can be found as

$$\sigma_f(x,t) = \frac{Ea_f h\gamma^2}{2}[\cosh \gamma x - C_A(\cos \gamma x + \cosh \gamma x) - C_B(\sin \gamma x + \sinh \gamma x)]\sin \Omega t \quad (11.3.19)$$

In a similar manner, for a thin beam clamped at $x = L$, one can find that

$$\sigma_f(x,t) = \frac{Ea_f h\gamma^2}{2}[\cosh \gamma x - \hat{C}_A(\cos \gamma x + \cosh \gamma x) - \hat{C}_B(\sin \gamma x + \sinh \gamma x)]\sin \Omega t \quad (11.3.20)$$

where

$$\hat{C}_A = \frac{1}{2}\left(1 + \frac{\sin \gamma L \sinh \gamma L}{1 - \cos \gamma L \cosh \gamma L}\right) \quad \hat{C}_B = \frac{1}{2}\left(\frac{\cosh \gamma L \sin \gamma L + \cos \gamma L \sinh \gamma L}{\cos \gamma L \cosh \gamma L - 1}\right) \quad (11.3.21)$$

For this case, the response becomes unbounded when

$$1 - \cos \gamma L \cosh \gamma L = 0 \qquad (11.3.22)$$

which is the frequency equation for the flexural vibration of a clamped-clamped thin beam. Accordingly, for this case, $\gamma_n L$ corresponding to the resonant frequencies are

$$\gamma_n L = \{4.730\ \ 7.853\ \ 10.996\ \ 10.996\ \ 17.279\} \text{ and } \gamma_n \cong (2n+1)\pi/2L \text{ for } n > 5 \quad (11.3.23)$$

Shown in Fig. 11.17 are the flexural natural frequency loci of a thin beam as a function of beam length L for two different materials, aluminum and copper. The cross-sectional dimensions of the beam are assumed to be $d = 45$ mm and $h = 0.2$ mm. The locus of curves shows the resonant vibration mode and the corresponding beam length at a given excitation frequency. For example, when $\Omega = 20$ kHz, the aluminum clamped-free beam will resonate at its first vibration mode if L is about 2.8 mm, whereas no resonance will occur if the beam is clamped at $x = L$. However, it can be noticed that the nth ($n \geq 1$) resonant frequency of the clamped-clamped beam is almost the same[4] as the $(n + 1)^{th}$ resonant frequency of the clamped-free beam. This indicates that, except for the first mode of the clamped-free beam, resonance will occur at the same length under either boundary conditions at $x = L$. That is, for example, for the aluminum beam with $L = 12$ mm and $\Omega = 20$ kHz, the second vibration mode will be resonated if the beam is clamped at $x = L$, whereas the third vibration mode will be resonated if the beam is free at $x = L$. It can be seen that the copper beam behaves in the same manner, with resonant beam lengths shorter than those of the aluminum beam.

---

[4] When higher order beam models such as the Timoshenko beam model that includes the effects of rotary inertia and shear deformation are used, the frequencies can be slightly different. The Timoshenko beam model is typically used for a beam whose slenderness ratio is less than 10.

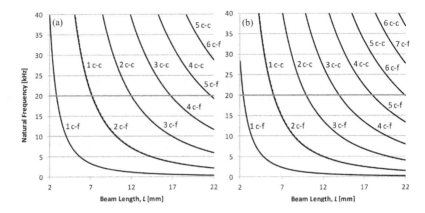

Figure 11.17. Flexural natural frequency loci of the thin beam (d = 45 mm and h = 0.2 mm) as a function beam length L for (a) aluminum and (b) copper. The solid (——) and dashed (- - - -) curves represent the clamped-free (c–f) and clamped-clamped (c–c) case, respectively. Notations for the markers are, for example, 4 c–f denotes the fourth vibration mode for the clamped-free beam.

11.3.2 Dynamic Stress in Battery Tab

As shown in Fig. 11.18, the battery tab and other weld parts are clamped between the sonotrode tip and anvil. In this study, the tab is modeled as a thin beam under both longitudinal (x-direction) and flexural (z-direction) vibrations excited by the oscillatory motion of the weld spot element, based on the following observations and assumptions:

1. Only one tab is considered in the model; other tabs and the bus bar (collectively called "other weld parts" in Fig. 11.18) are considered as stationary rigid bodies. It should be noted that the dynamic coupling between the tab and other weld parts is negligible as the coupling is only through the weld spot area where the oscillating sonotrode tip is in contact with the tab.
2. The thickness of the tab is much smaller than the other dimensions of the tab, especially the tab length in the x-direction.

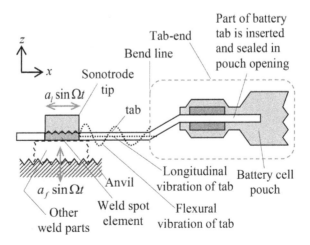

Figure 11.18. Schematics of the battery cell assembly (with the cell pouch partially shown) under ultrasonic welding.

3. The anvil vibrates in the z-direction with a constant amplitude during welding as indicated in Fig. 11.18, which causes the weld spot element to vibrate in phase and thus becomes the excitation source for the flexural vibration of the tab.

4. The weld spot element beneath the sonotrode tip is considered as a rigid body. It is assumed to oscillate in phase with the sonotrode tip and anvil.

5. The sonotrode tip oscillates in both x-direction and z-direction, where its motion in the z-direction is due to the rigid body coupling with the anvil via the weld spot element.

6. For modeling purpose, a term *tab-end* is defined for the cell-integrated tab. As indicated in Fig. 11.18, the tab-end includes part of the tab extended from the bend line and *some* part of the battery cell pouch that surrounds the inserted tab. The kinetic properties of the tab-end are represented by equivalent stiffness and mass in both longitudinal and transverse directions. The effects of rotary inertia and rotational stiffness of the tab-end are not considered in this study.

7. The longitudinal and flexural vibrations of the tab are not coupled. This is a reasonable assumption as the vibration amplitudes are at micron levels and also the fundamental frequency of the longitudinal vibration of the tab is much higher than the excitation frequency (within the practical ranges of tab length) at which flexural vibration modes resonate.

8. The characteristics of the sonotrode excitation during welding are not altered by strain hardening of the materials at the weld interface. This is a reasonable assumption as the kinetic of the oscillating sonotrode is massive.

The vibration characteristics of the tab are governed by the boundary conditions of the tab, then it can be seen from Fig. 11.18 that the tab-end constitutes natural (kinetic) boundary conditions for the cell-integrated tab. During ultrasonic welding, part of the vibration energy injected by the oscillating sonotrode tip travels along the tab, through the tab-end, and then eventually dissipates in the battery cell pouch which contains viscoelastic materials. Hence, the kinetic properties of the tab-end become an important factor in determining both longitudinal and flexural vibration characteristics of the tab during ultrasonic welding. In this study, as shown in Fig. 11.19, these kinetic properties of the tab-end are represented by the equivalent mass and equivalent stiffness. Because the tab-end undergoes both longitudinal and transverse motions, m_l and k_l represent the equivalent mass and stiffness, respectively, for the longitudinal motion; and m_f and k_f for the transverse motion of the tab-end. Due to complex geometry and material properties of the tab-end which consists of both parts of the battery tab and cell pouch, the determination of the equivalent mass and stiffness of the tab-end by analytical or numerical methods require extensive treatments including experiments. Experimental measurements of m_l and k_l of the tab-end

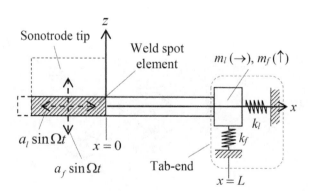

Figure 11.19. Schematic of tab and its boundary conditions with equivalent mass and stiffness.

for the longitudinal vibration are discussed in Section 11.2.3. It is, however, not a trivial task to experimentally measure m_f and k_f of the tab-end due to instrumentation challenges at present. Therefore, one objective of this study is to address the effects of m_f and k_f on the flexural vibration of the tab and resulting dynamic axial stresses through a parameter study by assuming a reasonable range of values for m_f and k_f. For instance, considering the geometry of the tab-end, it is reasonable to assume that $k_f < k_l$.

Axial Normal Stresses in the Unconstrained Tab During Welding

The boundary conditions at $x = L$ of the unconstrained battery tab are different from the ones of the cell-integrated tab used in the battery module, as previously discussed. When the unconstrained tab is clamped by the fixture during welding, the steady state axial stress distribution along the tab can be found by σ_l in Eq. (11.3.7) due to the longitudinal vibration and by σ_f in Eq. (11.3.19) due to bending caused by the flexural vibration of the tab. Figure 11.20, for example, shows the steady state σ_l and σ_f distributions along the aluminum unconstrained tab when the tab is free (Fig. 11.20(a)) and clamped (Fig. 11.20(b)) for $L = 17$ mm and $\Omega = 20$ kHz. Note that, as shown in Fig. 11.21, when $L = 17$ mm, Ω is very close to the fourth flexural vibration mode of the clamped tab and the third flexural vibration mode of the free tab, therefore the overall magnitude of σ_f is larger than σ_l for both boundary conditions. However, note that σ_l can be larger than σ_f, especially at $x = 0$, when L is long enough so that Ω is close to the fundamental frequency of the longitudinal vibration of the tab. These stress distribution curves also suggest that axial stresses at certain points along the unconstrained tab, especially near the weld area (i.e., $x = 0$), can exceed the yield strength ($\sigma_Y = 55$ MPa for aluminum) of the tab during welding when resonance occurs. Note that the aluminum battery tab considered in this study is made of annealed Aluminum 1100 that is commercially pure aluminum (at least at 99% aluminum composition), soft, ductile, low strength, and has excellent welding characteristics.

As previously mentioned, cracks occur near the weld area of the unconstrained tab when the lower end of the tab is not clamped by the fixture during welding. These cracks are believed to be fatigue fractures as a result of large vibration-induced axial stresses near

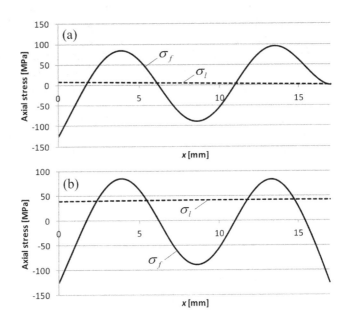

Figure 11.20. Axial stress distribution along the aluminum unconstrained tab when $\Omega = 20$ kHz and $L = 17$ mm for the (a) free boundary and (b) clamped boundary at $x = L$.

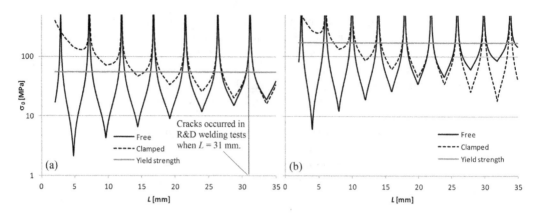

Figure 11.21. σ_0 of the unconstrained tab as a function of tab length L for (a) aluminum and (b) copper tabs when $\Omega = 20$ kHz.

the weld area. In order to evaluate the maximum stress near the weld area, denote σ_0 as the total axial stress at $x = 0$. Note that σ_0 is defined as the superposition of the individual stress magnitudes (i.e., $\sigma_0 = |\sigma_l(0)| + |\sigma_f(0)|$) caused by the two uncoupled vibrations by assuming that $\sigma_l(0)$ and $\sigma_f(0)$ are in phase, thus σ_0 can be considered as the possible maximum axial stress for the worst case of scenario from the tab design point of view. Shown in Fig. 11.21 is σ_0 as a function of tab length L for the unconstrained tab with two different boundary conditions at $x = L$. Notable findings are as follows.

- σ_0 of the unconstrained tab depends on the boundary conditions of the tab at $x = L$. σ_0 is larger when the tab end is clamped at $x = L$ up to L is about 30 mm for the aluminum tab and up to 20 mm for the copper tab. The gradual increase (decrease) of the lower bound of σ_0 is due to the increase (decrease) of the stress due to the longitudinal vibration of the tab.
- σ_0 is large, beyond the yield strength, when the tab resonates at one of its flexural vibration modes. For example, as shown in Fig. 11.21(a), σ_0 of the aluminum tab is higher than its σ_Y when $L = 31$ mm, however, it is significantly lower than σ_Y when $L = 30$ mm or $L = 29$ mm. Note that the aluminum tab with free end at $x = L$ resonates at its 7th flexural vibration mode when $L = 31.2$ mm. This confirms the experimental observations of fatigue cracks occurring near the weld area when $L = 31$ mm.

Axial Normal Stresses in the Cell-Integrated Tab during Welding
Figure 11.22 shows σ_0 as a function of tab length L for the cell-integrated aluminum tab with different values of k_f and m_f of the tab-end, where $k_l = 100$ kN/m and $m_l = 0.063$ g [3] are assumed. Notable findings are as follows.

- As shown in Fig. 11.22(a), σ_0 of the cell-integrated tab behaves in the same manner as the case for the tab-end free from constraints when $m_f = 0$; that is k_f has an insignificant effect on changing σ_0 unless k_f is very large. It is realistic to assume that $k_f < k_l$.
- The effect of m_f on σ_0 is more pronounced than k_f as shown in Fig. 11.22(b). Increasing m_f lowers the natural frequencies of the tab, and thus shortens the tab length L that resonates at 20 kHz. For example, if L is chosen to be between 8 and 10 mm, σ_0 may increase or decrease with increasing m_f depending on L; however, it can be seen that σ_0 is still lower than σ_Y. Noting that m_l ranges from 0.002 to 0.01 g (Section 11.2.3) for the aluminum tab, hence the range of values for m_f used in this analysis can be considered to be conservative.

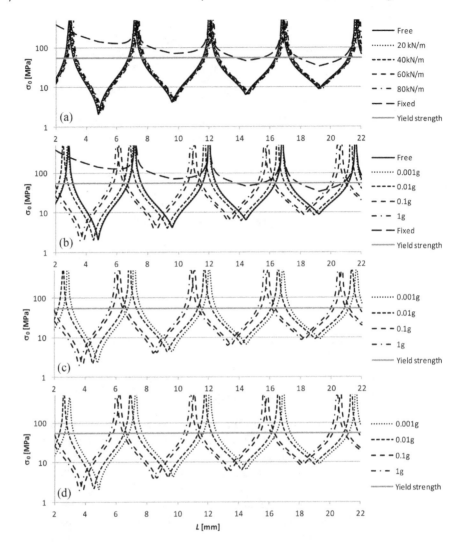

Figure 11.22. σ_0 of the cell-integrated aluminum tab as a function of tab length L. (a) Effect of k_f when $m_f = 0$, (b) effect of m_f when $k_f = 0$, (c) effect of m_f when $k_f = 25$ kN, and (d) effect of m_f when $k_f = 25$ kN.

- The effect of m_f on σ_0 with various non-zero values of k_f has been examined. Shown in Figs. 11.22(c) and 11.22(d) are two representative cases with $k_f = 25$ kN/m and $k_f = 50$ kN/m, respectively. When the two cases are compared, it can be seen that the effect of m_f remains almost unchanged. This is also true even for k_f larger than k_l as long as k_f is not unrealistically large.
- It can be clearly seen that the weld location has a critical impact on σ_0.

Shown in Fig. 11.23 is σ_0 as a function of tab length L for the cell-integrated copper tab with different values of k_f and m_f of the tab-end, where $k_l = 150$ kN/m and $m_l = 0.01$ g (see Section 11.2.3) are assumed. The overall behavior of σ_0 as well as the effects of k_f and m_f are similar to the aluminum tab. However, for this case, notice that the upper bound of the current practice range of L is close to one of the resonant lengths. It should be also noted that high axial normal stresses in the tab during welding increase the sonotrode force required for welding.

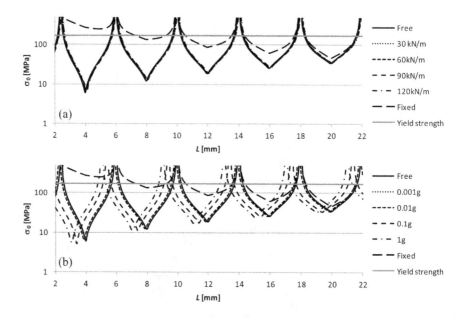

Figure 11.23. σ_0 of the cell-integrated tab as a function of tab length L. (a) Effect of k_f when $m_f = 0$ and (b) effect of m_f when $k_f = 0$.

11.3.3 Summary and Conclusions

The distribution of axial normal stresses in the battery tab during ultrasonic welding is studied in this work by applying an analytical mechanistic model. The battery tab is modeled as a thin beam under longitudinal and flexural vibrations due to ultrasonic excitation from the sonotrode. The main focus of this study is to assess the effects of the elastic vibration of the battery tab on the stress development near the weld spot area during welding. This study serves as the foundation for a scientific understanding of battery tab dynamics during ultrasonic welding and its effect on weld quality, and thus provides a guideline for design and welding of battery tabs. It is found that High stresses can develop when the ultrasonic welding frequency (nominally 20 kHz) is close to one of the tab's natural frequencies. The natural frequencies of the tab depend on the length between the weld spot and tab-end (interface between the battery tab and cell pouch), boundary conditions of the tab-end, cross-sectional area, and material of the tab. Therefore, it is important to design the weld position on the tab in the ultrasonic welding process such that the tab's natural frequencies stay away from 20 kHz as much as possible to minimize the tab stresses. Stresses near the weld area are mainly due to the flexural vibration of the tab during welding, which could exceed the tab material's yield strength and cause fatigue fracture. These stresses can be significantly reduced by reducing the anvil vibration. Stresses due to the longitudinal vibration of the tab during welding are insignificant.

Nomenclature

A	Cross-sectional area of battery tab (45×0.2 mm)
a_f	Sonotrode amplitude in the transverse direction (5 μm is used for calculations)
a_l	Sonotrode amplitude in the longitudinal direction (10 μm is used for calculations)
c_0	Phase velocity ($= \sqrt{E/\rho}$)
E	Young's modulus (70 GPa for aluminum and 110 GPa for copper)

k_f	Equivalent stiffness of the tab-end in transverse motion (see Fig. 11.19)
k_l	Equivalent stiffness of the tab-end in longitudinal motion (see Fig. 11.19)
L	Tab length (see Fig. 11.19)
m_f	Equivalent mass of the tab-end in transverse motion (see Fig. 11.19)
m_l	Equivalent mass of the tab-end in longitudinal motion (see Fig. 11.19)
t	Time
u	Longitudinal displacement of the tab
U_n	Normal mode function
w	transverse displacement of the tab
x	Longitudinal coordinate
γ	Wavenumber of a thin beam under longitudinal vibration
λ	Wavelength ($\lambda = 2\pi/\gamma$)
ρ	Mass density (2700 kg/m^3 for aluminum and 8940 kg/m^3 for copper)
σ_0	Axial normal stress at $x = 0$
σ_f	Axial normal stress due to flexural vibration
σ_l	Axial normal stress due to longitudinal vibration
σ_Y	Yield strength ($\sigma_Y = 55$ MPa for aluminum and $\sigma_Y = 172$ MPa for copper at 25°C)
Ω	Sonotrode frequency [rad/s] ($\Omega = 2\pi f$, f = sonotrode frequency [Hz])
ω_n	Natural frequency [rad/s]

11.4 VIBRATIONAL ENERGY LOSS ANALYSIS IN BATTERY TAB ULTRASONIC WELDING[5]

There are three quality indices in USMW; i.e., bonding effectiveness between weld parts [10], cracks/perforation on the weld surfaces [10], and bulging/distortion of the weld parts [3, 13]. The weld quality depends on a number of controllable factors such as mechanical and metallurgical properties of the weld parts, weld part geometry and dimensions, weld configuration, weld tool (e.g., the sonotrode and anvil) design, and welding process parameters—sonotrode amplitude, clamping pressure, and welding energy. In this regard, a significant amount of research has been made; for example, work by Lee et al. [5,10], Li et al. [17], and Zhao et al. [1].

The weld quality also depends a number of uncontrollable factors such as weld tool alignment, tool wear, work part surface variations and contaminations, and, as a unique characteristics in ultrasonic welding, the dynamics of the ultrasonic welding system, particularly the structural vibrations of weld parts and supporting structures (tools and fixtures). By experimental and finite element analyses, Jagota and Dawson [4] showed that the bonding strength of thin-walled thermoplastic parts by ultrasonic welding is strongly influenced by the lateral vibration of the weld parts. The impact of waveform designs, by controlling the wavelength of the ultrasonic input, on vibration response reduction of weld parts for the battery welding system was studied by Lee et al. [5]. The effect of dynamic responses of weld parts on the sonotrode force required for welding in USMW was studied by Kang et al. [3]. In our prior work [12], extensive experiments were also conducted to gain understanding of the vibration characteristics of the ultrasonic welding process of battery tabs. The experiments were designed to weld three tabs (which were not attached to battery cell pouches; the tab ends were clamped to a fixture) to the bus bar (Cu coupon). Vibration response of the welder system was measured by a high precision (resolution of 2 nm) Polytec single-point laser vibrometer. The vibrometer was synchronized with the welder system and a National Instruments DAQ system. The frequency of the sonotrode

---

[5] The content presented in this section has previously appeared in reference [11].

oscillation during welding was about 20 kHz and data was sampled at 200 kHz. Data was post-processed using the laser vibrometer software and MATLAB to obtain the response, FFT and other critical characteristics. In a set of experiments, the stiffness of the anvil was deliberately reduced, and Polytec laser vibrometer measured several microns more anvil vibration (almost doubled), adversely affecting the weld quality. In particular, some of the weld spots could debond and the tabs could also bulge. This experimental study demonstrated that undesirable anvil vibrations, even at the level of a few microns, could have significant adverse effects on the weld quality. This study also clearly indicated that although the sole vibration source is from the sonotrode, anvil does vibrate due to the coupling effect because the sonotrode applies high clamping force onto the work parts against the anvil.

Because the more system vibrates, the more energy loss is. Thus, the objective of this work is to study the observed phenomena from vibrational energy point of view. We believe it is very important to minimize vibrational energy loss by carefully designing the weld parts and tools, especially to avoid resonance of any of the weld parts and tools as considerable amounts of energy are consumed through resonant vibrations. Therefore, the present work examines the vibration energy loss of the bus bar coupon due to the longitudinal and flexural vibrations of the overhang (upper part of the bus bar extended from the anvil) during ultrasonic welding and assess the effects of this energy loss on the weld strength of battery tabs. The overhang of the bus bar is modeled as a thin beam extended in the direction parallel to the excitation direction of the sonotrode. Sections 11.4.1 and 11.4.2 present the principle of work and energy loss for forced longitudinal and flexural vibrations of thin beams. In Section 11.4.3, vibrational energy loss associated with the vibration of the overhang is discussed. Section 11.4.4 describes the experimental estimation of material damping of the bus bar coupon. Summary and conclusions are presented in Section 11.4.5.

11.4.1 Energy Dissipation by Material Damping in Longitudinal Vibration

In ultrasonic welding of battery tabs, the thickness of the bus bar coupon is much smaller than its other dimensions and the loading conditions are symmetric. Thus, in the present study, the overhang of the bus-bar coupon is modeled as a thin, internally damped beam extended parallel to the direction of the excitation of the sonotrode. An overview of the theory needed to calculate the vibrational energy loss of the bus-bar coupon is presented in this section. Using the modal analysis approach, the energy loss is expressed as a sum of the modal energies. The frequency characteristics of modal energy loss, which is essential to understand the vibrational energy loss in the bus bar coupon during ultrasonic welding, is presented using a single degree of freedom system in Chapter 10.

Consider a thin, infinitely long, undamped, straight bar with a uniform cross-section subjected to an arbitrarily distributed axial body force $P(x, t)$ (measured as a force per unit length) as shown in Fig. 11.24(a). The equation governing the longitudinal vibration of the bar can be found as [6]

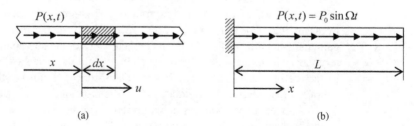

(a)   (b)

Figure 11.24. Thin bar with coordinate x and displacement u. (a) Infinitely long thin bar, (b) Fixed-free finite thin bar.

$$\rho A \frac{\partial^2 u}{\partial t^2} = EA \frac{\partial^2 u}{\partial x^2} + P(x,t) \qquad (11.4.1)$$

where $u = u(x,t)$ denotes the axial displacement of a cross-section, x the spatial coordinate, t the time, E the Young's modulus, A the cross-sectional area, and ρ the mass density of the bar. In the absence of the body force, Eq. (11.4.1) reduces to the classical wave equation:

$$\frac{1}{c_0^2} \frac{\partial^2 u}{\partial t^2} = \frac{\partial^2 u}{\partial x^2} \qquad c_0 = \sqrt{E/\rho} \qquad (11.4.2)$$

where c_0 is known as the phase velocity (or *bar velocity*) at which longitudinal waves propagate. Typical phase velocities in most metals are quite high compared to the velocity of sound in air of 340 m/s; for example, copper has $c_0 = 3{,}508$ m/s. The general solution to Eq. (11.4.1) can be found by assuming that

$$u(x,t) = U(x)G(t) \qquad (11.4.3)$$

where

$$U(x) = C_1 \cos \gamma x + C_2 \sin \gamma x \qquad (11.4.4)$$

$$G(t) = D_1 \cos \omega t + D_2 \sin \omega t \qquad (11.4.5)$$

where the radial frequency ω, wavenumber γ, and wavelength λ (the distance between two successive points of constant phase) are related by

$$\omega = c_0 \gamma = 2\pi c_0 / \lambda \qquad (11.4.6)$$

The arbitrary constants in Eqs. (11.4.4) and (11.4.5) depend on the boundary conditions and initial conditions. For example, consider a bar fixed at one end ($x = 0$) and free at the other end ($x = L$). The fixed boundary condition at $x = 0$ implies that the displacement at the end must be zero, therefore

$$u(0,t) = U(0)G(t) = C_1 G(t) = 0 \qquad (11.4.7)$$

Because $G(t) \neq 0$ for all time, Eq. (11.4.7) dictates that $C_1 = 0$. In addition, the free boundary condition at $x = L$ requires that the stress at the end must vanish; i.e.,

$$EA \frac{\partial u(L,t)}{\partial x} = EA \frac{dU(L)}{dx} G(t) = EA \gamma C_2 \cos \gamma L \, G(t) = 0 \qquad (11.4.8)$$

Because $C_2 \neq 0$, $\gamma \neq 0$, and $G(t) \neq 0$, it can be found that

$$\cos \gamma L = 0 \qquad (11.4.9)$$

which is the frequency equation for the fixed-free bar under longitudinal vibration. Eq. (11.4.9) is satisfied only when

$$\gamma_n = \frac{(2n-1)\pi}{2L} \qquad n = 1,2,3,\cdots \qquad (11.4.10)$$

Thus, the natural frequencies of the system are

$$\omega_n = \frac{(2n-1)\pi}{2L}c_0 \qquad n = 1,2,3,\cdots \tag{11.4.11}$$

These represent the discrete frequencies at which the system is capable of undergoing resonance. For a given n, the vibrational pattern (called the nth normal mode or mode shape) of the bar is described by

$$U_n(x) = \sin\gamma_n x \qquad n = 1,2,3,\cdots \tag{11.4.12}$$

Combining the time and spatial dependence for a given n, the assumed solution in Eq. (11.4.3) becomes

$$u_n(x,t) = (D_{1n}\cos\omega_n t + D_{2n}\sin\omega_n x)\sin\gamma_n x \tag{11.4.13}$$

The general solution is then obtained by superposing all particular solutions as

$$u(x,t) = \sum_{n=1}^{N} u_n(x,t) = \sum_{n=1}^{N}(D_{1n}\cos\omega_n t + D_{2n}\sin\omega_n x)\sin\gamma_n x \tag{11.4.14}$$

where the coefficients D_{1n} and D_{2n} are to be determined by applying the initial conditions of the bar.

Now, consider a fixed-free bar of length L, Fig. 11.24(b), with Kelvin-Voigt material damping (internal damping) and subjected to an axially distributed force $P(x,t)$. The corresponding equation of motion governing the longitudinal vibration takes the following form

$$\rho A \frac{\partial^2 u}{\partial t^2} = c\frac{\partial^3 u}{\partial x^2 \partial t} + EA\frac{\partial^2 u}{\partial x^2} + P(x,t) \tag{11.4.15}$$

Note that Kelvin-Voigt damping is a viscoelastic model commonly used for metals with relatively small damping. In this model, the stress σ, strain ϵ, and its rate of change with respect to time are related by:

$$\sigma = E\epsilon + c\frac{d\epsilon}{dt} \tag{11.4.16}$$

where c represents the viscosity of the material. The solution to Eq. (11.4.15) can be written in terms of the normal modes associated with undamped system as

$$u(x,t) = \sum_{n=1}^{N} q_n(t)U_n(x) \tag{11.4.17}$$

where $U_n(x)$ is the nth normal mode function for the fixed-free bar as shown in Eq. (11.4.12) and $q_n(t)$, referred to as time-dependent *generalized coordinates* or *modal coordinates* [16] in modal analysis of discrete systems, satisfies the following equation:

$$\ddot{q}_n + 2\zeta_n\omega_n\dot{q}_n + \omega_n^2 q_n = Q_n(t) \tag{11.4.18}$$

$$Q_n(t) = \frac{1}{\rho A\alpha_n}\int_0^L P(x,t)U_n(x)dx \qquad \zeta_n = \frac{c\omega_n}{2EA} \qquad \alpha_n = \int_0^L U_n^2(x)dx \tag{11.4.19}$$

Note that the basic problem of Eq. (11.4.18) is the vibration of a single degree of freedom system. $Q_n(t)$ is the *generalized force* or *modal force* in modal analysis of discrete systems associated with $q_n(t)$ and ζ_n is the modal damping ratio. If $P(x,t) = P_0\sin\Omega t$, i.e., a uniformly distributed harmonic body force, one can find that

$$q_n(t) = \frac{P_0 \int_0^L U_n(x)dx}{\rho A \alpha_n \omega_d} \int_0^t \sin \Omega \tau \, e^{-\zeta_n \omega_n (t-\tau)} \sin \omega_d(t-\tau) d\tau \qquad \omega_d = \omega_n \sqrt{1-\zeta_n^2} \quad (11.4.20)$$

Once $u(x,t)$ in Eq. (11.4.17) is found, the mechanical work W performed by the axial force on the harmonic motion of the bar over a time span of t_0 can be determined in a straight manner as follows

$$W = \int_0^L \int_0^{t_0} P(x,\tau)\dot{u}(x,t)d\tau \, dx$$

$$= \int_0^{t_0} \int_0^L P(x,\tau)\left(\sum_{n=1}^N \dot{q}_n(\tau)U_n(x) \right)dx \, d\tau \qquad (11.4.21)$$

$$= \rho A \sum_{n=1}^N \alpha_n \int_0^{t_0} \dot{q}_n(\tau)Q_n(\tau) d\tau$$

In addition, the kinetic energy T at $t = t_0$ is

$$T = \frac{1}{2}\rho A \int_0^L \left(\frac{\partial u}{\partial t} \right)^2 dx = \frac{1}{2}\rho A \sum_{n=1}^N \alpha_n \dot{q}_n^2(t_0) \qquad (11.4.22)$$

and the elastic potential energy V at $t = t_0$ is

$$V = \frac{1}{2}EA \int_0^L \left(\frac{\partial u}{\partial x} \right)^2 dx = \frac{1}{2}EA \sum_{n=1}^N q_n^2(t_0) \int_0^L \left(\frac{dU_n}{dx} \right)^2 dx \qquad (11.4.23)$$

Lastly, the energy W_d dissipated by material damping over a time span t_0 can be found as

$$W_d = -\int_0^L \int_0^{t_0} c\left(\frac{\partial^3 u}{\partial x^2 \partial \tau} \right)\left(\frac{\partial u}{\partial \tau} \right)d\tau \, dx$$

$$= -c\int_0^{t_0} \int_0^L \left(\sum_{n=1}^N \dot{q}_n(\tau)U_n''(x) \right)\left(\sum_{n=1}^N \dot{q}n(\tau)U_n(x) \right)dx \, d\tau \qquad (11.4.24)$$

$$= 2\rho A \sum_{n=1}^N \alpha_n \zeta_n \omega_n \int_0^{t_0} \dot{q}_n^2(\tau)d\tau$$

It should be noted that the work done W by the harmonic body force $P(x,t)$ in Eq. (11.4.21) and the energy dissipated by damping W_d in Eq. (11.4.24) include both the transient and steady-state responses as the solution in Eq. (11.4.17) includes both response solutions. Moreover, energies in Eqs. (11.4.21) to (11.4.24) are expressed in terms of the modal energies, i.e., energies associated with the modal coordinates, whose fundamental characteristics in the frequency domain have been described in Chapter 10.

11.4.2 Energy Dissipation by Material Damping in Flexural Vibration

Consider a thin bar, clamped at $x = 0$ and free at $x = L$, under flexural (transverse) vibration due to a body force $F(x,t)$ distributed over the span, as shown in Fig. 11.25. Denoting x as the spatial variable and t the time variable, the equation governing the transverse displacement $w(x,t)$ under the flexural vibration of the bar is [6]

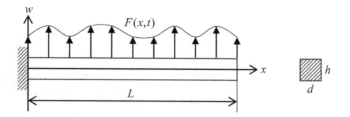

Figure 11.25. Thin bar with coordinate x and transverse displacement w.

$$\rho A \frac{\partial^2 w}{\partial t^2} + EI \frac{\partial^4 u}{\partial x^4} = F(x,t) \qquad (11.4.25)$$

where I is the second area moment of inertia of the bar; i.e., $I = dh^3/12$. In free vibration, the general solution of Eq. (11.4.25) can be found by assuming that

$$w(x,t) = W(x)G(t) \qquad (11.4.26)$$

Application of the above assumed solution to Eq. (11.4.25) leads to

$$W(x) = C_1 \cos \gamma x + C_2 \cosh \gamma x + C_3 \sin \gamma x + C_4 \sinh \gamma x \qquad (11.4.27)$$

$$G(t) = D_1 \cos \omega t + D_2 \sin \omega t \qquad (11.4.28)$$

where, the radial frequency ω and wavenumber γ are related by

$$\omega^2 = \frac{EI}{\rho A} \gamma^4 \qquad (11.4.29)$$

The arbitrary constants in Eqs. (11.4.27) and (11.4.28) depend on the boundary conditions and initial conditions. For clamped boundary conditions at $x = 0$, the displacement and slope must be zero. Hence,

$$w(0,t) = (C_1 + C_2)G(t) = 0 \qquad (11.4.30)$$

$$\frac{\partial w(0,t)}{\partial x} = \gamma(C_3 + C_4)G(t) = 0 \qquad (11.4.31)$$

In addition, the free boundary conditions at $x = L$ require that the bending moment and shear force at the end must vanish; i.e.,

$$EI \frac{\partial^2 w(0,t)}{\partial x^2} = -EI\gamma^2 (C_1 \cos \gamma L - C_2 \cosh \gamma L + C_3 \sin \gamma L - C_4 \sinh \gamma L)G(t) \qquad (11.4.32)$$

$$EI \frac{\partial^3 w(0,t)}{\partial x^3} = -EI\gamma^3 (C_1 \sin \gamma L + C_2 \sinh \gamma L - C_3 \cos \gamma L + C_4 \cosh \gamma L)G(t) \qquad (11.4.33)$$

Because $\gamma \neq 0$ and $G(t) \neq 0$, in order for Eqs. (11.4.30) through (11.4.33) to have a nontrivial solution, wavenumber γ must satisfy the following equation

$$\cos \gamma L \cosh \gamma L + 1 = 0 \qquad (11.4.34)$$

which is the frequency equation for the clamped-free thin bar under flexural vibration. The lowest five values of γL satisfying Eq. (11.4.34) are

$$\gamma_n L = \{1.875 \quad 4.694 \quad 7.855 \quad 10.996 \quad 14.137\} \qquad n = 1,2,\cdots,5 \tag{11.4.35}$$

and $\gamma_n L \cong (2n-1)\pi/2$ for $n > 5$. Accordingly, the natural frequency can be found from

$$\omega_n = \frac{\gamma_n^2}{L^2}\sqrt{\frac{EI}{\rho A}} \qquad n = 1,2,3,\cdots \tag{11.4.36}$$

These represent the discrete frequencies at which the system undergoes harmonic motion. For a given n, the nth normal mode (modeshape function) of the bar is

$$W_n(x) = \cosh \gamma_n x - \cos \gamma_n x - \frac{\sinh \gamma_n L - \sin \gamma_n L}{\cosh \gamma_n L + \cos \gamma_n L}(\sinh \gamma_n x - \sin \gamma_n x) \quad n = 1,2,3,\cdots \tag{11.4.37}$$

Combining the time and spatial dependence for a given n, the assumed solution in Eq. (11.4.26) becomes

$$w_n(x,t) = (D_{1n}\cos \omega_n t + D_{2n}\sin \omega_n t)W_n(x) \tag{11.4.38}$$

The general solution is then obtained by superposing all particular solutions as

$$w(x,t) = \sum_{n=1}^{N} w_n(x,t) = \sum_{n=1}^{N}(D_{1n}\cos \omega_n t + D_{2n}\sin \omega_n t)W_n(x) \tag{11.4.39}$$

where the coefficients D_{1n} and D_{2n} are to be determined by applying the initial conditions of the thin bar.

Now, consider a clamped-free bar of length L with Kelvin-Voigt material damping and subjected to a distributed body force $F(x,t)$. The corresponding equation of motion governing the flexural vibration is

$$\rho A \frac{\partial^2 w}{\partial t^2} + c \frac{\partial^5 w}{\partial^4 \partial t} + EI \frac{\partial^4 u}{\partial x^4} = F(x,t) \tag{11.4.40}$$

In the same as determining the solution for the longitudinal vibration problem in Section 11.4.1, the solution to Eq. (11.4.40) can be written in terms of the normal modes associated with undamped system as

$$w(x,t) = \sum_{n=1}^{N} q_n(t)W_n(x) \tag{11.4.41}$$

where $W_n(x)$ is the normal mode function for the clamped-free bar as shown in Eq. (11.4.37) and the nth time-dependent generalized coordinate $q_n(t)$ satisfies the following equations

$$\ddot{q}_n + 2\zeta_n \omega_n \dot{q}_n + \omega_n^2 q_n = Q_n(t) \qquad n = 1,2,3,\cdots \tag{11.4.42}$$

$$Q_n(t) = \frac{1}{\rho A \alpha_n}\int_0^L F(x,t)W_n(x)dx \qquad \zeta_n = \frac{c\omega_n}{2EI} \qquad \alpha_n = \int_0^L W_n^2(x)dx \tag{11.4.43}$$

Again, the basic problem of Eq. (11.4.42) is the vibration of a single degree of freedom system. $Q_n(t)$ is the generalized force associated with $q_n(t)$ and ζ_n is the modal damping ratio. If $F(x,t) = F_0\sin \Omega t$, i.e., a uniformly distributed harmonic body force, it can be found that

$$q_n(t) = \frac{F_0 \int_0^L W_n(x)dx}{\rho A \alpha_n \omega_d}\int_0^t \sin \Omega \tau\, e^{-\zeta_n \omega_n(t-\tau)}\sin \omega_d(t-\tau)d\tau \qquad \omega_d = \omega_n \sqrt{1-\zeta_n^2} \tag{11.4.44}$$

Once $w(x,t)$ in Eq. (11.4.41) is obtained in terms of the normal modes, the mechanical work W performed by $F(x,t)$ on the harmonic flexural motion of the clamped-free thin bar over a time span of t_0 can be determined in a similar manner as for the previous longitudinal vibration case, which is

$$W = \int_0^L \int_0^{t_0} F(x,\tau)\dot{w}(x,t)d\tau\,dx$$

$$= \int_0^{t_0} \int_0^L F(x,\tau)\left(\sum_{n=1}^N \dot{q}_n(\tau)W_n(x)\right)dx\,d\tau \qquad (11.4.45)$$

$$= \rho A \sum_{n=1}^N \alpha_n \int_0^{t_0} \dot{q}_n(\tau)Q_n(\tau)d\tau$$

The kinetic energy at $t = t_0$ becomes

$$T = \frac{1}{2}\rho A \int_0^L \left(\frac{\partial w}{\partial t}\right)^2 dx = \frac{1}{2}\rho A \sum_{n=1}^N a_n \dot{q}_n^2(t_o) \qquad (11.4.46)$$

and the elastic potential energy at $t = t_0$ is

$$V = \frac{1}{2}EI \int_0^L \left(\frac{\partial^2 w}{\partial x^2}\right)^2 dx = \frac{1}{2}EI \sum_{n=1}^N q_n^2(t_0)\int_0^L \left(\frac{d^2 W_n}{dx^2}\right)dx \qquad (11.4.47)$$

The energy W_d dissipated by material damping over a time span of t_0 for the clamped-free thin bar under flexural vibration is

$$W_d = \int_0^L \int_0^{t_0} c\left(\frac{\partial^5 u}{\partial x^4 \partial \tau}\right)\left(\frac{\partial w}{\partial \tau}\right)d\tau\,dx$$

$$= c\int_0^{t_0} \int_0^L \left(\sum_{n=1}^N \dot{q}_n(\tau)\frac{d^4 W_n(x)}{dx^4}\right)\left(\sum_{n=1}^N \dot{q}_n(\tau)W_n(x)\right)dx\,d\tau \qquad (11.4.48)$$

$$= 2\rho A \sum_{n=1}^N \alpha_n \zeta_n \omega_n \int_0^{t_0} \dot{q}_n^2(\tau)d\tau$$

Again, it should be noted that the work done W by the harmonic body force $F(x,t)$ in Eq. (11.4.45) and the energy dissipated by damping W_d in Eq. (11.4.48) include both the transient and steady-state responses as the solution in Eq. (11.4.41) is not limited to the steady-state response.

11.4.3 Vibrational Energy Loss of the Overhang

Figure 11.26 shows a schematic of the current ultrasonic welding setup for battery tabs and bus bar (U/W-channel), where the battery tabs and bus bar are clamped between the sonotrode tips and the anvil. The weld quality of battery tabs, measured by pull/peel tensile forces, perforation, and bulging, is affected by the dimensions of the bus bar, especially by the overhang length (L) of the bus bar. Longitudinal and transverse vibrations (in the x and y directions, respectively) of the anvil, of the order of several microns, can cause the overhang to vibrate in those respective directions. With different L, these vibrations are suspected to cause the differences in the weld quality. In this study, the vibrational energy loss associated with the overhang is estimated and correlated to the weld strength to assess

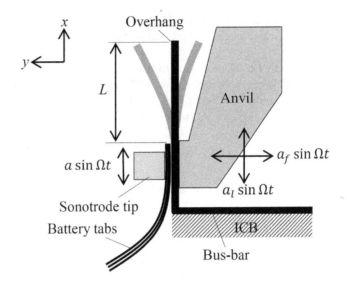

Figure 11.26. Schematic of the battery tabs welding setup.

the effects of the overhang length on the weld quality. We model the overhang of the bus bar as a thin bar vibrating in both the longitudinal and transverse directions under body force excitation due to the anvil vibrations.

The following observations and assumptions are imposed in our model:

1. The vibrations of the overhang of the bus bar are caused primarily by the vibrations of the anvil, i.e., the anvil can be considered a moving support for the overhang of the bus bar. For this case, the excitation force at the anvil and overhang interface can be transformed into an inertial body force uniformly distributed over the span of the overhang, especially when the excitation frequency does not resonate a high vibration mode of the overhang [18]. Under the current design of the bus bar and welding setup, $L \leq 10$ mm, and for such a short span length, the dominant vibration mode of the overhang is the fundamental (first) mode for both longitudinal and flexural vibrations. For example, when $L = 10$ mm and $t = 0.9$ mm (thickness), $\omega_1 = 5.1$ kHz and $\omega_2 = 32$ kHz for the flexural vibration and $\omega_1 = 87.7$ kHz and $\omega_2 = 263$ kHz for the longitudinal vibration.
2. The thickness of the overhang is much smaller than the other dimensions of the overhang.
3. The longitudinal and flexural vibrations of the overhang are uncoupled. This is a reasonable assumption as the natural frequencies of the longitudinal vibration are much higher than those of the flexural vibration. In addition, vibration amplitudes of the overhang can be considered very small so that linear elasticity theory is applicable.
4. The following values of the physical parameters are used in the numerical simulation results:
   - Material properties: $\rho = 8{,}940$ kg/m^3 and $E = 110$ for copper
   - Dimensions: $A = dh$, $d = 45$ mm, and $h = 0.4 - 0.9$ mm
   - Welding parameters: $a_l = 10$ μm, $a_f = 5$ μm, and $\Omega = 20$ kHz
   - $P_0 = \rho A a_l \Omega^2 = 25.4 - 57.2$ kN/m
   - $F_0 = \rho A a_f \Omega^2 = 12.7 - 28.6$ kN/m
   - Modal damping ratio: $\zeta_n = 0.001, 0.003, 0.01,$ and 0.02 for both longitudinal and flexural modes. A series of experiments was performed to estimate the damping ratio of the bus bar coupon in ultrasonic welding (see the Appendix at the end of

current chapter). The damping ratios chosen in the numerical simulations are based on the range of estimated values of ζ from the experiments.

Energy Loss Due to Longitudinal Vibration

The energy dissipated by material damping in the longitudinal vibration of the overhang is estimated. From Section 11.4.1, the mechanical work W performed by the axially distributed body force $P(x,t) = P_0 \sin \Omega t$ is

$$W = \rho A \sum_{n=1}^{N} \alpha_n \int_0^{t_0} \dot{q}_n(\tau) Q(\tau) d\tau \qquad (11.4.49)$$

and the energy W_d dissipated by material damping is

$$W_d = 2 \rho A \sum_{n=1}^{N} \alpha_n \zeta_n \omega_n \int_0^{t_0} \dot{q}_n^2(\tau) d\tau \qquad (11.4.50)$$

where, for our numerical simulations, $N = 10$ (the first ten normal modes), and $t_0 = 1$ second (typical welding time). Figure 11.27 plots W_d as a function of overhang length L of the bus bar for $h = 0.9$ mm with four different modal damping ratios. Note that $W > W_d$; however, their differences are so small that they basically overlap each other on the plots, indicating that the work required to set the overhang into longitudinal motion is negligible. Key findings of the simulation results are summarized as follows:

- The minimum length for which the first longitudinal natural frequency (ω_1) of the overhang matches with the ultrasonic excitation frequency ($\Omega = 20$ kHz) is 43.88 mm. In this case, there can be a large amount of vibrational energy loss. However, because $L \leq 10$ mm in current bus bar designs, this resonance will not occur in practice.
- For $L \leq 20$ mm, W_d due to longitudinal vibration of the overhang is less than 10 J within the range of modal damping ratio values. Note that $\omega_1 = 43.8$ kHz for $L = 20$ mm.
- In practice, for $L \leq 10$ mm, W_d due to longitudinal vibration of the overhang is negligibly small (less than 1 J) for the range of modal damping ratio values considered.
- In general, W_d increases with increasing damping. However, W_d decreases with increasing damping near resonance, as discussed in Chapter 10 for the single degree of freedom system.

Energy Loss Due to Flexural Vibration

Due to undesirable vibration of the anvil in the direction normal to the welding surface, the overhang of the bus bar is subjected to transverse excitation at the welding frequency.[6] The flexural vibration of the overhang caused by this excitation is suspected to lower the weld strength of battery tabs by channeling a significant amount of energy to the vibrational energy of the overhang. In this section, the amount of energy dissipated by material damping due to the flexural vibration of the overhang is estimated. From Section 11.4.2, the mechanical work W performed by the distributed inertial body force $F(x,t) = F_0 \sin \Omega t$ during the flexural vibration of the overhang is

$$W = \rho A \sum_{n=1}^{N} \alpha_n \int_0^{t_0} \dot{q}_n(\tau) Q_n(\tau) d\tau \qquad (11.4.51)$$

---

[6] Sub- and super harmonics of 20 kHz are occasionally observed in experiments, however their spectral power is much lower.

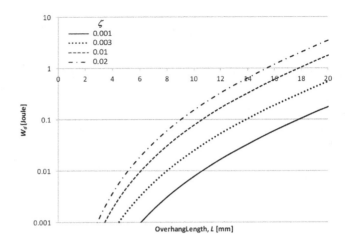

Figure 11.27. Energy (W_d) dissipated by material damping during longitudinal vibration of the overhang for $h = 0.9$ mm with different modal damping ratios.

and the energy W_d dissipated by material damping is

$$W = 2\rho A \sum_{n=1}^{N} \alpha_n \zeta_n \omega_n \int_0^{t_0} \dot{q}_n^2(\tau)d\tau \tag{11.4.52}$$

where $N = 10$ and $t_0 = 1$ second are used in the numerical simulations.

Shown in Figs. 11.28 and 11.29 are the plots of W_d for the flexural vibration of the overhang as a function of its length L for four different modal damping ratios and different bus bar thickness (from 0.4 to 0.9 mm). Again, note that $W > W_d$, but their differences are very small. Every peak in the plots corresponds to a length L for which the coupon overhang will resonate at the welding frequency (20 kHz). It should be noted that simulation results presented in the work are based on linear elastic vibration theory from which resonance merely predicts the conditions under which significant energy loss could occur.

- Unlike the case of longitudinal vibration of the overhang (see Fig. 11.27) in which the first resonant peak occurs when L is large (> 40 mm) which does not happen in practice, resonance of flexural vibration can occur when L is between 4 and 6 mm for the range of coupon thickness considered.
- Significant vibrational energy loss (of the order of hundreds of joules) can occur when one of the flexural natural frequencies of the overhang is close to the excitation frequency $\Omega = 20$ kHz. For example, with thickness $h = 0.6$ mm, the first natural frequency $\omega_1 = 20.225$ kHz for $L = 4.1$ mm, the second natural frequency $\omega_2 = 20.083$ kHz for $L = 10.3$ mm, and the third natural frequency $\omega_3 = 19.607$ kHz for $L = 17.3$ mm. When $h = 0.9$ mm, $\omega_1 = 19.607$ for $L = 5.1$ mm and $\omega_2 = 20.131$ for $L = 12.6$ mm. Such energy loss could account for reduced peel tensile strength.
- Based on the results of our analysis, the overhang of the bus bar should be kept as short as possible to minimize vibrational energy loss due to the flexural vibration of the overhang during welding. For the coupons under study ($h = 0.9$ mm), an overhang length of 2 mm or smaller results in an insignificant amount of energy loss.

Estimation of Material Damping in Bus Bar Coupon
Characteristics of material damping in mechanical systems can be estimated by theory of vibration. One of the most commonly employed techniques is the logarithmic decrement method [19]. Consider the free vibration of a single degree-of-freedom spring-mass-damper system, see Fig. 10.3 in Chapter 10. The equation of motion is

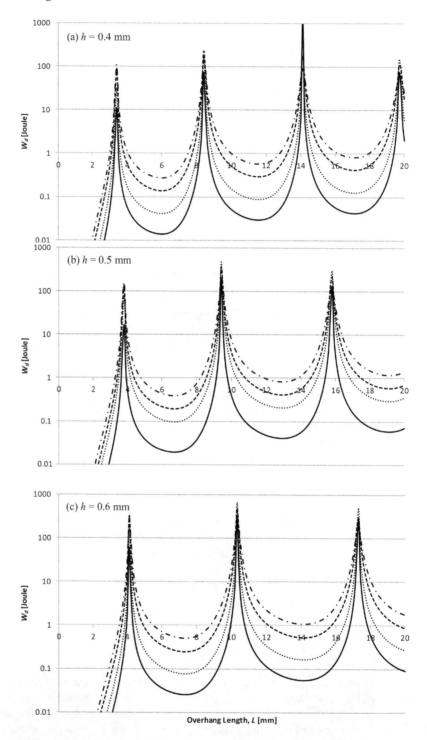

Figure 11.28. Energy (W_d) dissipated by material damping during flexural vibration of the overhang for $h = 0.4$, 0.5, and 0.6 mm with different modal damping ratios. See Fig. 11.27 for legend.

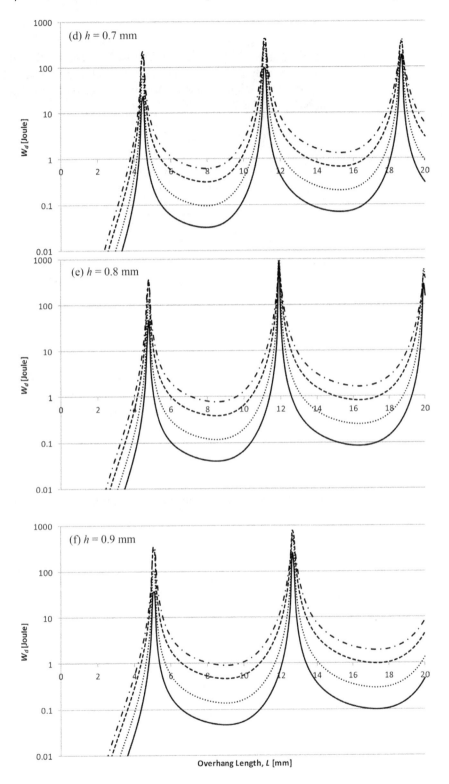

Figure 11.29. Energy (W_d) dissipated by material damping during flexural vibration of the overhang for $h = 0.7$, 0.8, and 0.9 mm with different modal damping ratios. See Fig. 11.27 for legend.

$$m\ddot{x} + c\dot{x} + kx = 0 \tag{11.4.53}$$

with initial conditions of $x(0) = x_0$ and $\dot{x}(0) = v_0$. We note that this simple model is fundamentally the same as those modal equations in Eqs. (11.4.18) and (11.4.42) for the longitudinal and flexural vibration of the bus bar overhang, respectively. The free response of the model can be obtained as

$$x(t) = Xe^{-\zeta\omega_n t}\sin(\omega_d t + \phi) \tag{11.4.54}$$

where, $\omega_n = \sqrt{k/m}$, $\zeta = c/2m\,\omega_n$ (to be estimated), and $\omega_d = \omega_n\sqrt{1-\zeta^2}$ have been previously defined, and the amplitude X and phase ϕ are obtained by imposing the initial conditions

$$X = \sqrt{\frac{(v_0 + \omega_n\zeta x_0)^2 + (x_0\omega_d)^2}{\omega_d^2}} \qquad \phi = \tan^{-1}\left(\frac{x_0\omega_d}{v_0 + \omega_n\zeta x_0}\right) \tag{11.4.55}$$

Figure 11.30 shows a sample plot of the solution given by Eq. (11.4.54). It is noted that the response of the system decays over time because of the presence of the viscous damping, and from Eq. (11.4.54), is enveloped by the curve $Xe^{-\zeta\omega_n t}$. Define the logarithm decrement as

$$\delta = \ln(x_1/x_2) \tag{11.4.56}$$

where $x_1 = x(t)$ and $x_2 = x(t + T_d)$, and $T_d = 2\pi/\omega_d$ is the period of oscillation of the damped system. In other words, δ is the natural logarithm of the ratio of successive amplitudes of the response over one period. From Eq. (11.4.54), the ratio of the amplitudes can be obtained as

$$\delta = \frac{2\pi\zeta}{\sqrt{1-\zeta^2}} \tag{11.4.57}$$

Inverting the above expression gives the damping ratio in terms of the measurable variable δ

$$\zeta = \frac{\delta}{\sqrt{4\pi^2 + \delta^2}} \tag{11.4.58}$$

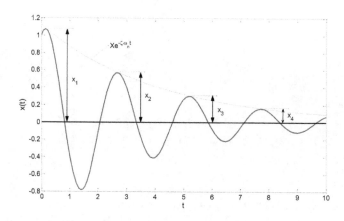

Figure 11.30. Decay of the free response over time.

Note that one can also obtain the following general relations for the logarithmic decrement

$$\delta = \ln(x_k/x_{k+1}) \quad n\delta = \ln(x_k/x_{k+n}) \quad k = 1,2,3,\cdots \quad (11.4.59)$$

The above relations allow a means of averaging the values of δ from experimental data. In practice, one would estimate the free vibration amplitudes from the response curve and then average the calculated values of δ. It should be noted that the application of the logarithmic decrement formulas Eqs. (11.4.56) and (11.4.59) is feasible only if the peaks in the response curve can be clearly and easily identified. The logarithmic decrement method can also be applied to the velocity data (laser vibrometer in the experiments collect velocity data). In other words, one can similarly define

$$\delta = \ln(v_1/v_2) \quad (11.4.60)$$

and apply the same approach to determine the damping ratio as outlined above.

Experiments were set up to estimate the material damping characteristics of the bus bar coupons. Response of the transverse vibration of the coupon was recorded near its bottom middle location by a laser vibrometer, (laser head model: OFV-505). According to the logarithmic decrement method, the damping ratio can be estimated by examining the free response of the coupon. The free response refers to the vibration of the coupon immediately after the welding process is completed, during which residual welding energy in the coupon will be dissipated through material internal damping.

Figure 11.31(a) plots the velocity data of the flexural vibration of the bus bar coupon obtained from one experiment. Figure 11.31(b) shows the free response of the coupon immediately after the welding process is completed. FFT of this decaying response shows that the fundamental period of oscillation is about 20 kHz with a super-harmonic at about 40 kHz, see Fig. 11.32. The super-harmonic results in a modulated signal as seen in Fig. 11.31(b), with the decaying response $Xe^{-\zeta\omega_n t}$ governed by the lower dominant frequency (20 kHz). It is noted that Fig. 11.32 is typical of a welding process, indicating that it is generally difficult to identify response peaks to effectively apply formulas, Eq. (11.4.56) or (11.4.59), for accurate numerical estimations of the material damping ratio. In such cases, a computer code should be developed to extract the values of the peaks and then curve fit these experimental data to the exponential model $x = ae^{bt}$ (the enveloped response is $Xe^{-\zeta\omega_n t}$) where the curve fitting parameter $b = -\zeta\omega_n$ with $\omega_n = 20$ kHz, from which the damping ratio ζ can be estimated.

In order to do the curve fitting, one must first determine the range of data to be considered and this should be examined for every set of data. The curve fitting procedure discussed above was applied to the data of Fig. 11.31(b) data between $t = 1.763$ and 1.77. The curve fitting result gives $b = -3.869 \times 10^2$, with a goodness of fit R-squared value, $R^2 = 0.993$ ($R^2 = 1$ for perfect fit). The damping ratio is thus estimated from $-3.869 \times 10^2 = -\zeta \times (2\pi \times 20 \times 10^3)$ or $\zeta = 0.0031$. This is consistent with the published values for copper (Irvine, 2004). We assume that the modal damping ratios are equal in the numerical simulations.

11.4.4 Summary and Conclusions

The vibrational energy loss of the bus bar associated with the longitudinal and flexural vibrations of the overhang (the upper part of the bus bar extended from the anvil) is studied in the present work by applying one-dimensional continuous vibration models. The overhang of the bus bar is modeled as a thin bar under both the longitudinal and flexural excitations

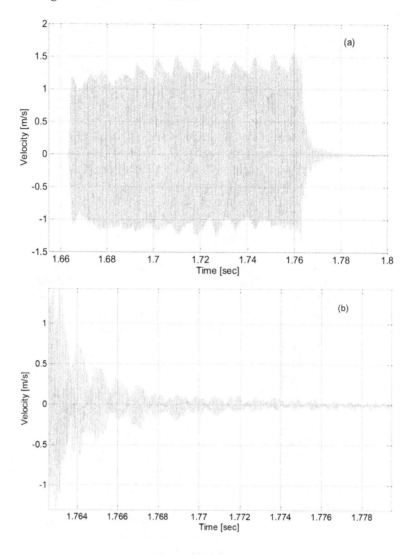

Figure 11.31. (a) Velocity data of bus bar coupon flexural vibration during welding; (b) zoomed-in view of the velocity data during the frce vibration of the coupon after welding.

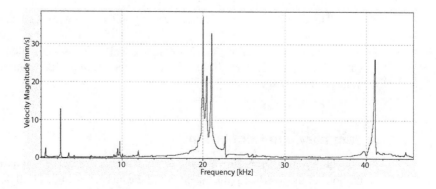

Figure 11.32. FFT of the free response of the bus bar coupon vibration (see Figure (b)).

from the anvil. Experiments were also performed to obtain the damping characteristics of the coupon in order to provide realistic values of the material damping ratio in the modeling. Our results lay a foundation for a scientific understanding of the bus bar dynamics during ultrasonic welding and its potential impact on the weld strength, thus providing guidelines for design and welding of battery tabs. Major findings are summarized as follows:

1. The energy loss due to longitudinal vibration of the bus bar overhang is negligible.
2. A substantial amount of energy loss can occur due to the flexural vibration of the bus bar overhang during welding when the overhang resonates at the welding frequency (about 20 kHz).
3. Vibrational energy loss through the bus bar can be significantly reduced by (a) suppressing the anvil vibration; and (b) optimizing the overhang length to avoid vibration resonance.
4. The energy loss is nil when there is no overhang.
5. The energy loss could account for the reduction of the weld strength.

Nomenclature

A	Cross-sectional area of overhang ($A = dh$)
a	Sonotrode amplitude
a_l	Displacement of anvil in the longitudinal direction of overhang
a_f	Displacement of anvil in the transverse direction of overhang
c	Viscous damping coefficient
c_0	Phase velocity ($= \sqrt{E/\rho}$)
d	Width of overhang
E	Young's modulus (110 GPa for copper)
h	Thickness of overhang
I	Second area moment of inertia of overhang ($I = dh^3/12$)
F_0	Inertial body force in the transverse direction of overhang [kN/m] (see Fig. 11.25)
P_0	Inertial body force in the longitudinal direction of overhang [kN/m] (see Fig. 11.24)
L	Overhang length (see Fig. 11.26)
u	Longitudinal displacement of overhang
U_n	Longitudinal normal mode function (see Eq. (11.4.12))
w	Transverse displacement of overhang
W	Work done by excitation force
W_d	Energy dissipation due to material damping
W_n	Flexural normal mode function (see Eq. (11.4.37))
x	Longitudinal coordinate (see Figs. 11.24 and 11.25)
γ_n	Wavenumber
ρ	Mass density (8,940 kg/m³ for copper)
Ω	Sonotrode frequency [rad/s] ($\Omega = 2\pi f$, f = sonotrode frequency [Hz])
ω_n	Natural frequency of the n-th mode [rad/s] (see Eq. (11.4.11) and Eq. (11.4.36))
ζ_n	Damping ratio for the n-th mode (see Eq. (11.4.19) and Eq. (11.4.43))

Acknowledgment

This chapter is based upon work supported by the United States Department of Energy (DOE) under Award Number DE-EE0002217.

REFERENCES

[1]   Zhao, J., Li, H., Choi, H., Cai, W., Abell, J. A., and Li, X., 2013, "Insertable Thin Film Thermocouples for in Situ Transient Temperature Monitoring in Ultrasonic Metal Welding of Battery Tabs," *Journal of Manufacturing Processes*, **15**(1), pp. 136–140.

[2]   De Vries, E., 2004, "Mechanics and Mechanisms of Ultrasonic Metal Welding," Ph.D. Dissertation, The Ohio State University, Columbus, OH.

[3]   Kang, B., Cai, W., and Tan, C. A., 2013, "Dynamic Response Of Battery Tabs Under Ultrasonic Welding," ASME *Journal of Manufacturing Science and Engineering*, **135**(5), p. 051013.

[4]   Jagota, A. and Dawson, P. R., 1987, "The Influence of Lateral Wall Vibrations on the Ultrasonic Welding of Thin-Walled Parts," *ASME Journal of Engineering for Industry*, **109**, pp. 140–147.

[5]   Lee, S. S., Kim, T. H., Cai, W. W., and Abell, J. A., 2014, "Parasitic Vibration Attenuation in Ultrasonic Welding of Battery Tabs," *International Journal of Advanced Manufacturing Technology*, **71**, pp. 181–195.

[6]   Graff, K. F., 1975, *Wave Motion in Elastic Solids*, Dover Publications, Inc., New York.

[7]   Gao, Y. and Doumanidis, C., 2002, "Mechanical Analysis of Ultrasonic Bonding for Rapid Prototyping," ASME *Journal of Manufacturing Science and Engineering*, **124**, pp. 426–434.

[8]   Kim, T. H., Yum, J., Hu, S. J., Spicer, J. P., and Abell, J. A., 2011, "Process Robustness of Single Lap Ultrasonic Welding of Thin, Dissimilar Materials," *CIRP Annals—Manufacturing Technology*, **60**, pp. 17–20.

[9]   Lee, S. S., Kim, T. H., Hu, S. J., Cai, W. W., and Abell, J. A., 2010, "Joining Technologies for Automotive Lithium-Ion Battery Manufacturing—A Review," *Proceedings of the ASME 2010 International Manufacturing Science and Engineering Conference*, Erie, PA, Paper No. MSEC2010-34168, October 12–15.

[10] Lee, S. S., Kim, T. H., Hu, S. J., Cai, W., Abell, J. A., and Li, J., 2013, "Characterization of Ultrasonic Metal Weld Quality for Lithium-Ion Battery Tab Joining," ASME *Journal of Manufacturing Science and Engineering*, **135**(2), p. 021004.

[11] Kang, B., Cai, W., and Tan, C. A., 2014, "Vibrational Energy Loss Analysis of Battery Tab Ultrasonic Welding," SME Journal of Manufacturing Processes, **16**, pp. 218–232.

[12] Tan, C. A., Kang, B., and Cai, W., 2012, "GOALI: vibration energy flow and mitigation via targeted energy transfer in power ultrasonic metal welding;" A proposal submitted to NSF, October 1, 2012.

[13] Kang, B., Cai, W., and Tan, C. A., 2013, "Dynamic Stress Analysis of Battery Tabs Under Ultrasonic Welding," ASME *Journal of Manufacturing Science and Engineering*, **136**, p. 041011.

[14] Sofronas, A., 2012, *Case Histories in Vibration Analysis and Metal Fatigue for the Practicing Engineer*, John Wiley & Sons, Inc., New Jersey.

[15] Mršnik, M., Slavič, J., and Boltežar, M., 2012, "Frequency-Domain Methods for a Vibration-Fatigue-Life Estimation—Application to Real Data," *International Journal of Fatigue*, **47**, pp. 8–17.

[16] Meirovitch, L., 2001, *Fundamentals of Vibrations*, McGraw-Hill Companies, Inc, New York.

[17] Li, H., Choi, H., Zhao, J., Li, X. C., Cai, W., and Abell, J. A., 2013, "Transient Temperature and Heat Flux Measurement in Ultrasonic Joining of Battery Tabs Using Thin-Film Micro Sensors," ASME *Journal of Manufacturing Science and Engineering*, **135**(5), p. 051015.

[18] Graff, K. F., 1974, "Process Applications of Power Ultrasonics—A Review," *Proceedings of IEEE Ultrasonics Symposium*, pp. 628–641.

[19] Inman, D. J., 2008, *Engineering Vibration*, 4th Edition, Pearson, New Jersey.

Chapter 12

![bar]

CONCLUDING REMARKS AND FUTURE WORK

Wayne Cai[1], and S. Jack Hu[2]
[1]Manufacturing Systems Research Lab, General Motors Global R&D Center
[2]Department of Mechanical Engineering, The University of Michigan

This book begins with an overview of the manufacturing, particularly joining processes used predominately in lithium-ion battery and battery electric vehicles. The rest of the book then focuses on the theories, methods and recent advances in battery ultrasonic welding, the detailed conclusions of which are included in each chapter. Each chapter focuses on a specific topic related to the battery ultrasonic welding process or system using either a physics-based or data-driven approach. In summary,

1. Chapters 2 and 3 start with the definition of ultrasonic weld quality followed by a discussion of post-weld attributes and weld qualities. Two complementary quality metrics for an ultrasonic weld, i.e., interfacial bond quality and circumferential material fracture, are then discussed. The chapters represent a first-ever systematic attempt to quantitatively define ultrasonic weld quality through material characterization and lay a foundation for post-process quality evaluation.
2. Chapters 4 and 5 describe two methods for real-time, in-process welding attributes measurements, i.e., in situ welding temperature and workpiece vibration measurements. The measurements are critical to the understanding of the welding physics, as well as the in-process weld quality evaluation.
3. Chapters 6 and 7 present metallo-thermo-mechanical models of ultrasonic welding processes, in which the welding temperatures, deformations, stresses, and microstructures can be simulated, and the bonding quality and weld fracture can be deduced.
4. Chapters 8 and 9 are research endeavors to devise in-process monitoring system of the ultrasonic welding processes for both the welding quality and weld tool conditions.
5. Chapters 10 and 11 investigate the effects of ultrasonic welding dynamics on the system by employing analytical resonance response models. Though the methods are limited to specific modeling conditions, they represent the most quantitative analyses of the dynamics, stresses, and energy losses in battery ultrasonic welding and can be readily broadened to other ultrasonic welding conditions.

Though this book includes many recent theoretical development and technological advancement in ultrasonic welding of batteries, it still leaves many future research and development opportunities. In our view, the following are areas of opportunities for future work.

12.1 UNDERSTANDING THE PHYSICS OF WELD FORMATION AND SYSTEM DYNAMICS

The Weld Formation Mechanism

The weld formation mechanism for USMW is not completely understood [1]. Literature states that one or more of the following four mechanisms may attribute to the weld formation: (a) metal interlocking due to plastic deformation, particularly the severe deformation caused by sonotrode knurls [Chapters 3 and 4], (b) chemical bonding (e.g., a few microns of micro-melting at the thin interface), (c) metallic bonding [Chapter 3], and (d) dynamic recrystallization [Chapter 7]. Interlocking is evident via optical and SEM microscopic analyses [Chapters 3 and 4]. Direct evidence of melting requires in-situ transient temperature measurement, which was hardly achievable even through unconventional techniques such as using embedded thin-film thermocouples as described in Chapter 4. To confirm metallic bonding, advanced microstructural characterization techniques such as SEM/EBSD, TEM/HRTEM, and X-ray diffraction are essential to study the crystallography [2]. The kinetics of phase transformation were reportedly studied in fusion welding [3], which is also be a powerful tool in ultrasonic welding. A better, scientific understanding of the weld formation mechanisms can lead to better designs and processes with improved welding quality.

Weld Propagation in Multi-Layered Configuration

Although one of the major advantages of ultrasonic metal welding lies in its ability to achieve multiple layered welding, the weld propagation in multi-layered configuration is seldom studied. It is necessary to develop a comprehensive understanding of the relations of the vibration input, the friction, deformation and plasticity behaviors at macro-scale [Chapter 6] and micro-scale [Chapter 7], and eventually the weld propagation among multiple layers of materials. Experimental methods such as in situ temperature measurement [Chapter 4] and high-speed imaging [Chapter 5] are well suited for this research. Future work should include surface scanning laser vibrometry to correlate the dynamics of the welding tool and multi-layered workpieces. A better understanding of the weld propagation will help produce homogeneous welding qualities at different weld interfaces.

System Dynamics

In ultrasonic welding, although it is known that a large percentage of input energy is converted to vibratory motions to form a weld [4], the mechanical waves also travel throughout the system, wasted and in most case detrimental to the entire system. Therefore, the system has to be designed to sustain the dynamics, particularly potential vibratory resonances, either with or without deliberately designed dampers. Such dynamics can lead to structural failure at high stress concentration areas. Although significant work has been done [Chapters 10 and 11] to understand the subject, the nature of high frequency (20 kHz and above) vibration makes it difficult to either predict or measure the dynamics due to very complex and highly localized vibration mode shapes.

12.2 WELD QUALITY PREDICTION

Ultrasonic welding is known to be sensitive to product/process conditions, such as materials (including surface conditions), tools, welding process parameters (such as pressure, ultrasonic amplitude and welding energy), stack-up configurations, damping, and boundary conditions. Weldability and quality welding is largely achieved through trial-and-errors. In addition, changes to existing conditions generally involve a new evaluation of the process and result in different weld quality. Therefore, a predictive capability, either through empirical models [5] or physics-based models [6, Chapters 6 and 7] are highly desirable. Even more imperative is the capability of direct prediction of the bonding quality by taking the surface interactions into consideration, which was little researched. As discussed in reference [7] and Chapter 3, a full predictive capability should include both interfacial bonding quality prediction at all interfaces and circumferential fracture prediction for the top layer(s).

12.3 WELD QUALITY EVALUATION, MONITORING, AND CONTROL

Quality evaluation, process monitoring and control are integral elements in any manufacturing life cycle. In this regard, post-process evaluation is essential to have a complete and thorough examination of weld qualities, usually done in an off-line fashion. In addition, real-time in-process monitoring is highly desirable to detect systematic or sporadic events in manufacturing due to product/process variations, process degradation or randomness. Built upon in-process monitoring, real-time feedback control can be further developed.

Post-Process Evaluation
Standards and guidelines for destructive, post-weld quality evaluation are well-established [8] for many types of welds, including ultrasonic spot welds [9, 10]. They generally prescribe the quality evaluation and testing procedures. As for Non-Destructive Evaluation (NDE), a variety of methods are developed using ultrasonic probes, eddy current, X-ray/CT, electrical resistance, etc. Jia et al. [11] reported that stereography method has the potential for accurate NDE for ultrasonic welds. Successfulness of any of the methods largely depends on the nature of the weld and defect types, and significant challenges exist in interpreting the test data.

In-Process Monitoring and/or Control
In terms of real-time, in-process welding process monitoring, no standards nor guidelines existed although many sensory technologies such as temperature sensors (including thermocouples, IR), force/pressure sensors (such as load cells), displacement (such as LVDTs), accelerometers, acoustic sensors can be used [12]. Chapter 8 proposed using selected in-process sensory data for process monitoring. Online monitoring and quality assurance methods were reportedly deployed in GM's Chevy Volt [13] and Cadillac ELR [14].

12.4 INNOVATIVE ULTRASONIC WELDING TECHNOLOGIES

For certain materials (such as Ni, anodized aluminum, or Ni-coated copper), certain stackup configurations (such as multiple layered thick metals), and situations where welding can only be accessed single-sided with less-rigid structure, innovative ultrasonic welding technologies are desired. Exemplary technologies are torsional ultrasonic welding [15], wire-bonding, hybrid welding (e.g., resistance-ultrasonic welding [16] and laser-ultrasonic welding).

REFERENCES

[1] Bakavos, D., and Prangnell, P. B., 2010, "Mechanisms of Joint and Microstructure Formation in High Power Ultrasonic Spot Welding 6111 Aluminium Automotive Sheet," *Materials Science and Engineering*, A 527, pp. 6320–6334.

[2] Xu, L., Wang, L., Chen, Y.-C., Robson, J. D., and Prangnell, P. B., 2016, "Effect of Interfacial Reaction on the Mechanical Performance of Steel to Aluminum Dissimilar Ultrasonic Spot Welds," *Metallurgical and Materials Transactions A*, **47**(1), pp. 334–346.

[3]   Elmer, J., 2008, "A New Path Forward for Understanding Microstructural Evolution During Welding," *Welding Journal*, **87**, pp. 149-s–166-s.

[4]   Gallego-Juárez, J. A., and Graff, K. F., 2015, *Power Ultrasonics: Applications of High-Intensity Ultrasound*, Woodhead Publishing.

[5]   Kim, T. H., Yum, J., Hu, S. J., Spicer, J. P., and Abell, J. A., 2011, "Process Robustness of Single Lap Ultrasonic Welding of Thin, Dissimilar Materials," *CIRP Annals—Manufacturing Technology*, **60**(1), pp. 17–20.

[6]   Siddiq, A., and Ghassemieh, E., 2008, "Thermomechanical Analyses of Ultrasonic Welding Process Using Thermal and Acoustic Softening Effects," *Mechanics of Materials*, **40**(12), pp. 982–1000.

[7]   Cai, W., 2017, "Lithium-Ion Battery Manufacturing for Electric Vehicles," *Advances in Battery Manufacturing, Service, and Management Systems*, Edited by Li, J., Zhou, S. Y., and Han, Y. H., John Wiley & Sons.

[8]   American Welding Society, 2007, "Standard Methods for Mechanical Testing of Welds," AWS B4.0.

[9]   US Department of Defense Military Standard, 1985, "Ultrasonic Welding of Aluminum and Aluminum Alloy Materials," MIL-STD-19471985.

[10] Society of Automotive Engineers, 2009, "Performance Specification for Ultrasonically Welded Wire/Cable Termination," SAE/USCAR-38.

[11] Jia, S., Hong, E., Katz, R., Lev, L. C., Smyth, S., and Abell, J., 2012, "Nondestructive Testing of Ultrasonic Welding Joints Using Shearography Technique," *ASME Journal of Manufacturing Science and Engineering*, **134**(3), p. 034502.

[12] Cai, W., Jeffrey, A. A., Tang, C. H. J., Wincek, M. A., Boor, P. J., Spacher, P. F., and Hu, J., 2014, "Method and System for Online Quality Monitoring and Control of a Vibration Welding Process," US Patent 8,702,882.

[13] University of Michigan Record Update, 2011, "GM, CoE create technology to maximize Volt's battery weld quality," from http://www.ur.umich.edu/update/archives/110624/battery

[14] Green Car Congress, 2013, "Ultrasonic welding in the battery pack for the Cadillac ELR," from http://www.greencarcongress.com/2013/08/elr-20130802.html

[15] Ultrasonic Welding with a Twist, from http://www.assemblymag.com/articles/90529-ultrasonic-welding-with-a-twist

[16] Yang, J., and Cao, B., 2015, "Investigation of Resistance Heat Assisted Ultrasonic Welding of 6061 Aluminum Alloys to Pure Copper," *Materials and Design*, **74**(June).

INDEX

Page numbers followed by f and t indicate figures and tables, respectively.

CPSIA information can be obtained
at www.ICGtesting.com
Printed in the USA
BVHW07*0712130818
524262BV00012B/112/P